ELECTRON TUBES
and SEMICONDUCTORS

ELECTRON TUBES

and SEMICONDUCTORS

by

JOSEPH J. DeFRANCE

Professor of Electrical Technology and
Head of Department, New York City
Community College

PRENTICE-HALL, INC.

Englewood Cliffs, N.J.

Library of Congress Catalog Card Number: 58–8261

First printing ....February, 1958
Second printing ....January, 1960
Third printing ....June, 1962
Fourth printing ....June, 1964
Fifth printing ....September, 1965

PRINTED IN THE UNITED STATES OF AMERICA

25015—C

PREFACE

This volume is intended primarily for use at the "technical institute" or semi-professional level for the training of electronic technicians. It is the outgrowth of courses given by the author at the United States Coast Guard Training Station at Groton, Connecticut, and presently being taught at New York City Community College.

Two outstanding features are claimed for this book. First is the styling —the author has used the same conversational or lecture style that proved successful in his previous texts. The book is easy to read and stimulating in its direct personal approach as contrasted to pedagogical and heavy third-person presentation. Second, the emphasis is on concepts and not on mathematical derivations. Where mathematics must be included, it is limited to algebra and basic trigonometry.

Prerequisite to the understanding of this volume is a good foundation in direct-current fundamentals, background in the principles of algebra, and a basic knowledge of elementary trigonometry. Prerequisite or co-requisite, a course in alternating-current fundamentals is strongly recommended.

As the title of this book implies, this is a tool subject and not a study of circuit applications. The student of electronics should know the characteristics and limitations of the various types of tubes and semiconductors before he can appreciate their selection and application to the many varieties of circuits for which each is suited. Therefore characteristics are presented and explained *per se*. Mention is made as to the possible circuit applications of each type discussed but, in general, no actual circuits are presented.

Circuity at this point would be an error of digression and furthermore could not be complete. For example, under "diodes," power-supply rectifier circuity might be included. But such a discussion would be incomplete unless power transformers, filter circuits, doublers, triplers, etc., were also included. But rectifiers need not be tubes. They could be of the metallic or semiconductor types. Should these also be discussed here? By now the reader has forgotten the original topic—diode characteristics. In addition to rectifier duty, the diode is also used as a mixer, demodulator, clipper, clamper, etc. Should these applications also be discussed under the topic of "diodes"? This introduces additional complications. These same functions are also accomplished with triodes! How far do we digress? These problems are easily solved by discussing only characteristics now. The circuits are then taken later, under their appropriate headings and using all circuit variations. Once the "tools" are understood, complete circuit discussions can readily be handled.

Joseph J. DeFrance

ACKNOWLEDGMENT

THE AUTHOR is indebted to many industrial organizations for their co-operation in furnishing photographs, tables, characteristics, and technical information on their products. Grateful appreciation of such service is acknowledged to:

> Allen B. Dumont Laboratories, Inc.
> Bell Telephone Laboratories
> CBS-Hytron
> General Electric Company
> General Motors Corporation (Delco Radio Division)
> General Transistor Corporation
> International Rectifier Corporation
> Radio Corporation of America
> Radio Receptor Company Inc.
> Raytheon Manufacturing Company
> Sylvania Electric Products Inc.
> Western Electric Company
> Weston Electrical Instrument Corporation

The author also wishes to express his appreciation to Professor I. Kosow, Head of the Department of Electrical Technology at Staten Island Community College and to Associate Professor E. N. Lurch, Head of the Department of Electrical Technology at Long Island Agricultural and Technical Institute, for their reviews of the original manuscript and their constructive recommendations.

JOSEPH J. DEFRANCE

CONTENTS

Chapter I. **BASIC VACUUM TUBE CHARACTERISTICS**   I

Work Function   2
Electron Emission   3
   Thermionic emission   4
Types of Cathodes   4
   1. Filament type or directly heated cathode   4
   2. Indirectly heated or separate heater-cathode . . .   4
   1. Tungsten   6
   2. Thoriated tungsten   6
   3. Oxide-coated   7
Space Charge   7
Diode Characteristics   8
   Current flow in a diode   8
   Voltage saturation   10
   Temperature saturation   11
   Plate resistance   12
   Applications of diodes   14
Triode Characteristics   15
   Triode characteristic curves   16
   Amplification factor (μ, mu)   19
   Plate resistance and conductance   21
   Transconductance or mutual conductance   22
   Interelectrode capacitance   24
Figure of Merit   25

Chapter 2. **DYNAMIC CHARACTERISTIC CURVES**   29

Load Line   31
Dynamic (Mutual) Characteristic   32
Standard Nomenclature and Symbols   34

Chapter 3. MULTIELEMENT TUBES   39

Tetrodes 39
   Action of screen grid on current flow 40
   Tetrode characteristic curves 41
   Tetrode tube coefficients 44
   Limitation of tetrodes 45
Pentodes 46
   Action of suppressor grid 46
   Pentode characteristic curves 46
   Pentode tube coefficients 50
   Remote cutoff pentodes 50
Power Output Tubes 54
   Beam-power tubes 55
Multielement Tubes 56
Multi-unit Tubes 57
Electron-ray Tubes 57
Limitations in Operating Conditions 60
Miniature and Subminiature Tubes 61
Ultra High Frequency (UHF) Tubes 64
Microwave Tubes 66
   Klystrons 67
   Magnetrons 68
   Travelling wave tubes 72

Chapter 4. GAS TUBES   76

Effect of Residual Gas on Tube Characteristics 76
Gas Diode—Hot Cathode 79
   Potential distribution in thermionic gas diodes 81
   Heater-cathode construction 82
   Limitations and precautions 83
Thermionic Gas Triode—Thyratron 84
   Action of control grid 85
   Thyratron control characteristics 87
   Thyratron action on alternating current 88
   Phase-shift control of thyratron firing 89
   Phase-shift circuit 91
   Hydrogen thyratrons 93
   Shield grid thyratron 94
Cold-Cathode Gas Tubes 96
   Gaseous conduction 96

Conduction stages in cold-cathode gas tubes 97
Ignitron 102
Multianode Mercury Pool Tubes 104

Chapter 5. CATHODE-RAY TUBE 107

Cathode-Ray Tube Construction 108
1. Envelope 108
2. Tube base 110
3. Electron gun assembly 111
4. Deflection plate assembly 112
5. Fluorescent screen 112
Effect of Control Grid Potential 113
Electrostatic Focusing 114
Electrostatic Deflection System 116
Deflection Sensitivity 118
Intensifier Bands 119
Positioning Controls 120
Balanced Deflection System 122
Electron-Beam Path 124
Electromagnetic Focusing 124
Electromagnetic Deflection 126
Ion Spots 128
Ion Traps and Magnets 129
Aluminized Tubes 131

Chapter 6. CATHODE-RAY OSCILLOSCOPE 134

Block Diagram of the Oscilloscope 134
Attenuator 134
Amplifiers 136
Time base—sweep generator 137
Synchronization 138
External horizontal input 140
Power supplies 140
Simple Sweep Circuit 140
Commercial Sweep Circuit—Thyratron 142
Applications of the Cathode-Ray Oscilloscope 144
Voltage measurement 144
Phase shift measurements 145
Phase measurements using external synchronization . . 152
Frequency measurements 153
Frequency response by square-wave testing 156

Chapter 7. SEMICONDUCTOR FUNDAMENTALS 160

Semiconductors 161
Valence Electrons 162
Semiconductor Crystal Lattice 163
Donors and Acceptors 164
Electrical Charge of N- and P-type Semiconductors . . . 166
Majority and Minority Carriers 167
P-N Junction 167

Chapter 8. CRYSTAL DIODES 170

Point Contact Rectifier Action 170
Types of Crystal Diodes 171
Crystal Diode Characteristic Curve 173
Diode Specification Data 176
Crystal Diode Advantages and Applications 177
Polarity and Graphic Symbol 177

Chapter 9. SEMICONDUCTOR POWER RECTIFIERS 180

Basic Principle of Area Rectifiers 181
Power Rectifier Cell Characteristics 182
Static characteristic 183
Forward current rating 183
Peak inverse voltage rating 183
Temperature 183
Aging 184
Self-capacitance 184
Copper-Oxide Rectifier 184
Magnesium-Copper Sulphide Rectifier 187
Selenium Rectifier Cell 188
Germanium Power Rectifiers 190
Silicon Power Rectifiers 194

Chapter 10. BASIC TRANSISTORS 198

Point-Contact Transistor 198
Current relations 200
Voltage and power gains 200
Limitations of point-contact transistor 201
Junction Transistors 202
Current relations 204
Current amplication (α) 205

Voltage and power gain 206
The P-N-P junction transistor 206
Transistor Graphic Symbols 207
Basic Current Amplification Factor (β) 208
Static Characteristic Curves 209
Transistor Configurations 211
Transistor Parameters 212
   1. Base resistance (r_b) 212
   2. Emitter resistance (r_e) 213
   3. Collector resistance (r_c) 213
Frequency Limitations 214
Power Transistors 215
Tetrode Transistor 217
Life Expectancy 219

Chapter 11. PHOTOTUBES AND PHOTOELECTRIC CELLS

226

Light Waves 227
Light Units 229
Light Energy 230
Photoelectric Emission 230
Vacuum Phototube 232
Gas Phototubes 234
Multiplier Phototubes 237
Photoconductive Cells 239
Semiconductor Photodiode 242
Phototransistors 243
Photovoltaic Cells 246
Sun or Solar Batteries 249

APPENDICES

256

1. Selected Vacuum Tube Characteristics 256
2. Selected Power Triodes 264
3. Selected Special Receiving Tubes 266
4. Selected Gas Diodes 268
5. Selected Gas Triodes and Tetrodes 270
6. Crystal Diodes 272
7. Registered RETMA Transistor Types 275
8. Selected Phototubes 280
9. Selenium Sun Batteries 282
10. Transistor Letter Symbol Standards 283

INDEX

285

CHAPTER 1

Basic Vacuum Tube Characteristics

For many years the vacuum tube was considered as the "heart" of an electronic circuit, and it had well earned this reputation.* It was not until the development of the vacuum tube that the electronics industries began to advance in leaps and bounds. At first there were very few types of tubes available, and these were used strictly for radio and telephone applications. Now there are very many forms available. Each year brings forth new types and new applications of this "miracle tool." During World War II, electronic tubes won a place in industry where they are now performing countless tasks more efficiently and accurately than have ever been done before. In almost every type of industry vacuum tubes have been used to measure and control such chemical and physical quantities as acidity, color, temperature, speed, pressure, and time.

A listing of the uses of electronic tubes would run into the thousands. There are almost no limitations to their capacities. Some tubes are available that are so sensitive they can measure the minute quantities of electricity in the muscles of the human heart. Others are sturdy enough to carry thousands of amperes, as required in welding operations or aluminum refining.

---

* Today this function is shared with semiconductor diodes and transistors. These will be covered in later chapters.

Despite the wide variety of jobs that electronic tubes are doing—despite the complexity of some electronic apparatus—the basic design of electronic tubes and their principles of operation are quite simple to understand.

Work Function

From earlier studies of electricity * you are probably familiar with the electron theory of matter. Let us briefly review some of the aspects important to our further discussion:

1. All atoms consist of a positive nucleus and negative electrons.
2. The electrons are arranged in shells around the nucleus.
3. The electrons rotate around the nucleus.
4. The force of attraction between the negative electron and the positive nucleus is balanced by the centrifugal force due to their rotation.
5. The electrons in the outermost shells have relatively weak binding forces to their own nuclei. These electrons may be able to break free from their "parent atom," and move *at random* from one atom to another. These electrons are called free electrons.
6. In their random motion, electrons drift in all directions, but the drift in any one direction is offset by equal drifts in the opposite direction and the net drift is zero.

Current flow was the result of motion of these free electrons in one general direction. To accomplish this it was necessary to apply external field forces (a voltage) to a *complete circuit*. If the circuit was broken, electrons could not jump through space, and the flow of current was stopped. Now, however, we shall see how electrons can be made to escape from the surface of a material and move out into space. This is known as *electron emission*. When electron emission is desired, metals are used because they have many free electrons.

If we consider a free electron in the middle of a piece of metal, we should realize that it must be surrounded by many positive and negative charges due to other electrons and nuclei. It is reasonable to assume that these surrounding charges are balanced (positive charges equal negative charges) and that the *average* force on this free electron is zero. In fact, that is why it is free to move at random.

Now let us examine the surface of the metal at a depth of one atom. At approximately the center of this layer, one atom thick, we would find

---

* DeFrance, J. J., *Direct Current Fundamentals*, 2nd Ed. (Prentice-Hall, Inc., Englewood Cliffs, N. J., 1955) Chaps. 1 and 2.

the nuclei of these outermost atoms. The upper half of this layer would contain only electrons. A free electron approaching this area would have many positive charges below it, attracting it back into the material, with few or no positive charges above it to balance the downward force. In addition this free electron would find a relatively strong concentration of negative charges above it also forcing it back down into the material. This combination of unbalanced forces creates a *surface barrier potential* which tends to prevent the escape of free electrons into space.

This potential barrier is made more effective by another action. If an electron should escape a short distance into space, the metal surface would become deficient by one electron and would acquire a positive charge. This is known as an *image charge*. A force of attraction would result between the two unlike charges, tending to pull the electron back. Theoretically, the electron would have to escape to an infinite distance to avoid this force. In order for electrons to escape, work must be done against these opposing forces. A measure of the amount of work done (or energy required) to remove one electron is called the *work function* (Φ) for that material. Since work is done against the opposing forces, and the forces are due to the charge on an electron, it follows that the work function is a ratio of work per charge. But work per unit charge is a measure of electric potential,* and is measured in volts. Similarly, work function (Φ) is given in *electron-volts* or simply *volts*. The value of this work function varies for different materials. One theory is that it depends on the spacing between the atoms of the material.

Electron Emission

Before an electron can escape from the surface of a metal, it must be supplied with *additional* energy equal to the work function. This liberating energy can be obtained in one of four ways.

1. *Thermionic emission.* When some metals are heated, electrons can gain sufficient energy to escape.

2. *Secondary emission.* When some metals are bombarded by electrons or other particles, kinetic energy of the striking particles can be absorbed by the electrons of the material.

3. *Field emission.* A very strong external electric field can overcome the attractive forces due to surface barrier and image charge and literally pull the electrons out of the material.

---

* DeFrance, *Direct Current Fundamentals,* page 25.

4. *Photoelectric emission.* When some metals are exposed to light, light energy can be absorbed by the electrons of the material.

Thermionic emission. If heat is applied to a material, some of the heat energy is converted to kinetic energy, causing accelerated motion of the electrons. When the temperature rises sufficiently, and the increase in kinetic energy equals the work function of the material, the electrons can overcome the attracting forces and fly off into space. Metals with lower work functions will require less additional energy and therefore will emit electrons at lower temperatures. Even so, the required temperature is quite high.

In a vacuum tube, the element which is heated to emit electrons is called the *cathode.* If the cathode were heated to the required temperature in open air, it would burn up because of the presence of oxygen in the air. Thomas Edison learned this in his experiments with the incandescent lamp. For this reason the cathode is placed in a glass or metal envelope and the bulb is evacuated.

Types of Cathodes

Since the cathode is sealed in a vacuum, the simplest way to heat it is electrically. On this basis, cathodes may be divided into two types depending on whether they are heated directly or indirectly.

1. Filament type or directly heated cathode. In this type the cathode consists of a metallic wire or ribbon. The heating current passes directly through this wire. The heating is a result of the I^2R loss due to the resistance of the filament wire. Typical filament structures are shown in Fig. 1-1(a).

2. Indirectly heated or separate heater-cathode. The indirectly heated cathode consists of a thin metal sleeve coated with the electron-emitting material. A filament or heater is enclosed within the sleeve and insulated from the sleeve. The cathode is heated by radiation and conduction from the heater. Useful emission does not take place from the heater itself. This type of construction is shown in Fig. 1-1(b).

Separate heater construction has many advantages. Since the cathode is completely separated from the heating circuit, it can readily be connected to any desired potential as needed, independent of the filament or heater potential. As you will learn when studying amplifier circuits, one such application is to make the cathode positive (with respect to ground).

The entire cathode structure will be at the same potential. In the filament type, due to the *IR* drop of the heating current each portion of the cathode structure is at a different potential. Furthermore, in electronic equipment

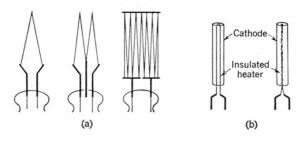

(a)   (b)

Fig. 1-1. Types of cathode structures: (a) directly heated; (b) indirectly heated; (c) cutaway view of commercial filament type tube.

(c)

it is preferable to use a-c in the heater circuit to simplify the power supply requirements. With filament type tubes, this may produce hum due to:

(a) variation of cathode potential,
(b) variation of cathode temperature,
(c) magnetic field around the filament.

All these faults are eliminated in the separate heater construction. On the other hand, filament type heaters require less filament power than a similar material indirectly heated and can be more easily designed to handle very high current requirements. For these reasons filament type tubes are often used in high power applications, for example, as transmitting tubes.

Cathodes may also be classified by the type of material from which they are made. The high temperatures required to produce satisfactory thermionic emission limit the number of substances suitable as emitters to a very few. Of these *tungsten, thoriated tungsten,* and *oxide-coated* emitters are the only ones commonly used in vacuum tubes. Each material has its advantages.

1. Tungsten. Tungsten (work function 4.52 electron-volts) is widely used for the filaments of large power handling tubes where very high plate voltages are encountered. They are the most rugged of the three types, can withstand overload and cathode bombardment by positive gas ions (see page 78) with minimum damage, and will give the longest life. On the other hand they must operate at very high temperature (2200°C, dazzling white) in order to emit sufficient electrons. A large amount of filament power is required. Since the filament efficiency is low, tungsten filaments are used only when other emitters cannot be employed.

2. Thoriated tungsten. At lower temperatures, the electron emission of thoriated tungsten is many thousand times better than for pure tungsten. This is due to its lower work function (2.63 electron-volts), and means that thoriated tungsten filaments can be operated at approximately 1650°C (bright yellow), with a consequent reduction in the filament power required. In their manufacture a small amount of thorium oxide is added to the tungsten (approximately 2%). After mounting the filament in the tube, it must be activated by heating the filament to higher than operating temperature (1850° to 2500°C) for a few minutes. This brings a very thin layer of thorium to the surface giving the filament its high emission. Thoriated tungsten emitters are used for intermediate power tubes at potentials between 500 and 5000 volts, where conditions are not so severe as to require pure tungsten. Overload may ruin the surface layer of thorium and reduce the emission properties of the filament. However they may be reactivated and put back into service.

Tungsten and thoriated tungsten emitters are made only in the directly heated or filament type cathode. Due to the lower heat transfer efficiency, too much filament power would be needed for indirect heating.

3. Oxide-coated. Emitters of this type consist of nickel (or nickel alloy) coated with barium and strontium oxides. The coating must be activated in a manner similar to the process used for thoriated tungsten filaments. This process brings a layer of barium to the surface giving the emitter its high emission quality (work function 1.1 electron-volts). The strontium adds mechanical strength to the coating. The oxide-coated cathode operates at comparatively low temperature (750°C, dull red). This type of emitter is the most efficient with regard to emission current per watt of heating power. It is therefore used wherever possible. Receiving tubes and transmitter tubes of lower power rating employ oxide-coated emitters, even up to plate potentials of several thousand volts. Oxide-coated emitters may be of the heater or filament type.

Tubes designed for battery operation (portables) are invariably of the filament type cathode, oxide-coated. The higher emission efficiency of the oxide coating plus the higher heating efficiency of the directly heated cathode combine to result in low filament power requirement which is desirable to minimize the drain on the batteries.

Space Charge

We have seen that as the temperature of the cathode is increased to the emission point of the material, electrons are thrown off into the space surrounding the cathode. Where do they go? They remain in a space surrounding the cathode in a sort of cloud. This effect is known as *space charge*. Since it is formed of electrons, the space charge is negative. Meanwhile, the cathode, having lost electrons, acquires a positive potential. The combined action of the repelling force due to the negative space charge and the attractive force of the positive cathode will tend to counteract the kinetic energy which throws the electrons off the cathode. Some of the electrons from the space charge return to the cathode. But meanwhile more electrons are being emitted by the cathode. In other words, the electrons in the space charge are not static, but in continuous motion. An equilibrium condition is soon reached where the number of electrons emitted is equal to the number of electrons attracted back to the cathode.

Let us assume that the operating temperature of the cathode is increased, by increasing the filament or heater current. The kinetic energy of the electrons in the cathode will also be increased, destroying the equilibrium condition. The number of electrons forming the space charge will increase. The higher the temperature of the cathode, the more electrons it will emit; the greater the rate at which they are emitted, the greater the number of electrons in the space charge; but again a new equilibrium condition is reached where the number of electrons emitted is balanced by the number of electrons returning to the cathode. Obviously the number of electrons forming the space charge depends on the cathode temperature. However, if too high a voltage is applied to the filament or heater, the increase in current (and temperature) may cause the filament or heater to burn out. Tubes should be operated at a safe filament or heater voltage as determined by the manufacturer. They are sometimes operated at slightly below rating (if the maximum current rating is not needed) to increase the life of the tube. Too low a voltage will result in insufficient emission and prevent proper functioning of the tube.

Diode Characteristics

The simplest type of vacuum tube contains two elements—the cathode and an *anode* or *plate*. (The heater of the indirectly heated cathode is not considered as an element.) Such a tube is called a *diode*. Figure 1-2 shows a diode connected to a source of heater and plate supply. This circuit can be used to study the effects of cathode temperature and plate potential on the diode characteristics. The plate of the tube is made positive with respect to the cathode.

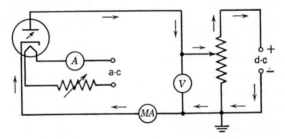

Fig. 1-2. Circuit for determining diode characteristics.

Current flow in a diode. If the cathode is at an operating temperature, electrons are being emitted to form a space charge. Remember that this space charge is in constant flux but that an equilibrium condition exists between the number of electrons being emitted and being returned to the cathode. Let us consider what will take place in this complete circuit of Fig. 1-2. We will start with the plate potentiometer set down to the very bottom. The plate potential is obviously zero. Up till now we have considered the space charge existing as a cloud around the vicinity of the cathode. This is essentially true. But some electrons are emitted with sufficient initial velocity to extend up to the plate. Now that we have a complete circuit, some of these electrons will return to the cathode via the external path (see arrows in Fig. 1-2). Current is flowing through the cathode-plate circuit even though no voltage is applied to the circuit! This phenomena due to the initial velocity of the electrons is known as the "Edison effect" in honor of Thomas A. Edison, who first noticed this action. However, since this current is extremely low (microamperes) compared to normal action (milliamperes) it can be neglected.

Now let us raise the setting of the plate potentiometer, applying a positive potential to the plate. Since the plate is positive, an appreciable number of electrons will be pulled from the space charge to the plate. These electrons will flow through the circuit back to the cathode. This *plate current* will be measured by the milliammeter. The meter could have been placed on the plate side of the circuit, but then it would have been at a high potential (with respect to ground). This would be dangerous to the operator. Since the same plate current also flows in the cathode, it is common practice to locate the meter as shown. Will this plate current destroy the equilibrium condition between space charge and cathode? Does the cathode emission change, to supply these extra electrons to the plate? The answer to both these questions is No! Cathode emission depends only on cathode temperature—and we have not changed the heater current. As for equilibrium, we know that the number of electrons emitted is balanced by the number of electrons returning to the cathode. Only now fewer electrons are returned from the space charge back to the cathode, the remainder are returned through the completed plate circuit as shown by the arrows in Fig. 1-2.

If we were to reverse the plate supply voltage, making the plate negative compared to cathode, would current continue to flow from cathode to plate? Of course not—the negative plate would repel the electrons. Even the small current due to Edison effect would cease as soon as the plate was made a few volts negative. Would current flow in the opposite direction? Definitely not! The plate is not hot enough to emit electrons, nor is it made of suitable emitter material. *Current can flow only in one direction, from cathode to plate and only when the plate is positive compared to cathode.* This is true of all vacuum tubes. Does that mean that plate current will not flow in *any circuit* if the plate potential is for example —50 volts? Think a minute before you answer that. Notice also the italics phrase three sentences back, the plate must be positive *compared to cathode.* In other words the plate potential can be negative if the cathode potential is even more negative. Remember that the operating voltage for any element of a tube is the voltage between that element and the cathode.

So—a plate potential of —50 is permissible if the cathode potential is for example —150 volts, since this makes the plate 100 volts positive compared to cathode. Remember this point well, when in your later studies you analyze circuits. Many television receivers, radar units, and industrial electronic circuits will use such seemingly odd potentials—yet the operating voltages will be correct.

Voltage saturation. We have seen that a positive plate potential will cause a plate current to flow. Let us check the relation between plate voltage and plate current.

What will happen if we raise the plate potential in steps? A more positive plate will attract electrons from the space charge at a greater rate. The plate current will increase. Will this effect continue indefinitely? Think a minute. For a given cathode temperature, the cathode emits electrons at a fixed rate. As the plate voltage is increased, the plate current keeps increasing as long as electrons are being supplied by the space charge. This continues until the electron supply forming the space charge is exhausted and electrons are being taken from the cathode as fast as they are given off. Beyond this point, further increase in plate potential can not cause a corresponding increase in plate current. This condition is known as *voltage saturation*. This maximum current is called the *saturation current,* and because it is an indication of the total number of electrons emitted it is also known as the *emission current* or, simply, *emission*.

Figure 1-3 shows the variation of plate current with plate potential. Curves are plotted for several cathode temperatures. Notice that all three curves coincide at low plate voltages. The reason for this should be ob-

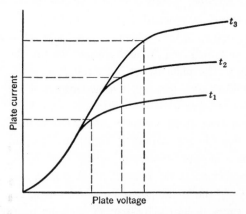

Fig. 1-3. Variation of plate current with plate voltage, showing voltage saturation.

vious: at low plate voltages so few electrons are pulled out of the space charge that even at reduced temperatures the cathode can supply sufficient electrons; on the other hand, with higher cathode temperatures the rate of emission is increased and the saturation point is delayed.

Tubes are designed to operate well below the voltage saturation point. The normal cathode operating temperature will supply sufficient emission so that saturation will not occur under normal operating conditions. The plate current at saturation level would be excessive and would ruin the tube. If it is desired to demonstrate saturation, the tube should be operated at considerably reduced heater voltage and current. In this way, voltage saturation can be made to occur within safe limitations of plate current. (See curve t_1 in Fig. 1-3.)

Temperature saturation. If the plate potential is kept constant while the cathode temperature is varied, another form of saturation is noticed. Such a curve is shown in Fig. 1-4, for two values of plate potential.

At low cathode temperatures (low heater current) there is no emission from the cathode, and no plate current can flow. As the heater current is increased, the cathode temperature rises. Emission begins, but at a slow rate. With this low rate of emission, *all* the electrons are attracted by the positive plate. No space charge is formed. The plate current is proportional to heater current or cathode temperature, regardless of plate potential. The two curves (for E_1 and E_2) coincide. (See Fig. 1-4 below temperature a.)

As the cathode temperature is increased further, emission takes place at a much higher rate. A low plate potential cannot draw the electrons

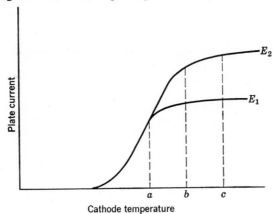

Fig. 1-4. Effect of cathode temperature on plate current, showing temperature saturation.

at a sufficiently fast rate—a space charge is formed. The negative space charge counteracts the attraction of the positive plate. The plate current levels off. This effect is known as *temperature saturation*. Since it is caused by the space charge it is also referred to as *space charge saturation*. Any further increase in cathode temperature merely increases the number of electrons in the space charge. The plate current shows very little increase. Now the plate current is nearly independent of cathode temperature. (See curve E_1 beyond temperature a.)

With a higher plate potential, the electrons in the cathode area are accelerated faster by the greater attraction of the plate. This faster motion of the electrons reduces the tendency to form a space charge. Saturation does not take place until a higher emission rate is obtained at some higher temperature. (See curve E_2 beyond temperature b.)

For normal operation the rated heater (or filament) current and voltage as recommended by the manufacturers will place the tube well beyond the temperature saturation point. This insures that the plate current of a tube will not be affected by small changes in cathode temperatures. Now the plate current will be affected only by changes in the plate potential. Such a condition is obtained by operating at temperature c in Fig. 1-4.

Plate resistance. In a d-c circuit we know that the current flowing through the circuit is proportional to the applied voltage—the proportionality factor being the resistance of the circuit. If we plot current versus voltage, and since the resistance for any given circuit is constant, the result will be a straight line. The slope of this line will be a measure of the resistance, i.e., the steeper the slope, the lower the resistance and vice versa. This is shown in Fig. 1-5 for three resistance values. The circuit

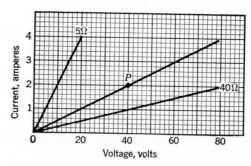

Fig. 1-5. Effect of resistance value on slope of *E-I* curve.

resistance for the middle curve is not marked. How can we find this resistance value? Let us see the method from a problem.

Example 1:

Find the resistance represented by the slope of the middle curve in Fig. 1-5.

Solution:

1. Select any point, *P*, on the curve.
2. Read the current (2 amp) and voltage (40 v) corresponding to this point.
3. Applying Ohm's law

$$R = \frac{E}{I} = \frac{40}{2} = 20 \ \Omega$$

How does this review of d-c apply to a vacuum tube? In a diode we saw that the plate current flowing through the tube varies with the applied voltage. In this respect, since the diode action is similar to a d-c circuit, the tube can be considered as having an internal resistance that limits the amount of current flow. Several factors contribute to creating the internal resistance of a tube. Physical structure—shape, size, and spacing—of the elements is important. Where low plate resistance is desired larger elements and closer spacing between elements are used. However, for a given physical structure, the negative space charge is largely responsible for the internal resistance of the diode. As you will see in a later chapter, a gas diode by neutralizing the space charge has much lower plate resistance.

Just as the ratio of voltage to current in a d-c circuit is the circuit resistance, similarly in a vacuum tube the ratio of the total plate voltage to the resulting total plate current is known as the *d-c plate resistance* (R_p). Figure 1-6 shows a typical plate voltage-plate current characteristic for a

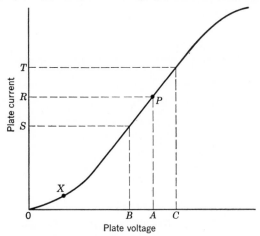

Fig. 1-6. Determination of plate resistance.

diode. Notice that this curve is not a straight line. This must mean that the current is not directly proportional to the voltage—or that the proportionality factor, plate resistance, is not constant. If the tube is operated at conditions corresponding to point X, the slope of a line from zero through this point approaches the horizontal—the plate resistance is high. Whereas at point P a straight line from zero through point P is steeper and the plate resistance is lower. It is therefore important, when evaluating plate resistance, that this quantity is determined at the actual operating point.

If this tube were to be operated at conditions corresponding to point P, the d-c plate resistance would be given by the ratio of OA (the total plate voltage) divided by OR (the total plate current).

Since tubes are generally used with a-c or with varying potentials, a much more important quantity is the *a-c plate resistance* (r_p). This value is obtained from the ratio of a *small change* in plate potential to the resulting *change* in plate current, or

$$r_p = \frac{\Delta e_b}{\Delta i_b}$$

(The symbol Δ, delta, is used to denote a small change.)

Due to the curvature of the diode characteristic, the a-c plate resistance will also vary depending on the operating point. For accurate results, not only should this value be determined at the operating point, but even more important, the small increment of voltage or current should be taken halfway on each side of this level. This procedure is shown in Fig. 1-6. The a-c plate resistance (r_p) for the conditions at point P is given by the ratio of BC (Δe_b) divided by ST (Δi_b).

Applications of diodes. Figure 1-7(a) shows an a-c sine-wave voltage applied to a resistive load through a diode. What effect would the diode have on the current through the circuit and on the voltage across the resistor? From the earlier discussion we can answer this easily. Current can flow only in one direction (cathode to plate) and only when the plate is positive compared to cathode. Therefore current flows only during the half-cycles of input which make the plate positive. We also know that in a resistive circuit the current is in phase with the voltage and (by Ohm's law) proportional to the voltage. Putting this all together, it should be obvious that the current must be sine wave in shape for *one half-cycle of input* and zero for the other half-cycle. This waveshape is shown in Fig. 1-7(b).

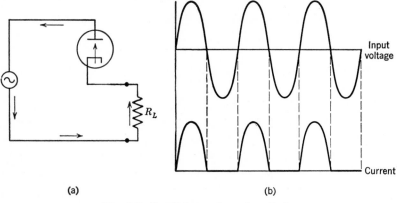

| (a) | (b) |

Fig. 1-7. Rectifying action of a diode.

From your knowledge of complex waves * you should recognize this as the output from a half-wave rectifier having a d-c component equal to 0.318 of the maximum value of the wave. In this application the diode is used as a *rectifier* to obtain d-c from an a-c supply.

Some other applications of the diode include detector circuits, automatic volume-control circuits, clipper circuits, and the d-c restorer circuit used in T.V. receivers to maintain proper background illumination of the screen. Each of these applications will be discussed when the individual circuits are studied.

Triode Characteristics

As the name implies, a triode has three active elements. Two of these we have already discussed—the plate and the cathode. The third element is called the *grid*. Figure 1-8 shows the schematic diagram of a triode and also a structural diagram. The grid structure consists of a mesh or helix of

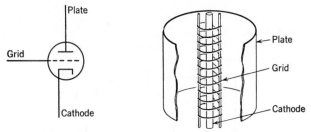

Fig. 1-8. Triode: symbol and construction.

* DeFrance, J. J., *Alternating Current Fundamentals,* 2nd Ed. (Prentice-Hall, Inc., Englewood Cliffs, N. J., 1957) Chaps. 3.

wire extending the full length of the cathode. The spacing between the turns of the mesh or helix is wide and the winding is made of fine wire, so that the passage of electrons from cathode to plate is practically unobstructed by the physical size of the grid structure. The grid is located between the plate and cathode, but much closer to the cathode than to the plate.

The purpose of the grid is to control the amount of plate current flowing through the tube, independently of the plate potential or cathode temperature. From this action it is often referred to as the *control grid*. This nomenclature is necessary to distinguish this grid from additional grid structures found in multigrid tubes. When the grid is made positive, it will counteract some of the limiting action of the negative space charge, and the plate current will increase. On the other hand, if the grid is made negative, the electric field around the grid structure will assist the space charge in holding back electrons, thereby reducing the plate current.

In normal operation of vacuum tubes the cathode temperature is kept constant at the recommended value, by applying rated voltage to the heater (or filament). The plate current flowing in a triode will therefore depend on the respective grid and plate voltages (compared to cathode). The grid is usually operated at a lower potential than the cathode, making the grid negative compared to cathode. This grid-to-cathode voltage is referred to as the *grid bias*. The plate current will increase or decrease as the grid bias is made less negative or more negative.

Triode characteristic curves. In order to study the operation of a triode and to pick suitable operating conditions, it is necessary to know the value of plate current that would flow for any value of plate and grid potentials. Such information can be obtained by experiment. The results are best shown graphically. A circuit suitable for obtaining this data is shown in Fig. 1-9.

If the grid voltage is kept constant at some value, and the plate voltage is varied in steps from zero to maximum, a series of plate current readings

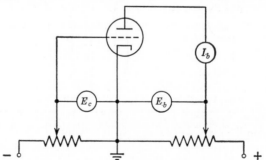

Fig. 1-9. Circuit for determining triode characteristics.

will be obtained. We can now plot a curve of plate current versus plate voltage for the fixed value of grid voltage. This curve is called a *plate characteristic* curve. Now we can change the grid voltage by a small amount and repeat the above procedure. We get a second plate characteristic curve. This process can be repeated for many values of grid voltage. The group of resulting plate characteristic curves is known as a *family* of plate characteristics for the tube. These curves can be obtained from tube manufacturers. Plate characteristic curves for a 6J5 (triode) are shown in Fig. 1-10.

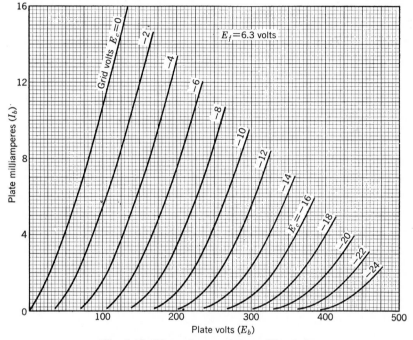

Fig. 1-10. Plate characteristics: 6J5 triode.

The same information could have been obtained with a sort of reverse procedure. That is, we could have held the plate voltage constant while we varied the grid voltage. The resulting curve is called a *mutual characteristic*. The term *mutual* is used because it shows the effect of the grid, (which is part of the input circuit), on the plate circuit, (which is part of the output circuit). By repeating this procedure for several values of plate potential, we get a *family* of mutual characteristics. Such a family of curves is shown for a 6J5 in Fig. 1-11.

The same information is presented by either family of curves. In general, the plate characteristics present the data in more usable form. Occasionally the mutual characteristics are preferable. However, it is a simple enough matter to construct the mutual characteristic curves from the plate family, or vice versa.

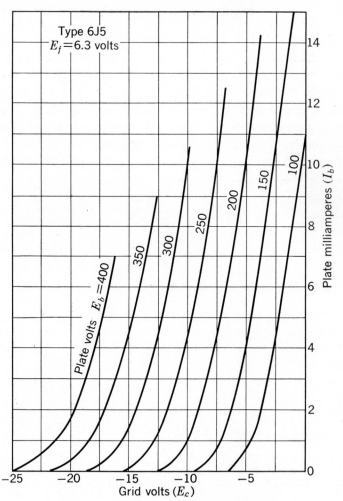

Fig. 1-11. Mutual characteristics: 6J5 triode.
[Note: 5/16 in. = 0.5 v (grid) or 0.2 ma (plate).]

You may have noticed in Figs. 1-10 and 1-11 that the plate current, plate voltage, and grid voltage were also referred to by the symbols I_b, E_b, and E_c, respectively. The use of the symbols I and E for current and voltage are already familiar to you. The subscripts will need further explanation, and will be discussed fully later. For the moment we will just say that the subscript b refers to a plate circuit value and the subscript c to a grid circuit value.

Let us see some simple illustrations of how these curves can be used.

Example 2:

Find the plate current that will flow in a 6J5, if the plate potential is 200 v and the grid potential is —6 v.

Solution:

Starting on the abscissa (*x* axis) at 200 v, move straight up till you intersect the curve $E_c = -6$. Now move to the left to the *y* axis and read (interpolate) 7.5 ma.

Example 3:

What plate voltage is required to give a plate current of 4.0 ma with a grid voltage of −8 v?

Solution:

Starting at 4.0 ma on the *y* axis, move horizontally to the right till you intersect the $E_c = -8$ curve, then down to the *x* axis, and read 207 v.

Example 4:

What grid voltage is necessary to limit the plate current to 8 ma with a plate potential of 250 v?

Solution:

Starting at 8 ma (*y* axis) move horizontally to the right, till you intersect the 250-v plate potential line. At this point imagine a new E_c line (or draw it in lightly), parallel to the E_c lines on each side ($E_c = -8$ and $E_c = -10$). Notice that this line is approximately one fifth of the distance between the −8 and the −10 grid voltage lines. The desired grid voltage can be estimated at −8.4 v.

The above problems were solved by using the plate family characteristics. They could also have been solved by using the mutual characteristics. In fact, the latter would have been easier to use for Example 4.

Amplification factor (μ, mu). The addition of a third element, the grid, to a vacuum tube makes the tube usable as an amplifier. Since the grid is much closer to the cathode than the plate, a small change in the voltage applied to the grid would have the same effect on the plate current as some large change in plate voltage. The *amplification factor* (μ) of a tube is a measure of the effectiveness of the grid voltage relative to the plate voltage in controlling the plate current. The value of the amplification factor of a tube depends on the relative size and location of its elements, but primarily on the grid structure itself. Larger grid wires, closer spacing of the grid wires, or greater distance between grid and plate all contribute to making the electric field of the grid more effective in controlling the plate current and will therefore result in a higher amplification factor. Triodes are classified as low-, medium-, or high-mu tubes depending on their amplification factor, which varies from as low as 3 (low-mu) to as high as 100 (high-mu). The simplest method for computing the amplification factor of a triode is to find what *small* change in grid voltage is necessary to counteract a *small* change in plate voltage *so that the plate current remains constant.* Expressing this relation by formula

$$\mu = \frac{\Delta e_b}{\Delta e_c} \quad (\text{for constant } i_b)$$

Are you wondering why the emphasis on a small change? It is a good question. However, to answer the question at this time is a little difficult —but only because we are not quite ready to use the tube in an actual circuit. And yet it is an important basic principle. So let us try to clarify the point, even if the details must be left to later.

From Figs. 1-10 and 1-11 we see that the characteristic curves of a typical triode are not straight lines. As a result, the amplification factor will vary depending on where along the curves we evaluate this quantity. This means that we must first select the operating point. (As you will learn later, amplifier tubes are operated in the straight-line section of their characteristics for best results.) This operating point is fixed by selecting the d-c grid bias and the d-c plate potential applied to the tube. In commercial applications, a signal voltage (a-c) is also applied to the grid circuit of the tube. The change in grid potential (above and below the d-c bias) will cause a change in plate current. The plate current is therefore a complex wave consisting of a d-c component due to the original operating point conditions, and an a-c component due to the a-c grid signal. The amount of change in plate current—the magnitude of the a-c component and consequently the degree of amplification—depends on the slope of the tube characteristic. A flat characteristic gives us a small plate current change. On the other hand, a steeper characteristic woud result in a much larger a-c component. But for a given tube the slope of the section of the characteristic curve used depends on the operating point chosen, and for small changes to either side of this operating point this section of the curve can be considered straight. So when evaluating the amplification factor, if we take small increments in grid bias—above and below the operating point— the effect of curvature of the characteristic curves is minimized, and the resulting answer will be accurate. Let us apply this to a problem.

Example 5:

Find the amplification factor of a 6J5 tube for an operating point of $E_c = -6$ v and $E_b = 200$ v.

Solution:

We will use the plate characteristic curves (Fig. 1-10) and take a change in grid voltage from −4 to −8 (2-v swing on either side of the operating point). Draw a horizontal line passing through the point $E_c = -6$ v and $E_b = 200$ v. The plate current for this operating point is 7.5 ma. To hold the plate current constant at this value when E_c is −4 v requires a plate potential of 160 v. Similarly for a grid voltage of −8, the plate potential must be 240 v. Therefore $\Delta e_c = 4$ v and $\Delta e_b = 80$ v, and

$$\mu = \frac{\Delta e_b}{\Delta e_c} (I_b \text{ constant}) = \frac{240 \text{ to } 160}{-8 \text{ to } -4} = \frac{80}{4} = 20$$

For best accuracy the change in voltage should be as small as possible. However, owing to the limitations of our characteristic curve plots, the ±2 volt grid swing to either side of the operating point was most convenient.

Plate resistance and conductance. As in the case of the diode, a triode tube also has an "internal resistance" that limits the amount of current for a given plate voltage. But now the grid potential also affects the plate current. In the diode we learned that the a-c plate resistance was given by

$$r_p = \frac{\Delta e_b}{\Delta i_b}.$$

To eliminate the effect of the control grid all we need do is *hold the grid potential constant,* and the same equation applies. It should be obvious that the a-c plate resistance will vary—again depending on the operating point. Plate resistances for triodes range from as low as 300 for low-mu tubes to approximately 100,000 ohms for high-mu tubes.

Example 6:

Find the a-c plate resistance for the tube of Example 5 (operating point $E_c = -6$ v and $E_b = 200$ v).

Solution:

Let us take a plate current change of 1 ma above and below the operating value of 7.5 ma. Since the grid potential must be held constant, our data is readily taken from the plate characteristic curves along a constant E_c line. In this case, it will be along the $E_c = -6$ line.

1. For $E_c = -6$ v and $I_b = 6.5$ ma, $E_b = 192$ v
2. For $E_c = -6$ v and $I_b = 8.5$ ma, $E_b = 208$ v

$$r_p = \frac{\Delta e_b}{\Delta i_b} = \frac{192 \text{ to } 208}{6.5 \text{ to } 8.5} = \frac{16}{0.002} = 8000 \ \Omega$$

Another value which is sometimes desirable is the converse of the a-c plate resistance or the *plate conductance* (g_p). Since conductance is the reciprocal of resistance, it should be obvious that

$$g_p = \frac{\Delta i_b}{\Delta e_b} \quad \text{(for constant } e_c \text{)}$$

In the above problem, the plate conductance would be

$$g_p = \frac{\Delta i_b}{\Delta e_b} = \frac{0.002}{16} = 0.000125 \text{ mho}$$

Conductance for vacuum tubes is so low that it is always expressed in micromhos. In the above case the plate conductance would then be given as 125 micromhos.

Transconductance or mutual conductance. We know what conductance means—the ability of a circuit to conduct current. We applied this to the *plate* circuit and saw that *plate* conductance is the ratio of change in *plate* current to change in *plate* voltage *for a constant grid potential.* Notice that both current and voltage changes are in the plate circuit. But we know that the grid voltage will also affect the plate current. There is therefore a *mutual* effect between plate and grid electrodes. *Transconductance, mutual conductance,* or *control grid-plate transconductance* (g_m) are all terms used to show the relation between plate current and grid voltage *for a constant plate voltage.* By formula:

$$g_m = \frac{\Delta i_b}{\Delta e_c} \quad \text{(for } e_b \text{ constant)}$$

If we remember the meaning of conductance and of the term "mutual," this formula should be obvious.

Example 7:

Calculate the mutual conductance for the tube in Example 5 (operating point $E_c = -6$ v and $E_b = 200$ v.)

Solution:

Let us use a grid swing of 2 v above and below the operating point. Since E_b must be kept constant, we can take our data along the vertical line corresponding (in this case) to $E_b = 200$.

1. For $E_b = 200$ v and $E_c = -4$ v, $I_b = 13.2$ ma
2. For $E_b = 200$ v and $E_c = -8$ v, $I_b = 3.4$ ma

$$g_m = \frac{\Delta i_b}{\Delta e_c} = \frac{3.4 \text{ to } 13.2 \text{ (ma)}}{-8 \text{ to } -4} = \frac{9.8 \times 10^{-3}}{4}$$
$$= 2.45 \times 10^{-3} \text{ mho} = 2450 \text{ } \mu\text{mhos}$$

These tube coefficients compare favorably with the values given in tube manuals for a 6J5 tube. Any discrepancy is due to the difference between our selected operating point and the operating point recommended in the manuals.

The amplification factor of a tube is given by the "μ" of the tube. In practical circuits, you will learn later, it is impossible to achieve the full amplification of the tube, due to the loss in its own internal resistance, r_p. To realize maximum gain in a circuit, a tube should have a high amplification factor but also a low plate resistance. For best results, the ratio of amplification factor to plate resistance should be as high as possible. But this ratio is the mutual conductance of the tube! This can be readily shown as follows:

$$\mu = \frac{\Delta e_b}{\Delta e_c} \tag{1}$$

$$r_p = \frac{\Delta e_b}{\Delta i_b} \tag{2}$$

Dividing (1) by (2) we get

$$\frac{\Delta e_b}{\Delta e_c} \times \frac{\Delta i_b}{\Delta e_b} = \frac{\Delta i_b}{\Delta e_c} = g_m$$

Therefore
$$g_m = \frac{\mu}{r_p}$$

Mutual conductance is one of the most important of the tube coefficients. It is widely used in the design of electronic equipment, both in the selection of suitable tubes and in the calculation of the a-c component of the plate current.

It is obvious from the above relation for the three tube coefficients that if we know any two values we can find the third. For example, from the results of Examples 5 and 6 ($\mu = 20$ and $r_p = 8000$) we could solve for mutual conductance:

$$g_m = \frac{\mu}{r_p} = \frac{20}{8000} \times 10^6 = 2500 \text{ } \mu\text{mhos}$$

This checks fairly well with the value (2450) previously found from the curves. The reason for the slight discrepancy can be readily explained. In Problems 5, 6, and 7 we used graphs and had to interpolate for values. A slight misjudgment in any interpolation would account for this small difference in the two values of our g_m coefficient.

We have mentioned earlier in this chapter that the values of the tube coefficients vary with the choice of operating point. This can be readiy verified by repeating Examples 5, 6, and 7 for various other initial values of grid bias and plate potential. Any change in these potentials will naturally affect the initial value of plate current. Figure 1-12 shows the variation of amplification factor (μ), plate resistance (r_p), and mutual conductance (g_m) with change in operating point, using the operating plate current as indication of the operation point.

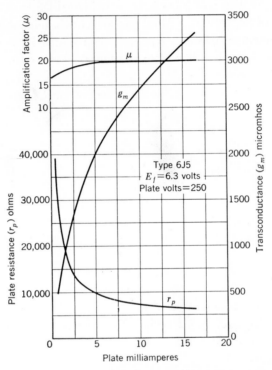

Fig. 1-12. Effect of operating point on tube coefficients.

Interelectrode capacitance. You already know that capacitance exists between any two conducting materials separated by a dielectric.* From this it is obvious that capacitance effects must exist between grid and cathode, grid and plate, and plate and cathode. These capacitances are called *interelectrode capacitances.* They are represented by symbols as follows:

Grid-plate capacitance: C_{gp}
Grid-cathode capacitance: C_{gk}
Plate-cathode capacitance: C_{pk}

---

* DeFrance, *Direct Current Fundamentals,* Chap. 20.

Interelectrode capacities are quite low, ranging from approximately 2 to 12 micromicrofarads. At low frequencies their effects are negligible. However these effects cannot be neglected at high frequencies.

At radio frequencies the grid-to-plate capacitance, C_{gp}, introduces serious complications. The reactance of even this small capacitance is low, and r-f currents from the output circuit of the tube are fed back to the input circuit. This may cause the tube to act as an oscillator producing its own sine waves in addition to amplifying the input r-f waves. These unwanted oscillations will prevent proper functioning of the circuit. Numerous "neutralizing" methods were devised to compensate for the effect of this interelectrode capacitance. The real cure, however, was the reduction of the grid-to-plate capacitance to negligible values. How this was accomplished will be discussed in a later chapter.

Figure of Merit

At the higher radio frequencies such as are used in television and ultra high frequency applications, the tubes selected for such service should have not only high mutual conductance, but also low input and output capacitances. The ratio of these two factors, $g_m \div (C_i + C_o)$, has been suggested as a measure of the usefulness of a tube at these frequencies. This ratio, called the *figure of merit,* should be high. At low frequencies, the shunting effect of the input and output capacities is negligible and only the mutual conductance (g_m) need be considered.

Review Problems

1. Explain "surface barrier potential" and its effect on emission.
2. Explain "image charge" and its effect on emission.
3. (a) What is meant by work function?
   (b) In what unit is it measured?
4. What general condition must be satisfied before an electron can escape from the surface of a material?
5. Name and describe briefly four practical ways by which electron emission can occur.
6. Discuss briefly the construction, operation, and relative advantages of the two types of commonly used cathodes.
7. (a) What materials are used for thermionic cathodes?
   (b) Compare the relative merits of each.
   (c) What type of cathode construction is generally used with each material?

8. (a) Explain the formation of a space charge.
(b) What is the effect of cathode temperature on the space charge?
9. Draw the schematic diagram of a diode and label the parts.
10. Explain how current flows through a diode.
11. (a) Explain "voltage saturation."
(b) What is the effect of increasing the heater current on the saturation level?
(c) Is a tube normally operated at or beyond the voltage saturation point? Explain.
12. (a) What is meant by temperature saturation?
(b) Explain the shape of the plate current versus cathode temperature curve.
(c) Why does the saturation point occur at a higher temperature when using a higher plate potential?
(d) Give another name for temperature saturation.
13. (a) What is meant by the d-c plate resistance of a tube?
(b) What is meant by the a-c plate resistance?
(c) State several factors that contribute to these effects.
14. (a) Give the equation for determining the d-c plate resistance of a diode.
(b) Give the equation for determining the a-c plate resistance of a diode.
(c) Why should small increments be used for the a-c determination?
(d) Why does the plate resistance vary with the operating point?
15. Figure 1-13 shows the characteristic curve of a commercial diode used in high voltage rectifier circuits of T.V. receivers.
(a) Find the current flowing through the tube when the voltage across the tube is 25 volts.

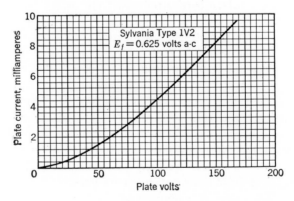

Fig. 1-13.

(b) Find the d-c plate resistance for this operation point.

(c) Find the a-c plate resistance at this same point.

16. From Fig. 1-13 and a plate voltage of 100 volts, find:

(a) plate current;

(b) d-c plate resistance;

(c) a-c plate resistance.

17. Draw the schematic diagram for a triode and label all elements.

18. Explain how the grid potential controls the plate current.

19. Draw a circuit suitable for determining the characteristic curves of a triode.

20. Explain how, with the above circuit, you would obtain:

(a) the plate characteristics;

(b) the mutual characteristics.

21. From the characteristic curves of a 6J5 (page 17) fill in the missing values in the table below.

	E_c	E_b	I_b
(a)	−2	120	?
(b)	−5	160	?
(c)	−7	180	?
(d)	?	240	6 ma
(e)	−12	?	4 ma

22. For a 6J5, corresponding to an operating point of 250 volts plate and −10 volts grid bias, find:

(a) amplification factor;

(b) a-c plate resistance;

(c) mutual conductance.

(d) Repeat (c) by calculation from the values obtained in (a) and (b) and compare with the answer from (c).

23. For a 6J5, corresponding to an operating point of 150 volts plate and −6 volts grid bias, find:

(a) amplification factor;

(b) a-c plate resistance;

(c) mutual conductance.

(d) Repeat (c) by calculation from the values obtained in (a) and (b) and compare with the answer from (c).

24. Figure 1-14 shows two mutual characteristic curves for a 7B4 high-mu triode. This tube is to be used in a circuit and the operating point is fixed by a plate potential of 250 volts and a d-c grid bias of −1.0 volts. An a-c signal of 0.141 volts is applied in series with the bias voltage. Find:

(a) the maximum value of the a-c signal;

(b) the maximum instantaneous grid potential;

(c) the minimum instantaneous grid potential;

(d) the maximum instantaneous plate current;

(e) the minimum instantaneous plate current;

(f) the change in plate current—or peak-to-peak value of the a-c component of plate current.

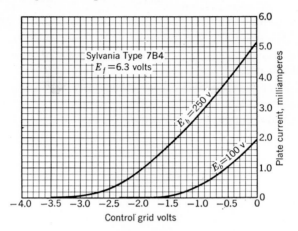

Fig. 1-14.

25. The above 7B4 is now operated at 250 volts plate and −2.0 volts grid. Again using an a-c signal of 0.141 volts, find (a) through (f) as in Problem 24.

26. The 7B4 of Problem 24 is now operated at 250 volts plate and −2.5 volts grid. Still using an a-c signal of 0.141 volts, find (a) through (f) as in Problem 24.

27. In each of the last three problems, the input a-c signal was the same. Explain why the a-c component of plate current is different. How does selection of operating point affect gain?

CHAPTER 2

Dynamic Characteristic

Curves

The triode characteristic curves shown in the previous chapter are known as *static* characteristic curves. Such curves are applicable only for a static or constant plate potential. They were obtained with the plate of the tube directly connected to the d-c supply voltage. In commercial applications of the triode, for example as an amplifier, you will learn that some form of load impedance must be connected between the plate of the tube and the power supply. Let us consider the effect of a simple resistance load R_b. Since the plate current flows through the load, a voltage drop I_bR_b will appear across this resistor. The plate potential will be less than the power supply voltage. To distinguish between plate potential and plate supply voltage the following subscripts are used:

E_{bb} for the plate supply voltage, and

E_b for the plate potential.

It follows that for any given plate current (I_b) the plate potential is

$$E_b = E_{bb} - I_bR_b$$

Let us see how this change affects our utilization of the static characteristic curves studies in the previous chapter. Figure 2-1(a) shows a triode (12AT7) with its grid connected to a bias supply of —2 volts and its plate connected through a plate load resistor of 30,000 ohms to a plate supply of 300 volts. The plate *static* characteristic curves for this tube are shown in Fig. 2-1(b). Can we find the plate current for the conditions given? We know that the plate current is determined by the intersection of the grid potential and plate potential values. Since we know the grid bias value is −2 volts, the plate current value must be found along the $E_c = -2$ line. But all we know about the plate potential, E_b, is that it is some value less than the supply voltage of 300 volts. How do we proceed?

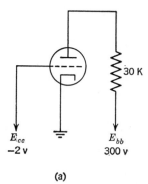

E_{cc}
−2 v

E_{bb}
300 v

(a)

Fig. 2-1. 12AT7 triode with load resistance and construction of load line.

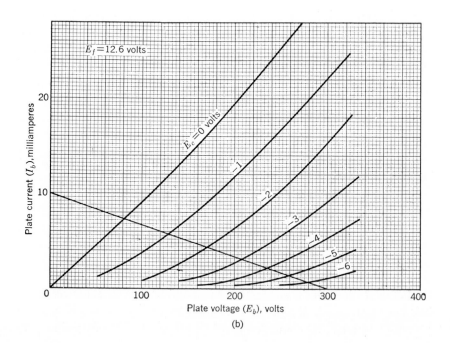

(b)

For the moment let us assume that the drop across the load resistor is 60 volts and that $E_b = 240$ volts. Then at the intersection of the 240 plate volt line and the —2 grid volt line we read a plate current of 9.4 milliamperes. Using this value of plate current to see if our assumed plate potential is valid, we get

$$E_b = E_{bb} - I_b R_b = 300 - 9.4 \times 10^{-3} \times 30,000 = 18 \text{ v}$$

Obviously our assumption of $E_b = 240$ volts was very inaccurate. Of course we could start again with a lower assumed value for E_b and repeat the process. If we are lucky or persistent, we will eventually get the true value for plate potential and plate current. However such a technique can hardly be considered a scientific approach.

Load line. There is a much more direct attack to solve the above problem. You will notice that the coordinates of the plate characteristic curves are E_b and I_b. We also know that because of the addition of the plate load resistor the relation between E_b and I_b is given by the equation

$$E_b = E_{bb} - I_b R_b$$

Since E_{bb} and R_b are fixed values, this is a first-degree equation and can be represented on the same axes by a straight line. This line is known as the *load line* and determines the locus of the E_b-I_b points for any given value of plate load resistance. It is therefore the *dynamic plate characteristic curve* for the given supply voltage and plate load resistance.

To add the load line to the characteristic curves all we need are two points. These two points are most readily established as follows:

1. When the plate current (I_b) is zero, the plate potential (E_b) is equal to the plate supply voltage (E_{bb}). This gives us our first point on the plate voltage axis corresponding to $E_b = E_{bb}$.

2. The plate potential will be zero at a current value that makes $I_b R_b = E_{bb}$, or when $I_b = E_{bb}/R_b$. This gives us our second point on the plate current axis at the value of E_{bb}/R_b.

3. By joining these two points we have our load line.

Example 1:

Using the plate characteristic curves of Fig. 2-1(b),
(a) Draw the load line for a plate load resistor of 30,000 ohms and a plate supply voltage of 300 v.
(b) Find the plate potential and the plate current for these circuit conditions, for a bias voltage of —2 v.

Solution:

1. Locate the two points for the load line
   (a) $E_b = 300$ and $I_b = 0$
   (b) $E_b = 0$ and $I_b = \dfrac{E_{bb}}{R_b} = \dfrac{300}{30,000} = 10$ ma
   (c) Draw the load line.
2. From the intersection of this load line and the $E_c = -2$ v line read $E_b = 170$ v and $I_b = $ **4.4 ma.**

Dynamic (mutual) characteristic. As we saw in the previous chapter, the mutual characteristic family of curves show the relation between grid voltage (E_c) and plate current (I_b) for several values of *constant plate potential.* But due to the plate load impedance used in commercial circuits, the plate potential will drop as the plate current is increased. Obviously no one of these *static* curves will represent the true condition of operation. Here again we must convert from static curves to the dynamic characteristic for the particular plate load resistance and supply voltage. Unfortunately, the solution is not quite as simple as the load line we previously drew on the plate characteristic curves. This time we will need a point-by-point determination since the mutual dynamic characteristic curve is not a straight line. The simplest technique is to use the plate characteristic curves with the proper load line added and pick off the plate current values corresponding to several grid voltage values. Let us apply this method to the 12AT7 triode used in Exampe 1.

Example 2:

Figure 2-2 shows the mutual characteristic curves for the 12AT7 triode. On this same diagram, draw the dynamic mutual characteristic curve for a plate supply voltage of 300 v and a plate load resistor of 30,000 ohms.

Solution:

1. Using the plate characteristic curves for this tube, draw the load line for the given values of supply voltage and load resistance. [See Fig. 2-1(b).]
2. At the intersection of this load line and each grid voltage curve read the plate current values.
3. Tabulate E_c and corresponding values of I_b.
4. Plot these points on Fig. 2-2 and draw the curve. (See light curve in Fig. 2-2.)

Notice how much straighter (and flatter) the dynamic curve is as compared to the static characteristics.

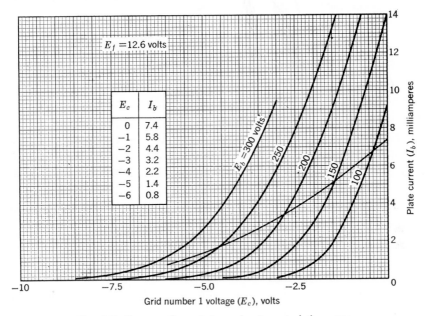

E_c	I_b
0	7.4
−1	5.8
−2	4.4
−3	3.2
−4	2.2
−5	1.4
−6	0.8

$E_f = 12.6$ volts

Grid number 1 voltage (E_c), volts

Plate current (I_b), milliamperes

Fig. 2-2. Construction of dynamic characteristic curve.

The load line shown in Fig. 2-1(b) is a dynamic characteristic curve for a given E_{bb} and R_b, plotted on the plate family of curves. Similarly the light line shown in Fig. 2-2 is *the same* dynamic characteristic curve, but this time plotted on the mutual family of curves. It is customary to refer to the former as the load line and the latter as simply the dynamic characteristic curve (the term mutual being dropped). But remember they are both dynamic curves (in fact one and the same curve) shown in different form. Sometimes it is preferable to use one form over the other.

You might be wondering, since the original static characteristic curves (plate or mutual) are not used as is, and these dynamic curves are so important, why doesn't the tube manufacturer supply dynamic curves rather than static curves? That is a natural error to fall into. It is true that the value of the static curves is merely that they enable us to construct dynamic curves. Yet remember that a particular dynamic curve applies only for a given value of plate load impedance and plate supply voltage. Obviously there are very many combinations of E_{bb} and R_b that could be used for any one tube. The circuit designer selects his values to fit his specific needs, and other circuit considerations. It would be impractical for the tube manufacturer to present dynamic curves for all possible combinations. On the other hand, with just one family of plate (or mutual) characteristic curves, the designer has all the information he needs.

Standard Nomenclature and Symbols

When dealing with electron tube circuits, various values of currents and voltages are encountered. It is important that we clearly identify each of these. To prevent confusion standard nomenclature and symbols are used. We have already employed some of them, for example, E_{bb} for the d-c plate supply voltage and E_b for the d-c plate potential. We are now ready to expand this concept. Figure 2-3 shows a 12AT7 triode with its plate connected as before through a load resistance of 30,000 ohms to a d-c plate supply voltage of 300 volts. Therefore the dynamic characteristic curve developed in Fig. 2-2 applies to this circuit. The d-c bias supply volt-

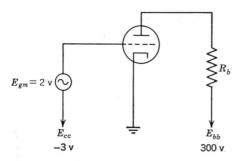

Fig. 2-3. Triode circuit with a-c signal voltage added.

age has been raised to —3 volts. This time, however, an a-c source, having a maximum value of 2 volts, is connected in series between the grid of the tube and the bias supply. This a-c source is used to represent a *signal* voltage applied to the grid circuit. Obviously, the instantaneous grid potential will vary, and will be the vector sum of the d-c bias and the instantaneous value of the a-c signal voltage. Consequently the instantaneous value of the plate current will also change. These changes must follow in accordance with the dynamic characteristic curve for this tube for the given operating conditions (E_{bb} = 300 volts, R_b = 30,000 ohms, and a d-c bias of —3 volts).

For convenience in analyzing these changes in voltages and currents, the dynamic characteristic (Fig. 2-2) has been redrawn to a larger scale as Fig. 2-4. Below the grid bias axis is shown a graphical representation of how the instantaneous grid potential varies with time, owing to the combined action of the d-c bias voltage and the a-c signal voltage. To the right of the dynamic characteristic curve is shown the resulting variation of plate current with time. During time interval *A-B,* the a-c grid signal voltage has not yet been applied, and therefore both the grid potential and plate current are constant. This has been done to show a comparison between the "no-signal" and "signal" conditions.

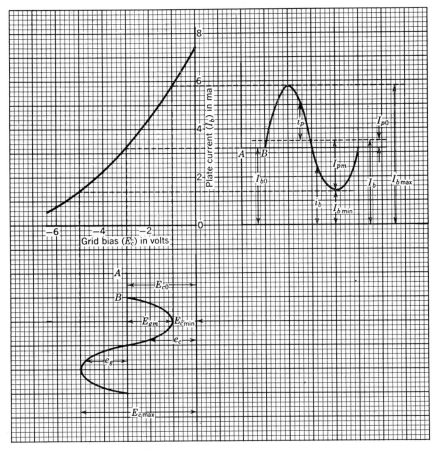

Fig. 2-4. Use of dynamic characteristic to show effect of grid signal voltage on plate current. Standard tube current and voltage nomenclature.

It should be noticed in Fig. 2-4 that the waveshapes for grid potential and plate current (except for time interval A-B) are complex waves having a d-c and an a-c component. The a-c component introduces the problem of distinguishing between maximum, effective, and instantaneous values. This is readily solved by using standard a-c nomenclature: E_m or I_m for maximum values; E or I for effective values; and e or i for instantaneous values. But we still have another problem in nomenclature and symbols. How do we distinguish between the a-c component values themselves and the total current or potential due to the combined effect of the d-c and a-c components? In the grid circuit, this is done by using the subscript *g* for the a-c or signal component, the subscript *c* for the total value, and the subscript *cc* for the fixed or d-c bias supply voltage. Plate circuit values are differentiated by using the subscript *p* for a-c component, *b* for the total value, and as you already know *bb* for the fixed or d-c plate supply voltage. This system of nomenclature is shown in Fig. 2-4.

One other point must be brought out. Notice the value of plate current before the signal voltage is applied (3.2 milliamperes). This is known as the *no-signal* or *quiescent* value of the plate current. This is the value that would be indicated by a d-c milliammeter in the plate circuit, before the signal is applied. When a signal is applied, the average value of the complex wave rises to 3.5 milliamperes. This is the *total average* value and represents the d-c component which would now be indicated by the d-c milliammeter.

Since the plate current varies, and the plate circuit contains a series plate load resistor, the plate potential must also vary. Therefore the plate potential waveshapes would also be complex waves containing an a-c and a d-c component. The same system of nomenclature as for plate current is used. Table I shows all nomenclature and symbols in convenient chart form.

Table I. Electron Tube Current and Voltage Values
(standard nomenclature and symbols)

COMPONENT VALUE	Grid CKT		Plate CKT	
	Current	Voltage	Current	Voltage
Power supply	......	E_{cc}	......	E_{bb}
Quiescent or zero signal value	I_{c0}	E_{c0}	I_{b0}	E_{b0}
Total value, average	I_c	E_c	I_b	E_b
Total value, maximum	$I_{c\,max}$	$E_{c\,max}$	$I_{b\,max}$	$E_{b\,max}$
Total value, minimum	$I_{c\,min}$	$E_{c\,min}$	$I_{b\,min}$	$E_{b\,min}$
Total value, instantaneous	i_c	e_c	i_b	e_b
Varying (a-c) component, maximum ..	I_{gm}	E_{gm}	I_{pm}	E_{pm}
Varying (a-c) component, effective ...	I_g	E_g	I_p	E_p
Varying (a-c) component, average	I_{g0}	E_{g0}	I_{p0}	E_{p0}
Varying (a-c) component, instantaneous	i_g	e_g	i_p	e_p

Filament or heater supply: E_{ff}
Terminal voltage: E_f
Current: I_f

Note: For multigrid tubes subscript numerals are used to distinguish between grids, i.e., E_{cc1}, E_{cc2}. Also, the single letter subscript *m* cannot be used for *total* values, since such quantities have minimum as well as maximum values.

Review Problems

1. Explain briefly why the static characteristic curves cannot be used directly in the design of commercial applications of a tube.

2. What symbols are used to distinguish between plate supply voltage and plate potential?

3. (a) What is the name given to the dynamic characteristic when plotted on the static plate family of curves?
(b) How does the curve differ from a static curve?

4. It is intended to operate a tube from a specific plate supply source, bias supply source and with a specific plate load resistor. The proper load line is drawn. Explain briefly, does this load line still apply if:
(a) the plate supply voltage is changed;
(b) the grid bias supply voltage is changed;
(c) the value of plate load resistor is changed.

5. (a) How many points are needed for constructing a given load line on the plate static characteristic curves?
(b) Specify how two such points can be obtained.

6. Using the plate characteristic curves of the 6J5 (page 17), draw the load line for a plate supply voltage of 300 volts and a plate load resistor of 20,000 ohms.
(a) Find the plate potential and plate current corresponding to a grid bias of —4.0 volts.
(b) Repeat (a) for a grid bias of —1.0 volts.
(c) Repeat (a) for a grid bias of —8.0 volts.

7. Using the plate characteristic curves of the 12AT7 (page 30), draw the load line for a plate load resistor of 22,000 ohms and a plate supply voltage of 340 volts.
(a) Find the plate potential and plate current corresponding to a grid bias of —3.0 volts.
(b) Repeat (a) for a grid bias of —1.5 volts.
(c) If a plate current of 8.0 milliamperes is desired what bias value should be used? What will the plate potential be?
(d) Repeat (c) for a place current of 4.0 milliamperes.

8. Using the data of Problem 6, tabulate values for the dynamic (mutual) characteristic curve. Plot this curve.

9. (a) What two subscripts are used to denote grid circuit values?
(b) Repeat (a) for plate circuit values.
(c) Explain briefly why two subscripts are needed in each case.

10. State briefly the meaning of each of the following symbols:
(a) E_{cc}
(b) E_{cc2}

(c) i_g

(d) E_{gm}

(e) I_{b0}

(f) $E_{b\,min}$

(g) I_p

(h) $I_{b\,max}$

(i) E_{p0}

11. Under what conditions will the no-signal d-c plate current differ from the d-c plate current reading when a signal voltage is applied?

12. A 12AT7 is to be operated with a load resistor of 22,000 ohms from a 340-volt supply. Using the plate characteristic curves on page 30:

(a) Tabulate values for the dynamic characteristic curve. Plot this curve.

(b) Plot grid voltage and plate current wave shapes for a d-c grid bias of −1.5 volts and a signal voltage, E_{gm}, of 1.0 volts.

(c) Give values for each of the following: $E_{c\,max}$, $E_{c\,min}$, I_{b0}, $I_{b\,max}$, $I_{b\,min}$, I_{pm}, I_{p0}.

13. A 6J5 is to be operated at the following conditions: $E_{bb} = 300$ volts; $R_b = 20,000$ ohms; $E_c = -4$ volts; $E_g = 1.414$ volts. Using the plate characteristic curves of page 17, repeat (a), (b), and (c) as in Problem 12.

CHAPTER **3**

Multielement Tubes

In Chapter 1 we were shown that although the triode made amplification of signal voltages possible, this tube presented two limitations—high input capacitance, due to Miller effect, and danger of producing unwanted oscillations particularly at higher operating frequencies. Actually, both these problems were created by the grid-to-plate interelectrode capacitance. Obviously both problems would be solved by reducing the grid-plate capacitance to negligible values. Research toward this solution led to the insertion of additional elements in the basic tube structure. This gave rise to the multielement tubes which will be discussed in this chapter.

Tetrodes

With the addition of a fourth element, the resulting tube is called a *tetrode*. The purpose of this new element is to shield the grid from the plate. Since electrons must flow through this new element to the plate, the element is made in the form of a grid. From its construction and purpose, it gets the name *screen grid*. A cross-section diagram of the tube structure is shown in Fig. 3-1.

The screen grid tube is also manufactured with a single screen structure. In this case the outer section of the screen structure (G_3 of Fig. 3-1) is eliminated. The shielding with this type of construction is not as complete and the grid-plate capacitance is slightly higher than with the dual screen

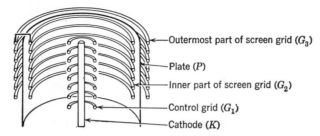

— Outermost part of screen grid (G_3)

— Plate (P)

— Inner part of screen grid (G_2)

— Control grid (G_1)

— Cathode (K)

Fig. 3-1. Cross-section view showing one type of screen grid construction.

sections. However, this latter construction is usually adequate. Most screens are now of this type. The schematic diagram for such a screen grid tube is shown in Fig. 3-2.

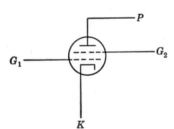

Fig. 3-2. Schematic diagram of screen grid tube.

Normally the screen is operated at a positive d-c potential. However, its a-c potential is held at ground level (zero) by connecting a suitable bypass capacitor from this element to ground. This grid serves as an electrostatic shield effectively preventing any interaction between the electric fields of the plate and grid. This shielding action eliminates nearly all the capacitive feed-back from plate circuit to grid circuit. The grid-plate capacitance of tetrodes is reduced to approximatey 0.005 micromicrofarad. The defects discussed in a previous chapter for triode tubes are now negligible except at extremely high frequencies.

Action of screen grid on current flow. A tetrode is normally operated with negative grid voltage, positive screen voltage, and still more positive plate voltage. *These voltages are all with respect to the cathode.* Very often the cathode of a tube is not at ground potential. This is especially common in "self-bias" circuits as you will learn later when studying voltage amplifiers. In such cases the cathode is operated with a positive potential. Then with the grid at ground potential, we have a negative bias on the tube, or the grid is negative *compared to cathode*. This illustration is being used not to discuss bias methods but rather to emphasize the importance of measuring all tube element voltages between the desired element and the cathode.

As for the triode, variation of grid potential will control the amount of current flowing within the tube. But now we have a screen grid which shields the plate from the space charge region. The electric field of the plate cannot pull electrons out of this area. *The plate current is therefore almost entirely independent of the plate potential.* How does plate current flow through the tube? The screen is positive. Electrons are attracted from the space charge toward the screen grid. Due to the strong attractive force, the electrons are accelerated and move toward the screen at high velocities. Remember that the screen is a grid structure. Most of the electrons shoot past the spaces of the grid structure and are now attracted to the more positive plate, forming a plate current flow. Some of the electrons hit this grid structure and flow through the screen grid and power supply back to the cathode. In a tetrode, therefore, the cathode emission produces a *screen grid current* as well as a plate current. The magnitude of the screen grid current will depend on the physical structure of this grid and on the relative potentials of the screen and plate.

Tetrode characteristic curves. Characteristic curves for a tetrode can be obtained in much the same manner as was shown for triodes. With the grid voltage held constant at some negative value, and the *screen voltage held constant* at some positive value, the plate potential can be varied from zero to maximum. The variation in plate current (and screen current) with plate potential can then be plotted. The process can be repeated for various fixed values of grid voltage to give a family of curves. Throughout this determination the screen voltage must be held constant at some posi-

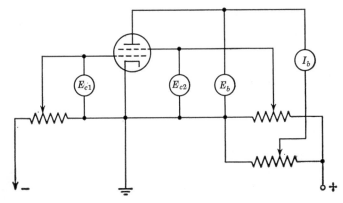

Fig. 3-3. Circuit for determining tetrode characteristics.

tive potential. The family of curves is therefore valid only for this screen voltage, and the data should be clearly and appropriately marked to show at what fixed value of screen voltage the curves were obtained. If the operating characteristics of a tetrode are desired for some other screen voltage a *new family* of curves must be obtained with the screen voltage *fixed at this new value.* A circuit suitable for experimental determination of the characteristic curves of a tetrode is shown in Fig. 3-3.

In Fig. 3-4 are shown a typical plate current and screen current characteristic obtained for a tetrode for one fixed bias and fixed screen potential. If we examine these curves, several peculiarities are noticed. Let us see what causes these effects. Remember that the screen is operated at some positive potential. The usual value of this screen potential is around $+100$ volts.

1. At *A*, a high value of screen current flows. This is readily explained; the high screen potential draws electrons from the space charge through the control grid structure (as in a triode). Electrons flowing to the screen are moving at fairly high velocity as they reach the screen. Since the screen is only a grid structure, some of these electrons will pass through the screen wires and continue on toward the plate. As they approach the plate, the electrons are decelerating rapidly. Since the plate is at zero potential, it does not attract these electrons. Disregarding Edison effect, we find that these electrons are attracted *back* to the positive screen. The screen current is high, the plate current is practically zero.

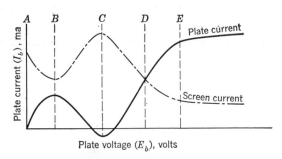

Fig. 3-4. Typical characteristic curves for a tetrode.

2. Between *A* and *B,* the plate potential is rising, but it is still much lower than the screen potential. Some of the electrons passing through the screen wires are attracted to the plate; fewer of these electrons return to the screen. As a result, the plate current begins to increase, while the screen current is decreasing. Meanwhile, due to the increased potential of the

plate, the electrons moving toward the plate are reaccelerated and reach the plate with higher velocity.

3. Between *B* and *C* the plate potential is becoming greater; electrons moving toward the plate are accelerated to such an extent that they hit the plate with sufficient velocity to knock *other* electrons off the plate itself. This type of emission by bombardment is called *secondary emission.* The secondary emission electrons are directed toward the screen, and since the screen is at a higher potential than the plate, these electrons are attracted to the screen, increasing the screen current. Meanwhile the plate current actually decreases. In fact, the secondary emission effect may be so great that the plate current may drop to zero and even reverse; the secondary emission current from plate to screen may be greater than the current flowing from the cathode to the plate.

4. Between *C* and *D,* the plate potential is still higher. The electrons moving toward the plate reach the plate at higher velocities. Secondary emission is increased. But now the plate potential is approaching the screen potential, and an increasing number of secondary emission electrons are recaptured by the plate. As a result, the plate current begins to increase again, while the screen current drops.

5. Beyond *D,* the plate potential is now higher than the screen potential. All the secondary emission electrons are attracted back to the plate. In addition all the electrons that pass through the screen wires are drawn to the more positive plate. The screen current is due only to those electrons that actually hit the screen wires. The plate current increases, while screen current drops.

6. Now remember that the number of electrons drawn from the space charge depends almost entirely on the grid bias and screen potential. The plate, *being screened from the space charge,* can have little effect on the space charge. With fixed grid and screen potentials, once the plate captures all the electrons passing through the screen wires and all the secondary emission electrons, the plate current can hardly increase further—regardless of further increase in plate potential. This levelling effect is noticed in the characteristic curve beyond point *E.*

Normally a tetrode is operated in this region beyond point *E,* that is, the plate potential should not be allowed to drop below the screen potential. Sometimes a tetrode is deliberately operated in the region between *B* and *C* on the characteristic curve (Fig. 3-4). Notice that the plate current in this region decreases as the plate potential increases. This is contrary to the action that would take place in a standard resistive circuit and represents a *negative resistance* characteristic. When a tetrode is operated in this manner, as an oscillator, it is known as a *dynatron oscillator*.

Tetrode tube coefficients. Tetrode tube coefficients have the same meaning and may be determined from characteristic curves in exactly the same manner as for triodes, with one slight modification. Since the screen grid potential affects the shape of the characteristic curves, this potential must be maintained constant during evaluation of the tube coefficients. Furthermore, coefficients calculated for one screen voltage will not apply at another screen potential. The coefficients must therefore be determined at the operating value of screen voltage. Since each family of curves is determined at a fixed screen potential, merely select the appropriate characteristic curves corresponding to the desired screen voltage. But the plate current–plate voltage curves of a tetrode are almost horizontal! As a result it is almost impossible to interpolate for small changes in plate current, plate voltage, or grid voltage with any degree of accuracy. Consequently, coefficients determined by graphical means are only approximate. In practice, tube coefficients are determined by dynamic measurements. Such methods are beyond the scope of this text; they may be found in more detailed books on vacuum tubes. Tube coefficients can be found in tube manuals published by the various tube manufacturers.

However, certain facts about the coefficients of a tetrode should be analyzed. What is the effect of the addition of a screen grid on their values as compared to the triode? Let us consider each coefficient in turn:

1. *Amplification factor.* The control grid (G_1) still exerts full control over the plate current. On the other hand, due to the action of the screen grid (G_2), the plate potential has little effect on plate current. A small change in grid voltage will cause a change in plate current. But now, because of the decreased effectiveness of the plate voltage, a large change in plate voltage is necessary to bring the plate current back to the original value. Since, for constant plate current, a small change in grid voltage (ΔE_c) corresponds to a large change in plate voltage (ΔE_b), the amplification factor of a tetrode is much higher than for a triode. Amplification factors for tetrodes range around 400.

2. *Alternating current plate resistance* (r_p). Plate resistance for a triode was evaluated in the previous chapter from the ratio of change in plate voltage (ΔE_b) to the resulting change in plate current (ΔI_b). The interaction of the remaining element, the grid, was eliminated by holding the grid voltage constant. Naturally this evaluation applied only for that par-

ticular fixed value of grid voltage. Now in the tetrode we have an additional element, the screen grid, and the potential applied to this element will also affect the amount of plate current change for a given plate voltage change. So—when evaluating the plate resistance of this type of tube, not only must we maintain the grid voltage constant, but we must also "fix" the screen voltage at the desired operating value. Again, the plate resistance value will apply only for these operating conditions. Furthermore, if we were to introduce additional elements into any tube structure, the potentials of these new elements would also affect the operating point, and in turn the plate resistance.

In view of the above discussion, a more general statement for the plate resistance of any multielement tube would be—the ratio of the change in plate voltage to the resulting change in plate current *with all other elements held at constant potential*. It must be realized, of course, that if the plate resistance is required for some other operating conditions, all voltages must be fixed at these new conditions. But this definition corresponds to the slope of the i_b-e_b curve, and in a tetrode we saw that the plate current curve is almost horizontal. This means that a very large change in plate potential is required for a small change in plate current. The plate resistance for a tetrode must therefore be much higher than for a triode. Plate resistance for tetrodes runs over 500,000 ohms.

3. *Mutual conductance* (G_m). We saw earlier that mutual conductance can be found by dividing the amplification factor by the plate resistance. The increase in amplification factor for the tetrode is offset by the greater increase in plate resistance. As a result, the mutual conductance of tetrodes is less than for triodes. Usual values of tetrode transconductance range around 1000 micromhos.

Limitation of tetrodes. In normal operation, with an a-c signal applied to the grid circuit, the plate potential of a vacuum tube varies as shown in Fig. 3-5. The waveshapes shown are complex waves, consisting of a d-c component (250 volts, in the example shown), and an a-c component having an amplitude of A or B. A discussion of how and why the plate potential varies in this manner must be delayed till amplifier circuits are studied. Here it is sufficient to point out that the voltage output and power output of a vacuum tube are dependent on the amplitude of this a-c component. Obviously, in Fig. 3-5, the solid curve (amplitude A) would result in greater voltage and power output.

How does this concern tetrode limitations? In the discussion of secondary emission it was stated that the plate potential should not fall below the screen potential. Assuming a normal screen potential of 100 volts, this would mean that the a-c component must be limited to an amplitude shown by B in Fig. 3-5. This limitation seriously reduces the maximum voltage

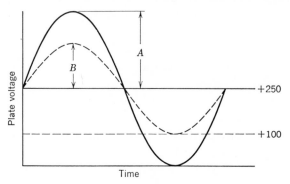

Fig. 3-5. Variation of instantaneous plate potential of a vacuum tube in normal operation.

and power output available from a tetrode. The range of operation could be greatly increased if the effects of secondary emission were eliminated.

Pentodes

The addition of a third grid structure to a vacuum tube accomplishes the above desirable effect. This new grid, called a *suppressor* (G_3), is located between the screen grid and the plate. The tube now has five active elements and is therefore classified as a *pentode.* With the advent of the pentode, tetrode tubes have become almost obsolete. Then why was so much time spent on tetrode characteristics? The reasons are twofold: first, to show the historical developments giving rise to the pentode and, secondly, because knowledge of the tetrode characteristics and limitations is basic to understanding pentode operation. Figure 3-6 shows the arrangement of elements in a pentode.

Action of suppressor grid. In normal operation the suppressor grid is connected to the cathode. In fact some pentodes are manufactured with this grid *internally* connected to the cathode. Most pentodes however have all three grids brought out to pin connections; the suppressor can then be tied to the cathode by external connection for normal operation, or connected to some other potential for special operating features.

The suppressor does not eliminate secondary emission. Secondary emission from the plate still takes place. But now, by the action of this new grid, the secondary electrons are recaptured by the plate even though the plate potential may be far below the screen potential. Therefore, the *effects of secondary emission are suppressed,* and the "dip" in the plate current–plate voltage characteristic curve is eliminated (see Fig. 3-7).

This desirable result is achieved as follows: Since the suppressor grid

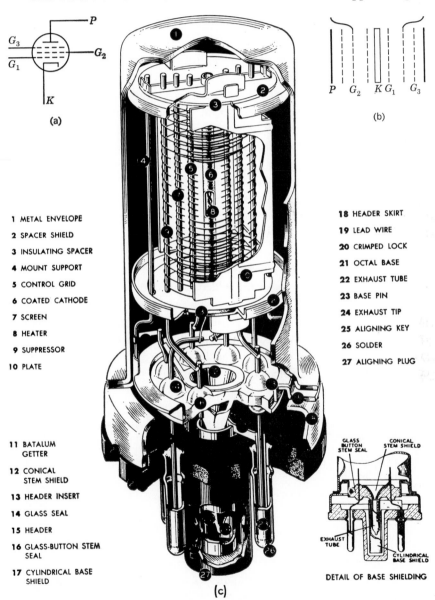

1 METAL ENVELOPE

2 SPACER SHIELD

3 INSULATING SPACER

4 MOUNT SUPPORT

5 CONTROL GRID

6 COATED CATHODE

7 SCREEN

8 HEATER

9 SUPPRESSOR

10 PLATE

11 BATALUM GETTER

12 CONICAL STEM SHIELD

13 HEADER INSERT

14 GLASS SEAL

15 HEADER

16 GLASS-BUTTON STEM SEAL

17 CYLINDRICAL BASE SHIELD

18 HEADER SKIRT

19 LEAD WIRE

20 CRIMPED LOCK

21 OCTAL BASE

22 EXHAUST TUBE

23 BASE PIN

24 EXHAUST TIP

25 ALIGNING KEY

26 SOLDER

27 ALIGNING PLUG

(a)

(b)

(c)

DETAIL OF BASE SHIELDING

Fig. 3-6. Pentode vacuum tube: (a) schematic diagram; (b) electrode arrangement; (c) cutaway view of metal case pentode.

is connected to the cathode, it operates at near zero potential. The positive electric field of the screen grid is unable to reach through the barrier of the suppressor grid and affect the region between suppressor grid and plate. The electrons from the cathode still produce secondary emission as they hit the plate with high velocity. But now, these secondary electrons are no longer attracted to the screen grid. Temporarily they may gather around the suppressor grid to form a *virtual cathode*. Almost immediately these electrons are recaptured by the plate, since the plate potential is positive with respect to the suppressor grid.

Because of this action of the suppressor grid, the plate potential limitation of the tetrode does not apply to the pentode. Consequently, the plate potential of a pentode can be allowed to swing far below the screen potential. Such operation results in greater maximum voltage and maximum power output ratings for pentodes. One additional, very important feature for the pentode is that it allows the tube to operate with equal supply voltage applied to the plate and screen. This is a distinct advantage in a-c/d-c and battery-operated receivers where the maximum power supply voltage available is around 100 volts.

Pentode characteristic curves. Using the same circuit diagram as for a tetrode (Fig. 3-3) and with the added connection of suppressor tied to cathode, it is a simple matter to obtain the characteristic curves for a pentode. Plate characteristics can be obtained by varying the plate potential from zero to maximum value, with fixed values of control grid and screen grid voltages. A family of curves can be obtained by repeating this procedure for several fixed values of control grid potentials. Such a plate characteristic family is shown for a typical pentode in Fig. 3-7. If data at some

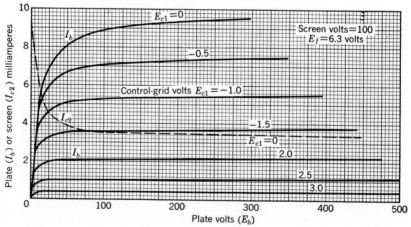

Fig. 3-7. Plate characteristics: 6SH7 pentode.

other screen potential is desired, a *new* family of curves must be obtained with the screen voltage held constant at the new desired value.

How could we obtain the mutual characteristic curves for a pentode? We know that a mutual characteristic shows the effect of grid voltage in controlling the plate current. The plate and screen voltages should be kept constant to prevent variation in plate current resulting from any control action of the screen or plate. So, with the same circuit as is used for plate characteristic curves, we now merely vary the grid potential from zero to maximum while holding the plate and screen potentials fixed at some value. In this way we obtain the data for plate current versus grid voltage along one constant plate potential line.

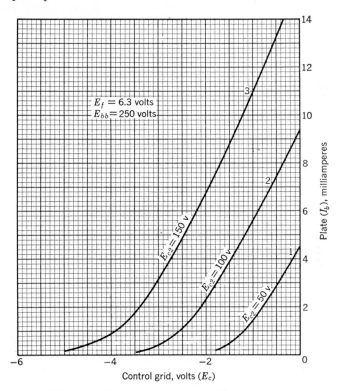

Fig. 3-8. Mutual characteristics: 6SH7 pentode.

By repeating the process for several different fixed values of plate potential, the mutual family of curves can be obtained. This family of curves applies only for the selected fixed value of screen voltage. Again, if data on the tube is required at some other screen voltage, the entire family of curves must be obtained with the screen voltage held constant at this new value. Figure 3-8 shows a mutual characteristic curve obtained with a

6SH7 at one constant plate potential. It also shows how this relation between plate current and grid voltage is affected by choice of the fixed screen potential.

Pentode tube coefficients. Comparison of the plate characteristic curves for a pentode (Fig. 3-7) and for a tetrode (Fig. 3-4) shows that the tubes are quite similar in performance (except for the dip found in the tetrode characteristic). Therefore, for the same reasons as explained under tetrodes, graphical determination of the pentode coefficients will give only approximate values. Accurate values for these coefficients can be found in tube manuals. Due to the additional shielding action of the suppressor grid, the plate potential in a pentode has even less effect on the plate current than in the tetrode. It is therefore not surprising to find that a pentode has a higher amplification factor and a higher plate resistance than the tetrode. Typical values for a pentode are:

1. Amplification factor, 1000 to 5000
2. Plate resistance, 0.5 to 2 megohms
3. Transconductance, 1000 to 9000 μmho

Usually the amplification factors for pentodes are not listed in tube manuals. As you will see later, calculations for pentode circuits are usually handled by using the combination factor, mutual conductance. However, the amplification factor, if desired, can be calculated from transconductance and plate resistance, by using the formula $\mu = G_m \, r_p$.

Remote cutoff pentodes. Pentodes are manufactured in two types— with sharp cutoff and with remote cutoff features. The sharpness or remoteness or cutoff refers to the slope of the mutual characteristic curve as it approaches low values of plate current. In a sharp cutoff tube, the slope of the curve is comparatively steep, and the plate current drops rapidly to zero. When the grid voltage is sufficiently negative, and the plate current is zero, the tube is "cutoff." For the 6SH7 tube discussed above, with a plate potential of 250 volts and a screen potential of 100 volts, a grid potential of approximately —3.5 volts is sufficient to cutoff the plate current flow. (See Fig. 3-8.) In a remote cutoff tube, the slope of the mutual characteristic curve becomes less and less steep as we approach lower and lower values of plate current. Therefore, the cutoff point is delayed or made remote. *In general much higher negative grid voltages are needed to produce cutoff in a remote cutoff tube.* An example of this type of pentode is the 6SK7. A grid bias of approximately —30 volts is necessary to cutoff the plate current in this tube even though the plate voltage and screen voltage are the same as for the above 6SH7. (See Fig. 3-10.)

The remote cutoff feature is obtained by special design of the control grid structure. The grid is wound in a spiral or helix around the cathode. At the upper and lower end of the cathode, the grid turns are close together, whereas in the central portion the spacing between turns is greatly increased. For low values of grid bias (and weak signals) the non-uniform spacing of the grid has little effect on the tube characteristics, and operation is essentially the same as for uniform spacing. As the grid bias is increased, the concentrated electric field at the ends cuts off the flow of current from these sections of the cathode. Meanwhile the electric field in the central portion with wide grid wire spacing is not strong enough to cut off current flow. This portion of the tube continues to operate, the plate current dropping gradually as less and less of the tube area remains operative until at high negative biases (approximately —30 for a 6SK7), the electric field in this portion is strong enough to cause complete plate current cutoff. The construction of this type tube can be seen in Fig. 3-9.

CATHODE PLATE

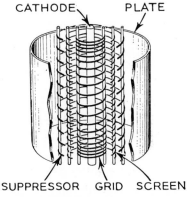

Fig. 3-9. Construction of remote cutoff tube.

SUPPRESSOR GRID SCREEN

The effect of this type of construction can best be seen from a comparison of the mutual characteristics of the sharp cutoff and remote cutoff tubes. Such a comparison is shown in Fig. 3-10, between the 6SK7 and the 6SH7. Notice how much more gradual is the decrease in plate current with increase in grid bias for the remote cutoff tube. Now comes the 64 dollar question. Of what value is this remote cutoff feature?

To answer this question requires a little more knowledge of tube operation and tube circuits. However, the following explanation should be adequate. To avoid distortion, a tube should be operated on the straight-line portion of its characteristic. For the 6SH7 tube, the straight-line portion as seen from Fig. 3-10, requires operation between 0 and —2.4 volts.

If the operating point is taken as −1.2, it will allow for a grid signal swing of ±1.2 volts (peak). Signals of larger amplitude would drive the tube into the curved or distortion area. For a 6SK7, the curvature at any point throughout the operating range is small. The tube is not driven to cutoff

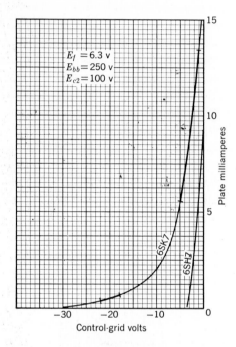

$E_f = 6.3$ v
$E_{bb} = 250$ v
$E_{c2} = 100$ v

6SK7
6SH7

Plate milliamperes

−30 −20 −10 0

Control-grid volts

Fig. 3-10. Comparison between sharp cutoff and remote cutoff tubes.

until very high negative biases are reached. This tube will handle much larger grid swings with a minimum of distortion. It can therefore be used to handle stronger signals.

There is still another advantage to the remote cutoff tube. You will recall that mutual conductance is the ratio of a small change in plate current to a small change in grid voltage at constant plate (and screen) potential. This corresponds to the slope of the mutual characteristic curve at any point. With the 6SH7, the slope of the curve is practically constant throughout the operating range. This tube has constant gain over this range. On the other hand, the slope of the mutual characteristic of the 6SK7 becomes more nearly horizontal as the grid bias is made more negative. The transconductance of this tube decreases as the operating point is made more and more negative. Notice that if the 6SK7 is operated at −20 volts bias, the characteristic is sufficiently straight between −18 and −22 and the tube can handle signals of ±2 volts swing without distortion. Also, the characteristic curve is almost horizontal in this region and the gain of the tube will be very low. Compare the a-c component of plate current obtained with an input grid signal of 2 volts maximum (± 2 volts), with operating points of -20 volts bias and -3 volts bias. (See Fig. 3-10.)

In radio receiver circuits using remote cutoff tubes, the volume level from the receiver was originally controlled manually by varying the grid bias operating point of the tube. In later receivers, this bias was varied automatically by the strength of the carrier being received. A strong

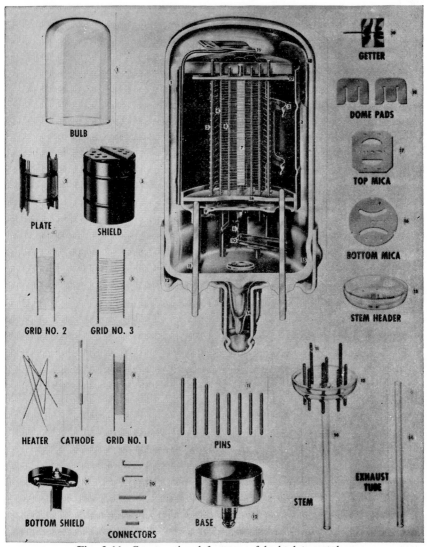

Fig. 3-11. Constructional features of locktal type tube.

signal caused a large bias to be developed and applied to the tube. This large bias caused the tube to operate on the lower, flatter portion of its characteristic, giving low gain, and thereby reducing the volume to the desired level. If a weaker signal were being received, the bias developed would be small; the tube would operate on the upper, steeper portion of its characteristic; the gain is increased; the volume is raised to the desired level. Such circuit action is called *automatic volume control* (AVC). These circuits are used to prevent a strong station from "blasting in" when the manual volume had previously been set for a weaker station.

Remote cutoff tubes find still another application when used as the first radio-frequency amplifier stage of a receiver. The receiver is tuned to the carrier of one station and its audio is heard from the loudspeaker. At the same time the audio signal from another station may be heard in the background. Such an effect is caused if the carrier of a strong local station drives the grid of the first tube into the curved portion of its characteristic. This first tube will act as a *detector* and the audio of the interfering station will "ride through" with the desired carrier. This effect is known as *cross-modulation*. By use of a remote cutoff tube, the possibility of driving the tube into extremely curved regions or cutoff is reduced and cross-modulation is largely prevented. From their action and applications remote cutoff pentodes are also known as *variable-mu* or *super-control* tubes. Details of the construction of pentode type tubes are shown in Figs. 3-6 and 3-11.

Power Output Tubes

Up to this point we have been considering tubes used primarily for *voltage amplification*. These tubes, used in proper circuits, will amplify a weak signal of only a few microvolts to several hundred volts. But the ultimate aim in any electronic equipment is to operate some load device —whether it is a relay, a motor, or a loudspeaker. For this purpose, specially constructed tubes called *power tubes* are used. The most familiar application of power tubes is in the last stage of radio receivers. Their purpose, in this case, is to deliver as much power as possible to the loudspeaker. But the power delivered to a speaker is a function of the current flowing through it (I^2R). For large power outputs, these tubes must be capable of passing high currents. In any other application the function of the power tube is to deliver large amounts of power to the operating device or "load." Again the plate current rating of the tube determines the power it can deliver to the load. Power tubes, therefore, have large emitting surfaces which may be of the direct or indirectly heated type. A typical triode power tube is the 6B4-G. Checking the tube manual data for this tube you will find that the normal plate current is 60 milliamperes. This is much higher than the normal current for the 6J5 triode (9 milliamperes) discussed in the previous chapter.

Power tubes are also available as pentodes. Power pentodes also have large emitting surfaces. In addition, when designed for power-tube application, the grid wires in pentodes are more widely spaced than in the 6SK7 or the 6SH7 types studied earlier. The more-open grid structures result in reduced shielding action and reduced suppressor action. However, much larger currents can now flow to the plate. The plate characteristic curves of the power pentode are not as flat as for voltage amplifier pentodes (6SH7 and 6SK7 type). Coefficients for the power tube can therefore be determined graphically with good accuracy. Owing to the reduction in shielding effect, the amplification factor and plate resistance of power pentodes are lower than for other pentodes. Values for a typical power pentode (6F6) are: amplification factor, 200; plate resistance, 80,000 ohms; transconductance, 2500 micromhos.

Beam-power tubes. In order to maintain the advantages of the pentode shielding and sensitivity, while still retaining the current-passing ability of the simple triode, a new power tube was developed. From its construction this tube is known as a *beam-power* tube. This tube should be classified as a tetrode in that it has only four electrodes: cathode, control grid, screen grid, and plate. In addition this tube has a pair of *beam-forming plates* that give it characteristics superior to those of a power pentode. Figure 3-12 shows the construction of a typical beam-power tube, the 6L6.

The cathode is made large to give the tube a high emission capability. In the 6L6 this cathode is indirectly heated. The control grid and screen grids are spiral windings of exactly the same size and shape wire. In addition the spirals are so arranged that each turn of the screen grid is directly in line with a turn of the control grid. This alignment of the two grids causes the electrons to travel in "sheets" through the spaces between the grid turns. Since the screen turns are "shielded" by corresponding control grid turns, very few electrons strike the screen wires. As a result, the screen current is lower than for a corresponding power pentode.

Let us now see the action of the beam-forming plates. Internally these plates are connected to the cathode; they are therefore at zero potential. These beam-forming plates effectively enclose the positive screen grid creating a zero potential region between the screen grid and the plate of the tube. As electrons from the cathode shoot past the highly positive screen at high velocity, they decelerate when they approach the zero potential region, particularly since the plate may be at a lower potential than the screen. This tends to produce a space charge effect or *virtual cathode* in

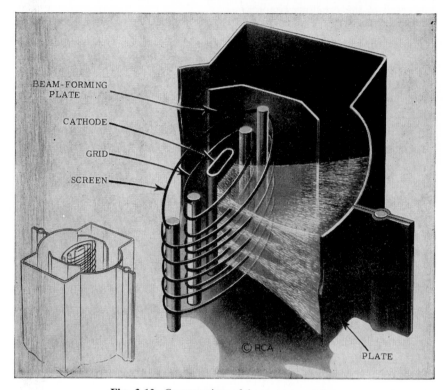

BEAM-FORMING PLATE

CATHODE

GRID

SCREEN

© RCA

PLATE

Fig. 3-12. Construction of beam-power tube.

the zero potential region. The effect of this virtual cathode is similar to the effect produced by the suppressor in a pentode tube. As a result, electrons emitted from the plate by secondary emission are repelled by the space charge or virtual cathode and caused to return to the plate. The beam-power tube therefore acts as a pentode. Since this tube does not have an actual suppressor, the added shielding action of this extra grid is eliminated. Because of this effect, and because of the alignment of control and screen grid wires, the beam-power tube has higher power output, lower plate resistance, and higher efficiency than a corresponding pentode.

Multielement Tubes

Some tubes for special or dual-purpose use have more than five active elements. For example the 6A8 pentagrid converter and the 6L7 pentagrid mixer each have five grids in addition to a plate and cathode. The 7A8 octode converter has a total of six grids. In general these tubes are used in circuits fed by two separate signals, or one signal and one or more control voltages. Typical applications are in superheterodyne receivers as mixers or converters, and in audio amplifiers as volume compressors or volume expanders. Since these tubes are used for special purposes, discussion of their operating characteristics will be taken up when the actual circuits are studied.

Multi-unit Tubes

Some tubes may seem at first to be multielement tubes. Closer investigation will reveal that these tubes are actually two or more separate tubes in one shell. Examples of multi-unit tubes are: 6H6 twin diode; 6N7 twin triode; 6R7 twin diode-triode; 6S8 triple diode-triode; 6F7 triode-pentode; 1D8 diode-triode-pentode. These tubes are used as "space-savers." For example, the 1D8 can perform the separate circuit function of a diode, a triode, and a pentode. In addition they are also more economical, in that one such tube costs less than the two or three tubes otherwise needed to perform the same functions, and also in that the multi-unit tubes have only one filament structure to heat the cathode emitting surfaces. Some multi-unit tubes have a common cathode structure serving each unit of the tube. An example of this type is the 6SC7 dual triode. On the other hand, the 6SL7 is also a dual triode, but each triode section has its own cathode structure. Although the common cathode structure is more economical in filament power requirement, the choice between common cathode structure or separate cathodes will depend on the specific circuit considerations. Unless the cathodes of the two tube functions have a common circuit connection, the separate cathode type tube must be used.

Multi-unit tubes need no further discussion. If you understand the principles of the individual basic tube types, then you know all that is necessary about multi-unit tubes.

Electron-ray Tubes

When an electron stream strikes a fluorescent material it produces a visible glow. You are already familiar with this effect from the fluorescent lighting fixtures used in homes and in industry. This property of an electron stream is also utilized in the construction of *electron-ray tubes*. The construction of a typical electron-ray tube, the 6E5, is shown in Fig. 3-13.

The tube consists essentially of a triode and an electron-ray indicator

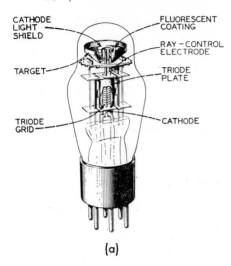

Fig. 3-13. Electron-ray tube: (a) construction; (b) schematic and characteristic.

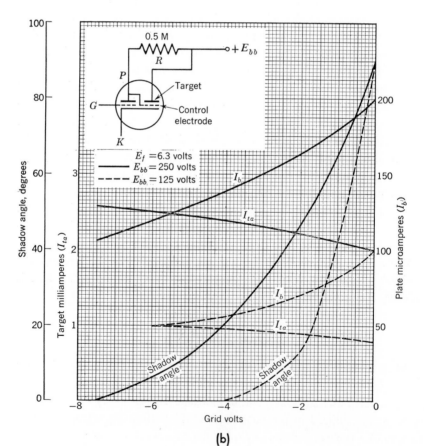

enclosed in the same bulb. The cathode supplies two separate currents: the triode plate current which is controlled by the triode grid potential, and the target current which is "directed" by the ray-control electrode potential. This ray-control electrode is connected internally to the triode plate. These two elements are therefore always at the same potential.

The operation of the tube is as follows: A high-value resistor (approximately 1.0 megohm) is connected between the triode plate and the target [see Fig. 3-13(b)]. The target in turn is connected to a high positive potential (+100 to +250 volts). If a high negative voltage is applied to the triode grid, very little plate current will flow in the triode section. The drop in resistor R will be negligible, and the target and control electrode are at the same potential. Under these conditions, the control electrode offers no barrier to the flow of target current. Electrons from the cathode strike all parts of the target causing complete fluorescence of this structure. As the triode grid bias voltage is reduced, more current flows through the triode section. The drop in resistor R increases, lowering the potential of the triode plate and of the control electrode. Now the control electrode is *negative compared to the target*. Electrons flowing to the target are repelled by the electric field of the control electrode and do not strike the portion of the target behind this electrode. This area of the target remains dark, or the "eye" of the indicator opens.

This is analogous to the situation encountered when a light source shines on a screen. If there is no barrier between the light source and the screen, the screen is completely and evenly illuminated. Now if a small barrier is placed between the light and the screen, a shadow is cast on the section of the screen behind the barrier. If the size of the barrier is increased, the shadow area is larger. Similarly, in the electron-ray tube, as the triode grid bias is further reduced, more triode plate current flows. The drop across resistor R increases. The potential of the triode plate and of the control electrode decrease further, making the control electrode still more negative compared to the target. This causes a greater electric field barrier effect and the shadow angle increases. When the triode grid potential is zero, the electrostatic field created around the control electrode is such as to cause a shadow angle of approximately 100 degrees on the target.

This tube is often used as a visual indicator replacing ammeters, voltmeters, frequency meters, volume indicators, etc. It is also used as a null indicator in bridge type circuits. The electron-ray tube does not measure the actual magnitude of the quantity but rather indicates when the quantity reaches some predetermined level. For example, in recording equipment, the degree of opening or closing of the eye is used to indicate minimum and maximum volume levels for good recordings. In receivers, it is used to indicate the best dial setting (correct tuning) for any desired station. In quality control circuits the electron-ray tube is used for quick inspection checks on tolerance limits of components. From such applications, this tube gets its popular name of *magic-eye*.

Limitations in Operating Conditions

In our discussions so far, the plate of a tube has been considered positive compared to cathode, with current flowing from cathode to plate. This is the normal situation. Now what would happen if the plate is made negative compared to cathode? The obvious answer would be—nothing; current cannot flow to the negative plate, and since the plate does not give off electrons because it is cold, no current can flow from plate to cathode. Normally, and up to a certain extent, this is true. No current can flow—in either direction—when the plate is negative compared to the cathode. But let us go back to basic fundamentals of electrostatic fields, conductors, insulators, and insulation breakdown. We know that if we apply a voltage across an insulator, such as a piece of wood, no current will flow, because wood does not have free electrons. However, if we increase the voltage across this insulator, a strong electric field is created. As the voltage is raised, this electric field becomes strong enough to *tear* electrons out of their orbital paths and force them to flow through the wood. This effect is called insulation breakdown.

The situation in a vacuum tube with reversed potentials (plate negative compared to cathode) is quite similar. The space between plate and cathode is an insulator. The plate is cold and does not give off electrons. There are no free electrons between plate and cathode. But as the plate is made more and more negative compared to the cathode, the electric field between these two elements is becoming stronger. The direction of this energy field is from plate to cathode. At some voltage, this field will be strong enough to *tear* electrons out of the cold plate. Current will flow from *plate to cathode*. This corresponds to an insulation breakdown and is undesirable. Insulation breakdown may also occur in lead-in seals. To aggravate the situation, no vacuum tube is a perfect vacuum. Some gas remains in the tube. One effect of this gas content, as you will see in the next chapter, is to lower the voltage at which this insulation breakdown will occur.

To avoid the possibility of this "inverse" current flow, manufacturers rate tubes with a *maximum peak inverse voltage*. This rating shows the maximum instantaneous or *peak* voltage that may be applied between plate and cathode, with the plate negative compared to the cathode. If this rating is exceeded, conduction in the reverse direction may take place. In rectifier service, this limitation of a tube is of extreme importance. Gas tubes—tubes in which a small amount of gas is deliberately added to improve certain operational characteristics (see Chapter 4)—are in general more critical with regard to inverse voltage rating.

Another limitation listed in tube manuals by the manufacturers is *maximum peak plate current*. This rating shows the highest instantaneous plate current that a tube can safely carry without damage to the cathode structure and without causing undue voltage drop within the tube. The safe value of this peak current depends on the electron emission available. This limitation is more important for tubes used in rectifier or pulse circuits.

It may sometimes happen that even though the maximum voltage and current ratings of a tube are not exceeded, the plate of the tube can be damaged. It is therefore necessary to put another restriction in tube ratings. This added limitation is *maximum plate dissipation*. As the plate is bombarded by electrons, the kinetic energy of these electrons is converted to heat, raising the temperature of the plate structure. If heat is produced faster than the plate can dissipate it, the temperature will rise to such a point as to either melt the plate or cause electron emission from the plate. Plate dissipation is measured in watts and is equal to the difference between the power supplied to the tube ($E_b \times I_b$) and the power output from the tube. To increase the allowable plate dissipation of a tube, large commercial tubes are designed with massive radiating fins for air cooling, or with hollow cylinders for water cooling. Figure 3-14 shows various types of commercial tubes.

If a tube has a screen grid, a similar limitation, *maximum screen dissipation,* must be considered. The product of screen voltage and screen current must not exceed this rating.

In indirectly heated tubes, it is general practice to apply a low voltage a-c to the heater of these tubes. The applied voltage should conform with the manufacturers' rating for the tube type used. Some of the more common heater voltages are: 2.5, 5.0, 6.3, 7.5 volts. When the proper heater voltage is applied, the resulting current (a-c) flowing through the filament will not only heat the heater itself, but by convection and radiation will also heat the cathode to the proper emission temperature. There should be no conduction between heater and cathode. Depending on the circuit in which the tube is used, the heater may be at a positive, zero, or negative

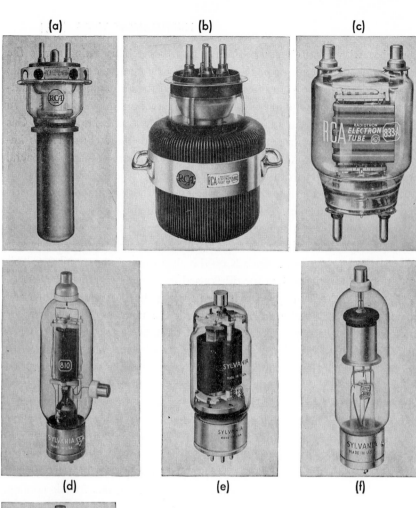

(a)   (b)   (c)

(d)   (e)   (f)

(g)

Fig. 3-14. Higher power commercial tubes:

  (a) Water-cooled power triode, output 110 kw; $24\frac{1}{2} \times 9\frac{1}{2}$ in.

  (b) Forced-air-cooled triode, output 27 kw; $17\frac{3}{8} \times 14\frac{1}{4}$ in.

  (c) Transmitter triode, output 2700 w; $8\frac{17}{16} \times 4\frac{19}{32}$ in.

  (d) Transmitter triode, output 725 w; $8\frac{3}{4} \times 2\frac{1}{4}$ in.

  (e) Beam-power tube, output 650 w; $7\frac{1}{2} \times 2\frac{9}{16}$ in.

  (f) Mercury-vapor rectifier, output 3200 v; 2.5 amp d-c; $8\frac{1}{2} \times 2\frac{5}{16}$ in.

  (g) High-voltage mercury-vapor thyratron; peak rating 15,000 v; 1.8 amp; $11\frac{1}{16} \times 3\frac{7}{8}$ in.

potential with respect to ground. Similarly, the cathode of the tube may have a positive, zero or negative potential. Usually the potentials of the heater and cathode are not the same. They may differ not only in magnitude but even in polarity. For example, the heater may be at ground (zero) potential while the cathode is at +20 volts with respect to ground; or the heater potential could be —45 volts and the cathode at +5 volts. In the latter case, the difference in potential, or voltage between heater and cathode is 50 volts. Normally this is not serious, but there is another rating or limitation given by the tube manufacturers that is sometimes overlooked. This is the *peak heater-cathode voltage* and represents the highest instantaneous value of voltage that a tube can safely stand between its heater and cathode. If this rating is exceeded a *leakage* current will flow between heater and cathode. Since the heater is energized from an a-c supply, this will introduce an unwanted a-c component in the cathode circuit current. In a radio receiver, the result will be heard as a hum in the loudspeaker output. In a television receiver, this defect will produce a black bar across the screen (or black at bottom and top of screen).

Miniature and Subminiature Tubes

As higher and higher frequencies were used in electronic applications another limitation was found in the operating characteristics of a vacuum tube. Conventional tubes were not suited to operation above 100 megacycles. This frequency limitation is due to *transit time* and interelectrode capacitance. The time required for an electron to travel from the cathode to the plate is known as the transit time. For low frequency operation, this time interval is of little importance, but at the higher frequencies the transit time may be too long compared to the period or time for one cycle of the signal frequency. At a television frequency such as 200 megacycles, the time for one cycle is 1/200 of a microsecond. A time delay of only 0.00125 microsecond would correspond to a 90-degree phase change in the signal voltage. So, it is quite possible for an electron to leave the cathode with a given phase relationship and to find drastic changes in phase relations by the time it reaches the plate.

The other objection, interelectrode capacitance, should be obvious. At very high frequencies the shunting reactance of the input and output capacitances would be so low as to cause serious attenuation of the signal frequency. Both problems were solved by designing tubes specifically for operation at these higher frequencies. One result was miniature tubes. By using closer spacing between elements, the transit time was reduced. The interelectrode capacitances were reduced by making the elements themselves smaller, and by eliminating the tube base structure. Typical of such tubes are the 6BA7, 6AK5, and the acorn tube, 954, shown in Fig. 3-15.

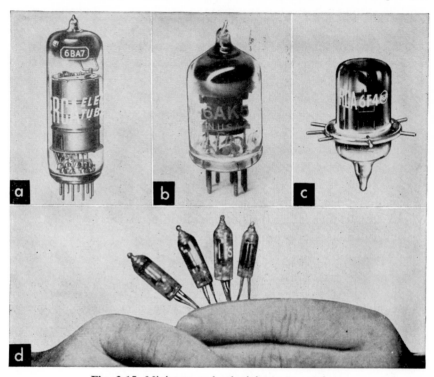

Fig. 3-15. Miniature and subminiature type tubes.

Where extremely small tubes are required, such as in hearing aid devices, this same principle was carried further, and subminiature tubes were developed. An idea of the smallness of these tubes can also be obtained from Fig. 3-15.

Ultra High Frequency (UHF) Tubes

The development of miniature tubes made it possible to extend the upper frequency limit of tubes, but when operation at ultra high frequencies (300 to 30,000 megacycles) was attempted, this solution failed. Again transit time, interelectrode capacitance, and now lead inductance from the tube element to the external pin connection prevented proper functioning of the circuits. One approach to this problem was to reduce these detrimental factors by radical changes in construction. To achieve

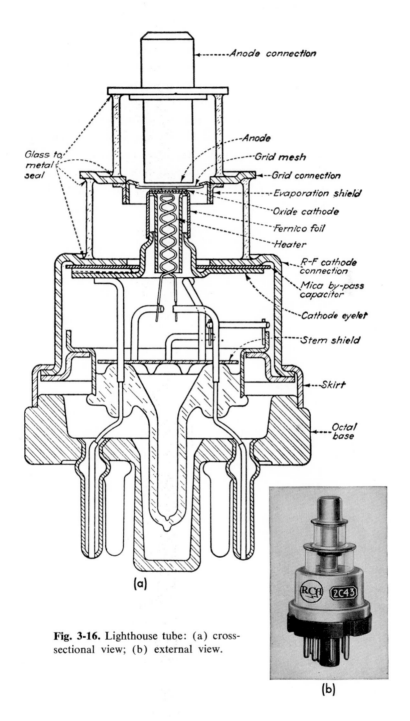

Anode connection

Anode

Grid mesh

Grid connection

Evaporation shield

Oxide cathode

Fernico foil

Heater

R-F cathode connection

Mica by-pass capacitor

Cathode eyelet

Stem shield

Skirt

Octal base

Glass to metal seal

(a)

Fig. 3-16. Lighthouse tube: (a) cross-sectional view; (b) external view.

(b)

65

this, the tube elements are arranged as parallel planes spaced very close together so as to reduce transit time. They are small so as to reduce capacitance. A short heavy metal ring in the center of the tube makes contact with the grid mesh and is used as the grid connection. Metal cylinders at opposite ends of the tube are used for the plate and cathode connection. This minimizes lead inductance. Glass-to-metal seals are then used to join the plate cylinder to the grid ring and the grid ring to the cathode cylinder. Because of this construction feature, these tubes are called *disc seal* tubes.

Figure 3-16 shows one type of disc seal tube known as a lighthouse tube so called because of its external appearance. Other forms of disc seal tubes are shown in Fig. 3-17.

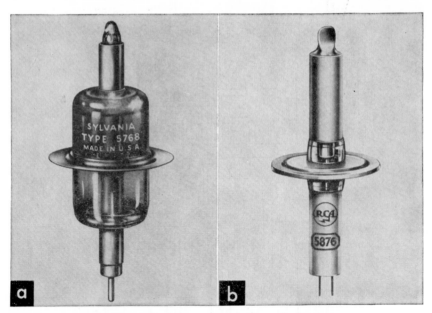

Fig. 3-17. Other types of disc seal tubes.

With the consequent reduction in transit time, interelectrode capacitance, and lead inductance, disc seal tubes are capable of operation as amplifiers or oscillators up to approximately 3000 to 3500 megacycles.

Microwave Tubes

At frequencies above 3000 megacycles, even with the small spacing of the disc seal tube, transit time again becomes appreciable compared to the time for one cycle of the signal. Further reduction of the electrode spacing is almost impossible. On the basis of the old adage "If you can't lick them, join them," design took a different line of attack. This led to the development of *klystrons, magnetrons,* and *travelling wave* tubes. In each case, the time of flight of the electrons is deliberately increased to some specific value and, in transit, kinetic energy imparted to the electrons by the power supply is converted to signal energy thereby producing oscillations or amplification.

Klystrons. Figure 3-18 shows a constructional view and external view of a dual-cavity klystron. The action of the cathode and smoother grid starts a beam of electrons moving at uniform velocity through the tube.

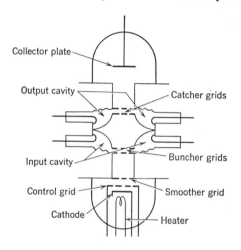

Fig. 3-18. Cross section and external view of a dual-cavity klystron.

An r-f field is applied to the grids of the input cavity resonators.* These grids, called *buncher grids,* impose a varying velocity on the electron stream. Depending on the instantaneous value of the r-f field, some electrons will be caused to speed up while at another instant others will be retarded. The variation in velocities will follow the variation in r-f field. Now the electron stream enters the *drift space.* Here those electrons that are moving faster will overtake those that were retarded in the previous portion of the r-f cycle, forming bunches. This bunching process produces strong pulsations in the electron stream at the r-f rate. At this point, the electrons reach the second pair of grids—the *catcher* grids. The catcher grids are connected to the output cavity resonator, and if the resonator is tuned to the proper frequency, strong r-f fields are set up. Power output is taken from this second resonator. The electrons, after giving up energy to the catcher grids, are attracted to the collector plate and through the power supply return to the cathode.

In the above application, the klystron tube was used as an amplifier. This tube could also be used as an oscillator if power from the output resonator is fed back to the input cavity. Another form of klystron having only a single cavity resonator is shown in Fig. 3-19. It is called a *reflex klystron.* Only one pair of grids are used, serving both as bunchers and catchers. In this tube, the plate is called a *reflector* and is made negative. As the electron stream approaches the reflector plate it is repelled back through the drift space. With the proper negative reflector potential, the electrons on the return trip will pass the grids at the instant of maximum bunching and give up energy to the cavity resonator. This tube can be used only as an oscillator, and is primarily used as a local oscillator in microwave superheterodyne receivers.

Magnetrons. The magnetron tube is essentially a diode. Its construction differs radically from the conventional diodes studied previously, and in addition it has a strong magnetic field parallel to the axis of the cathode. Before discussing the magnetron itself, let us consider the effect of a magnetic field on an electron in motion. With reference to Fig. 3-20, if the anode cylinder is made positive with respect to the cathode cylinder, electrons will travel radially from cathode to anode. One such path is shown by the dotted line *A*. Now let us add a magnetic field parallel to the axis of the cylinder, the lines of force coming out of the plane of the diagram.

---

* At ultra high frequencies, cavity resonators are used similarly to parallel resonant *L-C* circuits. The resonant frequency is a function of the volume and shape of the cavity.

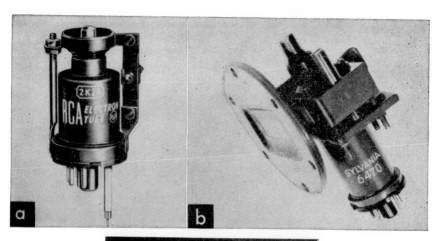

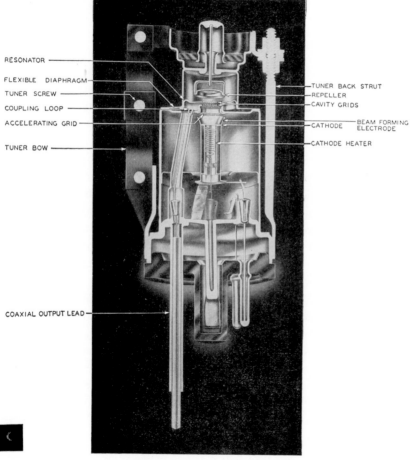

RESONATOR	TUNER BACK STRUT
FLEXIBLE DIAPHRAGM	REPELLER
TUNER SCREW	CAVITY GRIDS
COUPLING LOOP	
ACCELERATING GRID	CATHODE — BEAM FORMING ELECTRODE
TUNER BOW	CATHODE HEATER
COAXIAL OUTPUT LEAD	

Fig. 3-19. Reflex klystrons.

The dots on the diagram represent the heads of the arrows of the lines of force. The electrons in trying to move radially from cathode to anode cut these lines of force. A force reaction is produced that makes the electrons

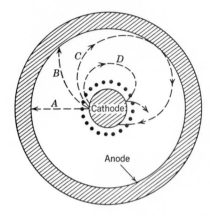

Fig. 3-20. Effect of magnetic field strength on electron path in a magnetron: *A,* no magnetic field; *B,* weak magnetic field; *C,* critical or cut-off field; *D,* strong field.

move at right angles to their original path.* The combination of the radial force of attraction from cathode to anode and the right-angle force of magnetic interaction causes the electron to move in a curved path. This shown in Fig. 3-20. If the magnetic field is weak, the curvature is small and is shown by path *B,* the electron reaching the anode. If the magnetic field is increased to a critical value, the electron will just graze the anode wall and then return to the cathode. This effect is shown by path *C.* With stronger magnetic fields, the electron will never reach the anode. The diverting force of the magnetic interaction is so great that the electron will be quickly returned to the cathode. From this point, the electron starts out once more toward the anode only to return to some new point at the cathode. This process is repeated with the electron hopping its way around the cathode.

Now let us look at a practical magnetron. Figure 3-21 shows an external view and cross-section view of this tube. Due to the action of the attractive force of the plate and the axial magnetic field, electrons travel in curved paths. As they spiral past the cavity resonators they give up

---

* This is the same principle (Fleming's rule) that you learned when studying basic instrument movements or direct-current motors. When a wire carrying current is placed in a uniform magnetic field, the interaction of the magnetic field around the wire and the original magnetic field will cause the wire to move in a direction mutually perpendicular to the direction of current flow and to the lines of force of the uniform magnetic field. In this case the stream of electrons takes the place of the wire carrying current, and the electrons themselves are diverted from their original path.

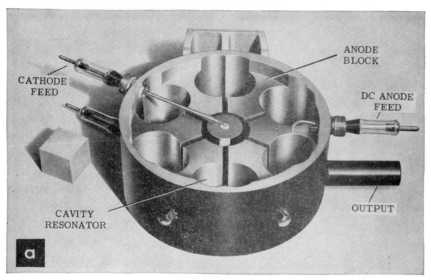

Fig. 3-21. Internal and external views of typical magnetrons.

energy, and oscillations are set up in the cavities. The frequency of oscillation depends on the size and shape of the cavities. This tube can be used only as an oscillator. Its main application is in radar and other equipment requiring short pulses of r-f power of high intensity. Magnetrons are available with peak power ratings as high as 300 kilowatts and for frequencies up to 30,000 megacycles.

Travelling wave tubes. So far, of all the tubes discussed, only the klystron is capable of amplification at frequencies above 3000 megacycles. However, the klystron produces a high noise level. The travelling wave tube, Fig. 3-22, was developed to meet this need. Basically the operation of this tube is as follows. Because of the high voltage on the anode gun, a beam of electrons is shot through the tube at relatively high velocity. The magnetic field of the focus coil aims this beam so that it passes through the center of the helix winding to the collector plate. Signal energy in the

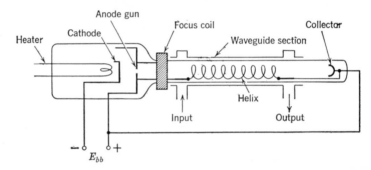

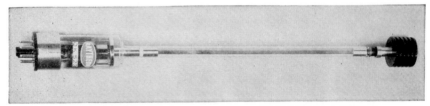

Fig. 3-22. Travelling wave tube.

form of electromagnetic waves enters at the input end of the waveguide section surrounding the helix. A short stub to which the helix is connected at this point picks up this energy in much the same manner as an antenna picks up energy from a broadcast station. The electromagnetic energy travels along the helix at about the speed of light. However the *forward velocity* through the tube is greatly reduced. Another short stub at the output end of the helix transfers energy to the output of the waveguide.

Gain is a result of the interaction of this electromagnetic field and the electron beam. The anode gun and collector potential are adjusted so that the electron beam travels through the helix at a velocity slightly greater than the forward wave velocity. We can therefore consider the wave as standing still and the electrons slowly moving past it. When the electrons reach a positive electric field, they take energy from the field, gain speed, and move through quickly. Conversely, wherever the electric field is negative, electrons are retarded and energy is transferred from the electron stream to the wave. Electrons are under the influence of a retarding field for a longer period of time than in passing through a positive or accelerating field. The net result is that the wave is receiving more energy than it is giving up. The amplitude of the wave increases as it travels along the helix. Since the output is greater than the input, amplification has been obtained.

Review Problems

1. Draw the schematic diagram of a tetrode and label all elements.
2. What disadvantage of the triode was overcome by the addition of the screen grid? Explain.
3. Explain why the plate current in a tetrode is practically independent of the plate potential.
4. Compare and explain any differences in the coefficients for triode and tetrode.
5. (a) What serious disadvantage is inherent to a tetrode?
   (b) What effect does this have in the output capabilities of the tube?
6. Explain how this disadvantage (Problem 5) is eliminated in a pentode.
7. Draw the schematic diagram of a pentode and label all elements.
8. Draw the schematic diagram of a circuit suitable for determining the characteristic curves of a pentode.
9. (a) Determine the amplification factor, plate resistance, and mutual conductance of a 6SH7 around an operating point of 250 volts plate, −2 volts grid, and 100 volts screen.
   (b) Compare these values with tube manual data.
   (c) Why is the graphical method of determining these coefficients inaccurate?
10. Figure 3-8 shows three mutual characteristic curves for a 6SH7, each obtained at 250-volt plate, but for various values of screen potentials. Using the plate characteristic family of Fig. 3-7, tabulate data and plot a similar mutual characteristic curve for 200-volt plate and 100-volt screen.

11. Using Fig. 3-7, can you obtain the data for a mutual characteristic curve for plate voltage of 200 volts and screen voltage of 150 volts? Explain.

12. How do the pentode coefficients (μ, r_p, and G_m) compare with the typical tetrode tube? Give reason for any changes.

13. Explain the difference between the sharp cutoff and remote cutoff pentode.

14. State three advantages gained by use of a remote cutoff tube.

15. What is meant by AVC? Explain briefly why and how this is used in a receiver.

16. How is the pentode construction modified for use as a power tube?

17. Is the beam power tube similar to a tetrode or pentode in: (a) number of elements; (b) characteristics? Explain.

18. Explain the advantage of a beam power tube over a power pentode.

19. (a) What is meant by a multielement tube?
    (b) Give an example. (Consult a tube manual; do not use a tube previously discussed.)
    (c) Draw its schematic diagram.

20. (a) What is meant by a multi-unit tube?
    (b) Give an example not previously mentioned in the text.
    (c) Draw its schematic diagram.

21. (a) Explain the operation of a 6AB5 tube. (Consult a tube manual.)
    (b) State two applications for this tube.

22. What is the meaning of the maximum inverse voltage rating of tubes? Why is this limitation necessary?

23. Explain the maximum peak plate current rating of tubes.

24. (a) Why is a maximum plate dissipation rating necessary?
    (b) How is this rating increased in some commercial tubes?

25. (a) Under what conditions may a leakage current flow between heater and cathode of a tube?
    (b) How can such undesired current be prevented?
    (c) What is the effect of such leakage current?

26. State two reasons why standard tube construction is not suitable for high frequency operation.

27. (a) What is meant by transit time in a vacuum tube?
    (b) Why is transit time of importance at high frequencies?

28. Explain why miniature type tubes can be used at higher frequencies than conventional type tubes.

29. State an application of miniature vacuum tubes, other than for high-frequency operation.

30. (a) What is the approximate upper frequency limit for miniature tubes?

(b) What is the general name given to tubes particularly designed for use in the UHF range?

(c) Name two specific types of tubes used in this range.

31. Name three types of tubes specifically designed for use at microwave frequencies.

32. (a) Name the elements in a klystron tube.

(b) Describe its operation briefly.

33. What is a reflex klystron used for?

34. (a) To what basic class of tubes does the magnetron belong?

(b) What additional feature does a magnetron have that is not normally found in other tubes?

(c) For what type of service is a magnetron used?

35. (a) For what type of service is a travelling wave tube used?

(b) Describe its construction.

(c) Explain briefly how amplification is obtained.

CHAPTER 4

Gas Tubes

▀▄

In the tubes we have been discussing so far, extreme care is taken to produce as perfect a vacuum as possible. The glass and metal parts of the tube are heated to sufficiently high temperatures as to drive out any occluded gases in the material. This is done both before assembly and during exhaust of the tube. In addition, an active chemical material called a "getter" is placed in the tube, and flashed or vaporized by high frequency induction heating, just before the tube is sealed. This getter tends to absorb residual gas. The action of the getter continues to absorb any gases that may be released during operation of the tube. (A commonly used getter material is an alloy of barium and magnesium.) Although no system can achieve a perfect vacuum, yet the results obtainable are such that the residual gas has a negligible effect. These tubes are, therefore, referred to as *high-vacuum* types.

Effect of Residual Gas on Tube Characteristics

Let us see what would happen if the envelope of a tube is not completely evacuated. The space between cathode and plate of the tube will contain gas molecules. Electrons flowing between these elements will collide with the gas molecules. If the velocity of these electrons is sufficiently high, they will knock other electrons off the gas molecules, creating free electrons (negative charges) and *positive gas ions*. This process is called *ionization.* The additional free electrons will flow to the plate together with the original electrons. However, the increase in plate current due to these added electrons is practically negligible. But what happens to the positive gas ions? Since they are positive they are attracted toward the cathode and toward the negative grid (if the tube is a triode, tetrode, or pentode). But these ions are relatively massive. (Remember that the weight of any atom, or molecule is due almost entirely to the nucleus). Because of this, the positive ions move very slowly and remain in the field between cathode and plate for a very long time. But these ions are positive and therefore neutralize the field created by the negative space charge.

What will happen to the plate resistance of the tube? In the first chapter we saw that the main cause of plate resistance was the negative space charge. Obviously, since the effect of this space charge is neutralized, the plate resistance will be greatly reduced. What will happen to the plate characteristic of the tube? At low plate potentials, the normal electron flow between cathode and plate is at low velocity—no ionization takes place and a tube having residual gas content will operate similarly to a normal high-vacuum tube. As the plate potential is raised, the plate current increases, again as for normal high-vacuum tubes. But the velocity of the electrons is also increasing. At some higher plate potential, the velocity of these electrons will be sufficient to start ionization. This plate potential, known as the *ionizing potential,* varies with the type and amount (pressure) of gas in the envelope. Let us analyze this situation more slowly. In a normal high-vacuum tube (or a tube with gas, but with the plate-cathode voltage below the ionization value) the amount of plate current for any plate potential is limited by the internal plate resistance. The value of this plate resistance depends primarily on the amount of electrons in the space charge. But in a tube that is not perfectly evacuated, once the ionizing potential for the particular type and pressure of residual gas is reached, ionization starts. The electrons of the normal plate current are accelerated toward the plate at high velocity. In their travel they collide with the gas atoms or molecules with sufficient force to knock other electrons off the gas molecule. As mentioned above, the positive gas ions so created drift slowly toward the cathode and since they are positive they neutralize, to some extent, the effect of the negative space charge.

With a weaker space charge field, the plate resistance of the tube decreases, and the plate current increases above the high-vacuum normal value—without any increase in plate potential! But an increase in plate current means more collisions; more collisions mean further ionization; further ionization means further neutralization of the space charge; this in turn causes further reduction in plate resistance and a greater increase in plate current—and all this occurs without any change in plate potential. Obviously these effects are cumulative, and the current rises sharply. When does it stop? Not until the current reaches saturation value. Since with normal filament temperature, saturation takes place at a current value well beyond rated value, this gas effect in a tube may quickly ruin the tube. In practical applications, the maximum current value may be limited by the resistances in the associated circuit. As the current tries to rise toward the saturation value, the IR drop across these circuit resistances will reduce the effective plate-to-cathode voltage across the tube. This reduction in plate voltage may offset the reduction in plate resistance, preventing any further increase in plate current. However, if the total circuit resistance is low, the gas effect may still ruin the tube.

There is a second detrimental effect due to imperfect evacuation. Normally positive ions drift rather slowly toward the cathode. But if the negative space charge were missing—or if sufficient gas ions were produced to more than completely cancel the space charge effect, then these positive ions would be attracted more strongly to the cathode. Under such conditions they would bombard the cathode at high enough velocities and in such quantities as to destroy the cathode. This is especially true for thoriated tungsten and oxide-coated cathodes.

Gas content can cause another problem in triodes or other tubes with control grids. In normal operation the control grid of a tube is operated at a negative potential and there is an external resistive path between grid and cathode. For resistance-coupled amplifiers, as you will learn later, it is desirable to make this grid-to-cathode resistance as large as possible. But if there is any trace of gas in a tube, the maximum value that can be used for this resistance is seriously limited. Some positive ions will be attracted to the negative grid. Grid current will flow through this external resistance to the grid and from the grid back to the cathode. The direction of this current is such as to tend to make the grid end of the external resistor positive. But this is in opposition to the original negative grid potential! The action is cumulative—the grid becomes less negative; the plate current increases; more ionization takes place; the grid current increases —and we are back on a merry-go-round. If the resistance in the grid circuit is high enough the control grid potential will suddenly become positive due to this cumulative action. The excessive plate current resulting from a positive control grid potential will ruin the tube. Tube manufacturers are aware that perfect evacuation cannot be achieved and therefore specify the maximum value that may be used for control grid to cathode resistance.

Another serious disadvantage of residual gas is that the effect of the positive ions on the space charge is irregular. Therefore irregularities will exist in the electron flow from cathode to plate. This will greatly increase the tube noise known as *shot effect,* and will limit the maximum usable amplification that can be realized from an amplifier.

When the amount of gas in a tube is quite high, the degree of ionization produced may be sufficiently intense to produce a visible glow. This glow may sometimes be noticed in an old high-vacuum rectifier or power tube. It may be due to an imperfect seal of the envelope or more likely due to the liberation of gas imprisoned in the tube elements themselves, with continued operation. Such tubes are said to have gone "soft," or gassy.

Gas Diode—Hot Cathode

From the above discussion on the effects of gas it may seem that gas in a tube should be avoided like the plague. Yet gas does produce some definite advantages, such as reduction of plate resistance. Therefore, for certain applications, gas is *deliberately* introduced into the tube envelope. These tubes are known as gas tubes. The tube is first evacuated and then a special gas is added. The gas pressure used is under careful control. Some of the commonly used gases and the typical values of ionizing potentials required with each are:

Argon	15.7 volts
Neon	21.5 volts
Helium	24.0 volts
Mercury vapor	10.4 volts

A typical example of a gas tube is the gas diode with a hot cathode. One of the main applications of such a diode is as a *rectifier,* to change alternating current to direct current. When the requirements are not severe (that is comparatively low current, or constant current), or when variation of terminal voltage with load is unimportant, high-vacuum tubes are used. But such tubes have a high internal resistance. Therefore, on heavy loads, or where good regulation (small change in voltage with varying load) is needed, gas diodes are more generally used.

At very light loads, the gas in the tube is not ionized and the tube acts similar to a high-vacuum tube—the *IR* drop in the tube increases with load. This action continues until the *IR* drop equals the ionizing potential for the particular tube. (Remember that the ionizing potential depends on the type of gas and gas pressure used.) Once this potential is reached, the gas begins to ionize. The positive ions created tend to neutralize the effect of the space charge, decreasing the internal resistance. Any further increase in load increases the degree of ionization and further decreases the internal resistance. As a result, increase in load is offset by the decrease in plate resistance and the *IR drop within the tube remains constant*. Therefore, with a gas diode, not only is the drop within the tube small (equal to the ionizing potential), but also it remains constant with load. This results in better efficiency and better regulation than for a high-vacuum tube when used in rectifier circuits. Figure 4-1 shows a comparison of the internal voltage drop for a gas tube and a corresponding high-vacuum tube.

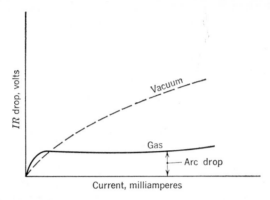

Fig. 4-1. Comparison of internal voltage drop between gas diode and high-vacuum diode.

The curves shown in Fig. 4-1 are actually the characteristic curves (E_b-I_b curves) for each diode. This would be recognized more readily if the *IR* drop were made the abcissa and labeled E_b. We have already seen from Fig. 1-2 how this curve for a vacuum diode is obtained. The identical circuit could be used to determine the characteristics of a gas diode. For convenience such a circuit, with minor variations, is shown here as Fig. 4-2(a). The heater circuit variable resistor has been removed. This is important. The reason will be explained later. *Gas tubes must be operated at rated heater current*. Currents under or over the rated value can damage the tube almost instantly. Also notice the dot in the tube symbol. Such a dot is used to distinguish gas tubes from vacuum tubes.

As was mentioned just above, the characteristic curve of Fig. 4-2(b) is really the same curve shown in Fig. 4-1, and the explanation for the shape of this curve has been given. It is interesting to note, however, that any attempt to raise the plate potential (E_b) above the ionizing value *O-A* is fruitless. Moving the potentiometer arm higher, toward the maximum E_{bb} value, results in higher plate current (I_b), and larger drop across resistor R; but the voltage across the tube (E_b) as measured by the volt-meter remains constant. As explained above, this is so because of reduced plate resistance due to greater ionization.

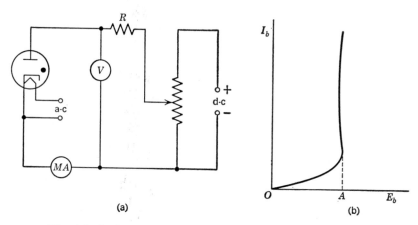

Fig. 4-2. Gas diode test circuit and typical characteristic curve.

Would removal of resistor R cause E_b to increase? No! Remember E_b is the IR drop across the tube, and within operating limits of current will remain constant. Then what is the function of this resistor? It is a safety measure. Because of the low value of the internal resistance, plate current can rise dangerously high with only a slight change in supply voltage. This resistor will limit the current. Its value should be so chosen that at maximum supply voltage the current, E_{bb}/R, should not exceed the maximum current rating of the tube.

Potential distribution in thermionic gas diodes. If we could measure the voltage between the cathode and some point in space between the cathode and the plate of a vacuum tube, we would find that the voltage rises *almost* linearly from zero at the cathode to the full plate potential value at the plate. Such a distribution or voltage gradient seems quite un-derstandable, i.e., half the distance, half the voltage drop. In practice, the curve is not quite linear but slightly concave upward. Near the cathode, the voltage is somewhat less than the linear value due to lowering effect of the negative space charge. This voltage distribution is shown as the dotted line in Fig. 4-3.

The solid curve represents the voltage gradient for a hot cathode gas diode. Notice the drastic difference. Almost the full voltage drop occurs between the cathode and a region quite close to the cathode as shown by the dotted line 1. It is almost as if the plate had been moved up to position 1. Most of the space between the electrodes (between regions 1 and 2) is called the *plasma* region. In the plasma are found electrons, positive

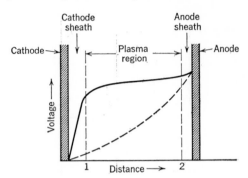

Fig. 4-3. Potential gradient between cathode and plate in a gas diode.

ions, and neutral gas atoms. Because of the presence of these ions and electrons the conductivity in this region is very good, and the voltage drop or potential gradient is very low—just enough to cause the positive ions to drift toward the cathode and the electrons toward the plate.

The region between the cathode and the plasma is known as the *cathode sheath,* or *positive ion sheath.* The negative space charge found in vacuum tubes has been neutralized by heavy concentration of positive ions, and the potential rises rapidly almost to the full value. A third region near the plate is sometimes referred to as the anode sheath. In this region the potential may have a slight drop or rise depending on shape of the plate structure, amount of current, type and pressure of gas.

Heater-cathode construction. Gas tubes are used as rectifiers for much higher loads as compared to vacuum diodes. Higher currents require higher emission from the cathodes. This could be obtained by using higher heater currents to achieve higher temperatures. But higher temperatures would cause evaporation of the active cathode material thereby reducing the life of the tube. Luckily there is a better method. In a gas tube, the electron path need not be a direct line between cathode and plate and so heat shields can be used to reduce heat losses. The hot cathodes, usually oxide-coated, can be placed inside hollow metal cylinders. This reduces radiation losses. In addition the heaters or emitting surfaces can be convoluted in such a manner that one surface heats the other. An example of this type of construction is shown in Fig. 4-4. This cathode combines direct and indirect heating, in that both the heating element (center spiral) and the *inside*

Fig. 4-4. Cutaway view of an 866A mercury-vapor gas diode, showing high efficiency cathode structure.

surface of the heat shield cylinder are oxide-coated and will emit electrons.

Limitations and precautions. Unfortunately the above type of cathode construction, although more efficient, introduces a complication. It takes a much longer time for these cathodes to reach operating temperature. Heating times of 5 or 10 minutes are not uncommon. Some larger tubes may require even longer. Because of this, whenever a gas-tube circuit is energized, filament power should be applied to the tube long enough to enable the cathode to reach full operating temperature before the plate voltage is applied. This precaution is necessary to insure that a strong enough space charge has built up to protect the cathode against positive ion bombardment. Commercial gas-tube equipment often employs time switches or relays that will delay the closing of the plate circuit (from 30 seconds to 10 minutes) after the filament power is applied. In the smaller (low current—low voltage) gas tubes used as rectifiers in receiver circuits, ion bombardment is low and the above precautions are not necessary.

Short-circuits in high-vacuum diode rectifiers are not too destructive since heavy overloads are prevented by the high internal resistance of the tube itself. But a gas diode has low internal resistance. A short-circuit would allow excessively high currents and ruin the tube. It is, therefore, important that protective devices be used with gas tubes to prevent damage to the tube or associated components. Such circuits will often incorporate quick acting fuses, relays, or current-limiting resistors.

Gas tubes are also more critical than vacuum tubes with regard to inverse voltage rating. Conduction may take place between the cold anode and the cathode as you will see later in this chapter when we discuss cold cathode tubes. This limits the peak inverse voltage to values lower than allowable for vacuum tubes. In fact, the higher the gas pressure, the lower the peak inverse voltage rating.

Thermionic gas diodes are available from such low current ratings as 115 milliamperes for the type 82 up to values approaching one hundred amperes for rectifiers used in large radio broadcasting stations. The type 866-A shown in Fig. 4-4 has a peak current rating of 2.0 amperes at a peak inverse voltage of 2500 volts or 1.0 ampere at 10,000 volts. Tubes with higher ratings are generally enclosed in metal containers. Their external appearance is similar to the ignitron shown in Fig. 4-18(a). Gas diodes are often known by trade names such as *Phanotrons* for low pressure mercury vapor tubes and *Tungar* or *Rectigon* for higher pressure inert gas tubes. These latter tubes are usually found in low voltage applications such as rectifiers for charging automative storage batteries.

Thermionic Gas Triode—Thyratron

In the gas diode previously discussed, it was noticed that the ionizing potential for any one tube type is fixed, depending on the type of gas used and the gas pressure. Very often it is necessary to control the point at which ionization is to start. Such control is obviously impossible with the previous tube. However, the addition of a third element makes this control feature practical. This new tube, a gas triode, is known by the trade name of *thyratron*. The third element in the thyratron is called a grid. However, it does not resemble the grid structures as used in vacuum tubes. Instead, this control electrode is a metal cylinder surrounding the cathode structure, with one or more perforated discs near the center. A cross section of this type of construction is shown in diagrammatic form in Fig. 4-5(a). An older type of grid structure using perforated sheet metal for the grid cylinder is also shown. The cathodes used in these tubes are of the heat-shielded high efficiency types. Thyratron tubes are available in a wide range of ratings from currents as low as a few milliamperes to peak currents of over one hundred amperes. Tubes with low ratings resemble glass-envelope receiving tubes in appearance. Two such tubes are shown in Fig. 4-6. Larger capacity thyratrons are often enclosed in cylindrical metal containers. In fact the housing itself may be used as the grid structure.

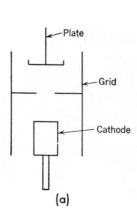

Fig. 4-5. Grid structures used in thyratron tubes.

Action of control grid. Let us analyze the effect of the grid in a gas tube. Obviously, before ionization takes place, this tube must exhibit characteristics similar to a high-vacuum triode—and it does. The plate current will increase as the plate voltage is increased, and for any fixed value of plate voltage, the current flowing will depend on the grid bias. At low plate potentials the gas is not ionized and the grid has full control of the amount of plate current flowing. At some plate potential, the tube ionizes and positive ions tend to neutralize the effect of the space charge. As for a gas diode, this results in low voltage drop within the tube. Large currents can flow from cathode to plate, and the tube has good efficiency and regulation. But now, in addition, positive ions will be attracted to the negative grid. A positive ion field surrounds the grid, neutralizing the effect of the normal negative field of the grid, and thereby preventing the grid from

Notice that the control characteristic is shown as a shaded *area* rather than a single curve.

The single curve obtained by the test procedure described above is for that *one specific tube* under the exact conditions as tested. The range of control characteristics as shown by the shaded area is for *any* GL 5544, new or old; for temperature ranges between 25 to 50°C; for heater voltage variations of ±5%; and for grid resistor values from 10,000 to 100,000 ohms. There is actually only one basic reason for the wide variation of the control characteristics, and that is gas pressure. At higher pressures (within reason) ionization is easier and will occur at lower plate potential for a given grid voltage—or at more negative grid potentials for a fixed plate voltage. Age of the tube, operating temperature, and heater voltage will affect the gas pressure.

Why does the value of grid resistor affect the critical grid voltage point? Surely this has no bearing on gas pressure. True—but it does affect grid voltage. In a thyratron, grid current flows even though the grid is negative. This current may be due to a combination of factors:

1. Some positive ions exist in the tube even before breakdown. These positive ions are drawn to the negative grid and can pull electrons out of the grid by field emission.

2. Bombardment of the grid by these positive ions can cause grid current by secondary emission.

3. The grid can be contaminated by emitting material from the cathode, and thermionic emission from such portions of the grid can occur.

4. There is a large interelectrode capacitance between grid and cathode, and if a-c is applied to the grid circuit, grid current will flow as this grid-cathode capacitor charges and discharges.

Due to this grid current, the voltage drop across the grid circuit resistor will change the grid bias, thereby affecting the control action. Since the grid current and temperature effects are variable, no one control characteristic curve would apply to any tube of a given type. Most manufacturers therefore show range of control area.

Thyratron action on alternating current. If a-c is applied to the plate-cathode circuit, it should be obvious that current cannot flow during the "negative" half cycle—when the plate is negative compared to cathode. Also, it should be obvious that current can flow during the "positive" half cycle. But will current flow for this full half cycle? Not necessarily—before the tube can conduct the plate potential must overcome the critical grid voltage control action. For example, referring to Fig. 4-7(b) for the GL 5544 thyratron you can see that at zero or positive values of grid voltage, the tube will conduct almost immediately on the positive half cycle. On the other hand, if the bias is —8.0 volts, using the left edge of the control area, what plate voltage is needed for the tube to fire? The —8.0 bias line intersects the critical voltage curve at approximately the 460-volt anode potential line. So—if the peak value of the applied a-c supply were less than 460 volts, the tube would not conduct at all. In other words, variation of grid bias can be used to control the duration of plate current flow per cycle.* This technique is shown in Fig. 4-8 for three bias values. Notice

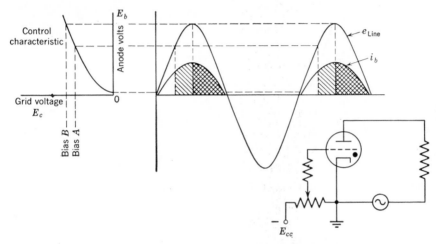

Fig. 4-8. Effect of grid bias on conduction cycle.

that at zero grid bias the tube is conducting for almost the full half cycle. At bias *A,* conduction is for approximately 135 degrees, as shown by the total shaded area, and at bias *B,* conduction is reduced to approximately 90 degrees. This is shown by the cross-hatched area. What would happen if the bias is made still more negative? For the plate voltage as given, the tube would not conduct at all!

Phase-shift control of thyratron firing. The d-c control system described above can reduce the conduction period to about one-half time or one-quarter cycle. Further reduction is impossible since higher grid bias will cut the tube off completely. This method of control has another drawback, in that changes in plate voltage, heater emission, or tube temperature can easily upset the conduction period. Where more exact timing is desired, phase-shift control is used. Alternating current from the same source as the

---

* Bias control is used with thyratron rectifiers to control the output (d-c) voltage and current.

plate voltage is applied to the grid. The phase of the grid voltage can be varied from zero to 180 degrees with respect to the plate voltage. The start of conduction depends on the relative phasing. If the grid voltage lags, start of conduction is delayed. This can be shown by a combination of the critical grid-voltage control characteristic and a wave-time analysis (Fig. 4-9). First we must transfer the critical grid voltage line to the time diagram. This construction can be seen from Fig. 4-9(a). Control characteristics, the left-hand portion of Fig. 4-9(a), are usually plotted with dif-

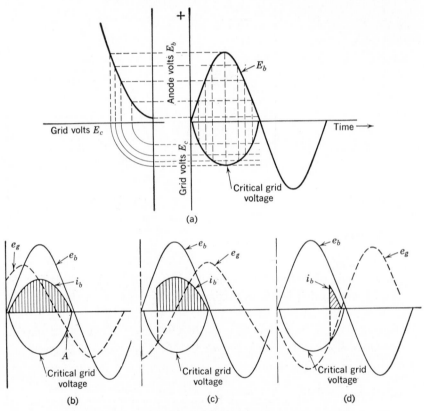

Fig. 4-9. Effect of grid-plate phasing on conduction period.

ferent scales for voltages E_c and E_b. This is natural, since the grid voltages are much lower than the anode voltages. Since the transfer construction does not alter scales *it is important to remember that on the time diagram, right side of Fig. 4-9(a), grid voltages are shown using the E_c scale but anode voltages are at the E_b scale. Two separate voltage scales are used in the same drawing.*

Now that the critical grid voltage curve has been plotted against time, we can show how the phasing of the grid voltage will alter the conduction time. In (b) of Fig. 4-9, the a-c signal (e_g) applied to the grid is leading the anode voltage (e_b) by approximately 45 degrees.* Since the grid signal voltage is less negative than the critical grid value, the tube will fire soon after the plate goes positive and conduction is for almost the full half cycle as shown by the shaded area. Notice that at time A, the grid signal voltage becomes more negative than the critical grid voltage value. Will the tube deionize and stop conducting? NO—remember once a tube fires, the grid loses control until the plate voltage drops to below the ionization value for the gas at that pressure.

We mentioned earlier that if the grid voltage lags (with respect to the plate voltage), start of conduction is delayed. This effect can be seen in Fig. 4-9(c). The grid voltage is lagging by about 90 degrees. Now as the plate voltage starts to rise, the grid is more negative than the critical value. The tube does not fire until approximately one-quarter cycle later, when the grid potential swings less negative than the critical value.

The condition shown in Fig. 4-9(d) is approaching complete cutoff. The value of the grid signal is greater than the maximum value of the critical grid voltage. Also the grid signal lags the anode voltage by almost 180 degrees. As can be seen from the diagram, the grid remains more negative than the critical value for almost 135 degrees. The conduction period is reduced to less than 45 degrees. The phase-shift method of control will give continuous control from full value to zero. In addition the firing time will remain more nearly constant since any change in the plate voltage or in the value of the critical grid voltage will affect the grid signal voltage in like manner and tend to compensate for the changes.

Phase-shift circuit. From the above discussion you will notice that in order to get a full range of control, it is necessary to shift the grid signal by as much as 180 degrees. With an ordinary R-C or R-L circuit the maximum practical phase shift obtainable is approximately 60 degrees. Beyond 60 degrees the output voltage is so low as to be of little value, and so, the theoretical maximum phase shift of 90 degrees cannot be obtained. Figure 4-10 shows a circuit commonly used to obtain phase shifts from zero to a full 180 degrees. In addition, this circuit has a second advantage in that the output voltage remains constant regardless of the degree of phase shift.

---

* This grid signal is much lower in amplitude than the anode voltage. Remember that different voltage scales are used for each.

The proof of the above phase and magnitude relations can be seen from the vector diagram Fig. 4-10(b). The total voltage E_T across the inductance is used as reference. This is the anode voltage and can be applied

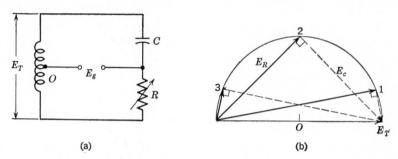

(a)   (b)

Fig. 4-10. Circuit diagram and vector diagram for a 0-180 degree phase-shift circuit.

across the center tapped inductance or can be induced in this winding by transformer action from a suitable primary winding. This voltage, E_T, causes current to flow in the R-C circuit, the value of current depending on the variable resistor, R. However, regardless of the current value, the vector addition of the voltage drops E_R and E_C across the resistor and capacitor respectively must equal the total voltage E_T.

$$\dot{E}_T = \dot{E}_R + \dot{E}_C$$

Also the relative magnitudes of these voltages (E_R and E_C) will depend on their respective oppositions. Since the capacitor is a fixed value, the voltage ratio depends on the value of the resistor R. When R is large: E_R is large; E_C is small; and since the circuit approaches a pure resistive circuit, E_R is almost in phase with E_T. The converse is true as R is made smaller: E_R is small; E_C is large; the circuit approaches a pure capacitive circuit; and E_R leads E_T by almost 90 degrees. Also remember that at all times E_R and E_C are 90 degrees apart. By geometric analysis, this places the junction of E_R and E_C at the perimeter of a semicircle with E_T as the diameter. Such a vector diagram is called a *circle diagram*.

In the circle diagram of Fig. 4-10(b) three conditions are shown: condition 1 for a large value of R (approximately $5X_C$); condition 2 for $R = X_C$; and condition 3 for a small value of R (approximately $1/5X_C$).

Now if you refer back to the circuit diagram, you will see that the output (phase-shifted voltage, E_g) is taken from across point 0, the center top of the inductance (or transformer winding), and the junction of the R-C circuit. On the vector diagram, this corresponds to a voltage line from point

0 to points 1, 2, or 3 depending on the value of R. In each case this line is a radius of the circle, and is constant in magnitude. Also notice that voltage 0-1 is almost in phase with E_T, while at the other extreme, voltage 0-3 leads E_T by almost 180 degrees.

Hydrogen thyratrons. Where more exact timing is required, thyratrons using hydrogen or inert gases such as argon and zenon are used. These tubes may be operated over a wide range of temperature without affecting the control characteristic. Hydrogen thyratrons have an additional advantage, particularly when used as "trigger" tubes. The speed at which a trigger tube can be used is limited by the time required for ionization and deionization. Ionization in tubes is quite rapid, in the order of 10 to 20 microseconds. But deionization time can run as long as 1000 microseconds. By careful design this can be reduced to approximately 100 microseconds. With hydrogen thyratrons, deionization time can be further reduced to 10 microseconds. This is because hydrogen is a monatomic gas—its molecule has only one atom. As a result, its positive ion is relatively light (compared

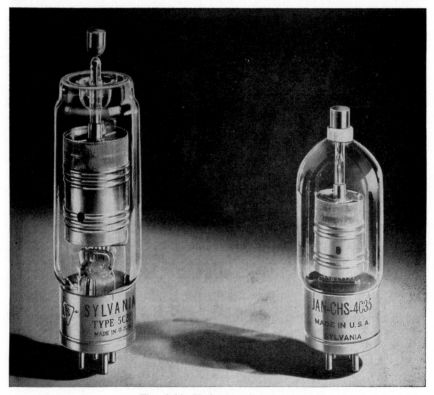

Fig. 4-11. Hydrogen thyratrons.

to other gases) and can move much faster. Deionization, or recombination of positive ions and electrons occurs more rapidly. Two hydrogen thyratrons are shown in Fig. 4-11.

Shield grid thyratron. The three-element thyratron has much greater flexibility than the gas diode because the ionization value of plate potential can be varied by control of the grid bias. It therefore finds great use in commercial applications, particularly in grid-controlled rectifier circuits. However, it does have a limitation. Let us suppose that an ionization potential of +300 volts is desired, and that from the thyratron characteristic curves this point corresponds to a grid bias of —5 volts. Let us also assume that for certain circuit reasons, it is impossible to apply —5 volts to the grid, but that we could apply a —3 potential to this element. But a —3 volt grid bias would cause ionization at a lower plate voltage value and this lower ionization potential is not desirable. What can we do? A new thyratron tube could be designed with characteristics such that —3 volts grid would cause ionization at +300 volts plate. Fine! But then to meet all possible circuit applications we would need thyratrons with innumerably different characteristics. Naturally such a solution is impractical.

The problem was readily solved by adding a fourth electrode in the form of a shield around the grid. The shield grid is operated at some low potential and may be made positive or negative compared to the cathode. Variation of the shield grid potential will vary the characteristics of the thyratron. This can be seen from the control characteristic curves of the 2D21 shield grid thyratron, Fig. 4-12. For example, with the control grid voltage held constant at —3 volts, the tube will ionize at +300 volts when the shield grid potential E_{C2} is zero; if the shield grid is made positive by 2 volts, the ionization potential—*for the same control grid bias*—drops to 180 volts; on the other hand, if the shield grid potential is made —1 volt, ionization does not take place until the plate potential is raised to +600 volts. The shield grid thyratron can therefore be adapted to fit any circuit requirements merely by resetting the shield-grid operating potential.

In addition to greater flexibility, the shield grid tube has the added advantage of lower grid current. This is directly attributable to the changes in construction. The shield grid is a hollow cylinder surrounding the other elements—much like the control grid of a three-element thyratron. (See Fig. 4-13.) This cylinder is subdivided into three "compartments" by baffles. The cathode is in the lower compartment, the control grid in the center, and the plate or anode in the top compartment. In this way the grid is shielded from the other elements—directly, to reduce cathode con-

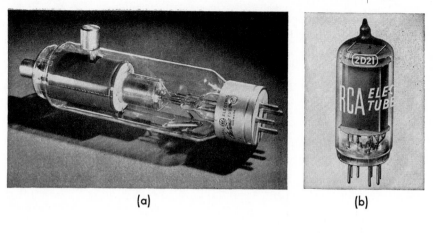

(a)   (b)

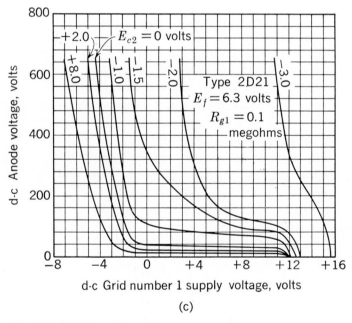

(c)

Fig. 4-12. Typical shield grid thyratrons and control characteristic.

tamination; thermally, to reduce thermionic emission; and electrostatically, to reduce interelectrode capacitance effects. In this last connection, the much smaller size of grid structure also results in reduced capacitance. Due to the lower grid current two operational advantages are obtained. The tube has a higher input impedance. This is of importance if the thyratron action is controlled from a high resistance source such as a phototube.

Also notice that the control curves (Fig. 4-12) are shown as lines—not areas. In other words, because of lower grid current, the shield grid tube has more exact control characteristics.

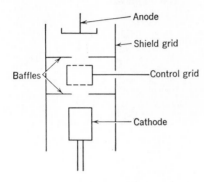

Fig. **4-13.** Diagrammatic cross section of shield grid thyratron.

Cold-Cathode Gas Tubes

The tubes previously discussed were all of the hot-cathode type, the cathode being either directly or indirectly heated by current flowing through the filament or heater wires. Cold cathodes differ in that they have no filament or heater to raise the cathode to emission temperature. Most cold-cathode tubes used in electronic applications are diodes. The following discussion will be limited to such types.

Cold-cathode diodes consist essentially of two elements, cathode and plate, mounted fairly close together in an envelope filled with inert gas, usually neon, argon, or helium. The tube symbol is changed to indicate the cold-cathode feature. This is shown in Fig. 4-14(a). In tubes used for high power applications, a pool of mercury is used as the cathode. The symbol for this type of tube is shown in Fig. 4-14(b).

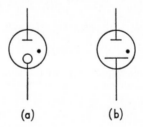

(a)   (b)

Fig. **4-14.** Cold-cathode gas tube symbols: (a) metallic cathode; (b) mercury-pool cathode.

Gaseous conduction. In order to explain the operation of cold-cathode tubes, it is necessary that we analyze gaseous conduction more carefully.

A normal gas atom has no charge. It is not affected by positive or negative fields and does not contribute to conduction. However, in any atom an electron can gain enough energy (equal to the work function) and escape. The atom is now ionized. Instead of a neutral atom we now have a negative charge (the electron) and a positively charged ion (the rest of the atom). Energy for ionization can be obtained in several ways. In studying thermionic gas tubes we saw one way, by collision. Electrons emitted thermionically by the hot cathode were accelerated by the positive anode potential and in their path toward the plate struck gas atoms, knocking out an electron.* In this process the fast moving electron gives up energy and the ion gains some energy. The ion later gives up this energy (usually as heat) when it recombines with some other free electron and becomes a neutral atom.

Sometimes the energy gained from a collision is less than the work function of the material, and therefore is not enough to cause an electron to escape. However, outer shell electrons can gain sufficient energy to move further away from their nucleus—or to a new energy level. In this condition, the atom is said to be in an *excited state*. In most cases, excited electrons give up the extra energy and move back to their normal level. *The energy released is in the form of electromagnetic waves. Depending on the type of gas (and other factors), these waves may be light waves.*

Energy for ionization is also available from *natural* sources. For example, this energy can be supplied from cosmic rays, ultraviolet rays from the sun, or radioactive particles in the air. These natural sources are the underlying reasons for the start of conduction in cold-cathode gas tubes.

Conduction stages in cold-cathode gas tubes. Figure 4-15(a) shows a circuit that can be used to investigate the current-voltage characteristics of a cold-cathode gas tube. As before, the resistor R is used in gas tubes to prevent "runaway" currents, that is, limit current values when the tube fires. Electrical conduction in these gas tubes passes through three successive discharge phases. They are known as the Townsend discharge, the glow discharge, and the arc discharge. These three stages are shown in Fig. 4-15(b). The current range for the full curve starts at values far below one microampere and can approach one hundred amperes in the electric arc region. It should be noted that, due to this extremely wide range of current values, *the current is plotted on a logarithmic scale*. It is also customary to plot this curve with the current as the abscissa. Now we can proceed to explain why this E_b-I_b curve is obtained.

---

* In general this is not a physical impact, but a reaction between electric fields.

It should be recalled from our earlier discussion that some ions are always present in a gas tube, due to ionization energy from natural sources. Therefore, if a voltage is applied between the cold electrodes some current

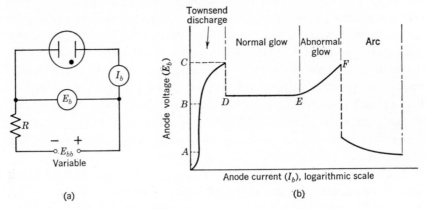

Fig. 4-15. Conduction stages in a gas discharge tube.

can flow. In the circuit of Fig. 4-15, if the applied voltage is increased from zero to some value such as B, it will be found that a small current will flow. The current will rise fairly rapidly at first, until voltage A is reached and then remain constant, even though the voltage value at B is appreciably higher. Obviously we have a saturation condition. This can be explained as follows. The rate of ionization from natural sources is very low. As the few electrons produced are drawn to the plate, (and the positive ions to the cathode), the supply of electrons is quickly exhausted— even at this very low voltage. After this, any further increase in voltage cannot cause any increase in current. (This condition corresponds to voltage saturation in a vacuum diode at low cathode temperatures.) *It must be realized that this saturation current value is very low, and unless an extremely sensitive instrument is used, no current deflection will be noted.*

Now, as we continue to raise the applied voltage beyond B, the current will start to increase. At this point, the few electrons produced by "natural" ionization are being accelerated by the higher plate voltage to fairly high velocities. Some electrons gain sufficient kinetic energy to cause ionization by collision with other gas atoms. As the applied voltage is increased further toward C, more electrons gain sufficient energy and the ionization by collision proceeds at a faster rate. The effect tends to become cumulative. The current is increasing rapidly. Again, however, we must point out that this current value is still low—possibly less than one microampere (it varies with tube geometry, gas, and pressure).

This stage of conduction up to voltage C is known as the *Townsend discharge*,* and is a *non-self-maintained discharge,* because it requires an external source (cosmic rays, ultraviolet rays, etc.) to produce the original ions and electrons. At any point in this conduction range within the Townsend discharge region, if the external source action could be stopped, the electrons and ions in the tube would soon be swept away and all conduction would cease.

At some critical voltage such as $C,$ not only do the gas electrons gain enough energy to cause ionization, but also the more massive positive ions are accelerated and gain appreciable kinetic energy. These ions are attracted toward the cathode. They bombard the cathode with sufficient force to produce electrons by secondary emission. In addition, the heat produced, as the positive ions give up energy and become neutral atoms, can raise the cathode to emission temperature. Now we have a new source of electrons—the cathode. These electrons, whether produced by secondary or by thermionic emission are accelerated toward the plate. In their paths they will collide with gas atoms, producing more positive ions and electrons. In turn, the positive ions bombard the cathode—increasing electron emission from the cathode. This is a cumulative chain reaction, and the current will rise rapidly. In fact, were it not for the resistor R in the circuit (Fig. 4-15), the current could rise to destructive values. Now the discharge has become *self-maintained.*

The critical voltage (C), at which this cumulative action *starts* is known as the *striking potential, ignition potential,* or *breakdown potential.* Almost immediately, however, due to the tremendous increase in ionization, the internal resistance of the tube drops and the voltage across the tube (E_b) drops to an appreciably lower value. This lower value (D) is determined by the *ionizing potential* for the type of gas and the gas pressure used. Meanwhile a visible glow will be seen in the gas and on a portion of the cathode. This is the start of the second conduction stage known as the *glow discharge.*

Notice from Fig. 4-15(b), that for the first portion of the glow discharge region $(D$ to $E)$, the voltage across the tube remains constant even though there is appreciable increase in current. The amount of current is determined by the value of circuit resistance. Any increase in supply voltage (E_{bb}) causes more current to flow; the drop across resistor R increases; but the voltage across the tube (E_b) remains constant. Since current is increasing, E_b can remain constant only if the internal tube resistance is decreasing—and that is exactly what happens. At higher current levels, the

---

* This volt-ampere characteristic was first investigated by J. S. Townsend in 1901.

degree of ionization increases; a greater portion of the cathode is bombarded and gives off electrons. (This can be seen by the fact that the cathode glow covers a greater area of the cathode surface.) The ionized gas path between cathode and anode has a thicker cross section. (In conduction through wires, this is similar to using a wire of larger area.) Consequently, the internal resistance of the tube decreases, and the product IR or voltage drop across the tube remains constant. This region of constant voltage drop across the tube is known as the *normal glow* region.

Once the cathode glow covers the entire surface of the cathode, the cross-sectional area of the gas path cannot increase further. The internal tube resistance can no longer decrease. This condition is reached at around E in Fig. 4-15. Now if the supply voltage is raised, not only will the circuit current increase but the drop across the tube (E_b) will start to rise again. Since the current through the tube has increased, and the conducting area is constant, the current *density* must increase. This is evidenced by a more intense visible glow. This region E to F is known as the *abnormal glow* region.

As the current density in the abnormal glow region is increased, cathode temperature rises drastically, emission zooms, and suddenly the voltage across the tube drops to a very low value. At the same time an intense glow is seen in the tube. The discharge has become an electric *arc*. An arc discharge has a "negative resistance" characteristic; that is, the greater the arc current, the lower the resistance of the arc. In fact, the decrease in resistance is so great that in spite of increased current, *less* voltage is required to send current through the tube. If there were no external circuit resistance, the current would increase until some circuit component fails.

This covers the complete range of conduction that may occur in cold-cathode gas diodes. However, this complete range cannot be obtained with all diodes. Unless the tube, and particularly the cathode, is designed for high currents and operation in the arc stage, tube failure will occur before this condition is reached.

One group of cold-cathode gas diodes are also known as *glow tubes* because of their characteristic glow when the gas ionizes. Some of the typical applications in which these tubes can be found are:

1. As power supply rectifiers (type OZ4), used mainly in mobile radio equipment;
2. As variable light sources (type R 1130) for use in recording sound on film;
3. As relay and trigger tubes (type 5823);
4. As voltage regulator tubes (type OD3).

These tubes, shown in Fig. 4-16(a)-(d), are designed to operate in the normal glow region. This is especially true for voltage regulator tubes. You will recall that within this region (*D-E* of Fig. 4-15), the voltage

Fig. 4-16. Typical cold-cathode gas diodes.

across the tube was practically constant over a wide range of current. This portion of the full discharge curve and a simple regulator circuit application are shown in Fig. 4-17. The unregulated d-c input voltage must exceed the striking potential (*A*) for the particular tube used. Once the tube ionizes, the voltage across the tube—and across the load—will drop to the ionizing voltage for the particular gas and gas pressure used.

Should the supply voltage increase, more current would flow through the regulator tube, the drop across resistor *R* would increase, but the load voltage would remain constant. The reverse would be true should the supply voltage decrease. However, if the supply voltage decreases to the point where the tube current falls below the minimum value, the tube loses con-

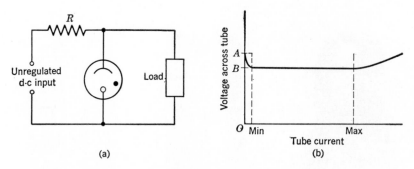

Fig. 4-17. Simple voltage regulator action of a cold-cathode gas tube.

trol as it begins to deionize. Also, should the supply voltage rise so that the tube current exceeds the maximum value, operation would shift to the abnormal glow region, and again the tube would lose regulator action. These tubes are available for various voltage ranges depending on type of gas and gas pressure. Maximum currents range from 25 to 50 milliamperes.

Tubes used in the familiar neon signs are also cold-cathode gas diodes, the gas in this case being neon, and the tube is called a neon tube. The neon gives a reddish-orange glow. Other gases will give other colors; for example, yellow for helium, and blue for mercury. Fluorescent lamps are another example of gas diodes used for lighting. However, these lamps may use either cold cathodes or heated (thermionic) cathodes.

Another application of the cold-cathode gas diode is in high-speed photography and stroboscopic work. Here, high intensity flashes of light are needed. The tubes used (such as types 631P1 and R 4330 shown in Fig. 4-16(e)-(f)) operate in the arc discharge region with peak currents of several amperes to give a brilliant flash for only a few microseconds.

Ignitron

Where high currents are required for continuous operation, the metallic cathodes used in the above tubes could not withstand the heavy bombardment. For this type of service mercury pool cathodes are used. One such tube is the *ignitron*. Figure 4-18(a) shows a water-cooled, steel-jacketed tube of this type. This tube has a maximum peak current rating of 1500 amperes at a peak inverse voltage of 1200 volts. The ignitron consists essentially of a mercury pool cathode, a graphite block for the anode, and a third electrode called the *ignitor*. This electrode is made of a high resistance ceramic material such as silicon carbide or boron carbide. It is important that the material used is not wet by the mercury. A diagrammatic sectional view and the symbol for this tube are also shown in Fig. 4-18.

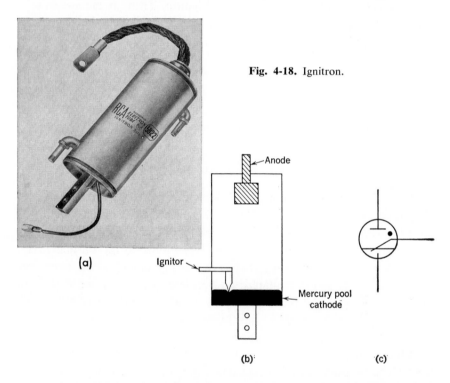

Fig. 4-18. Ignitron.

(a)

Anode

Ignitor

Mercury pool cathode

(b)

(c)

Notice that the ignitor rod dips into the mercury pool. However, remember that the mercury does not wet this material. The surface of the rod has many microscopic sharp points, so that when a voltage is applied between the ignitor and the mercury pool, current flows but sparks are produced at the points of contact. These combine into an arc. Due to the high resistance of the ignitor rod and the resulting potential gradient between the top of the ignitor and the mercury pool, the arc travels up the ignitor. Gas ionization increases. If the anode is positive, the arc transfers to the anode. Since this is an arc discharge, the voltage across the tube is low when the tube fires. The full firing process takes only a few microseconds.

Ignitrons are used to a great extent as high current rectifiers for power applications. Several tubes can be used together in polyphase (3-, 6-, 12-phase) systems, to produce a smoother d-c output. For any one tube, conduction can take place only for the half cycle when its anode is positive. During the negative half cycle, the anode current drops to zero and the tube deionizes. It is therefore necessary to re-ignite the tube for each positive half cycle. This can be done by shunting another rectifier (usually a thermionic gas tube) between anode and ignitor. Then, as the anode voltage starts to rise, the auxiliary rectifier conducts immediately and fires the main tube. Once the ignitron fires, the resulting low voltage between anode and ignitor reduces the auxiliary circuit current to negligible value. The output of the ignitron can be controlled by changing the phasing of the voltage applied to the auxiliary rectifier. By delaying the flow of current in the ignitor, the firing time of the anode is delayed and conduction time can be reduced to only a portion of the positive half cycle.

Multianode Mercury Pool Tubes

One of the earliest mercury pool tubes to be used as a rectifier was a glass tube, with two anodes and a starting electrode. The glass bulb was tipped to start current flow between the mercury and the starting electrode. Then when the tube was levelled, an arc was formed as the starting circuit was broken, and the arc transferred to one of the anodes. Since there were two anodes, each anode conducted on opposite half cycles, and it was not necessary to re-fire the tube each cycle. However, because of their poor heat dissipation and fragility, these tubes were limited to relatively low current (50 amperes or less) applications.

Multianode, water-cooled, steel-jacketed rectifiers were introduced in the 1920's. By use of many anodes and a polyphase a-c supply, it was possible to get much smoother d-c output than from the earlier glass tubes. Also steel jackets gave mechanical sturdiness, and water cooling made possible much higher ratings. However, these rectifiers also had their disadvantages. Since the anodes are all in the same tank, it is possible for an arc to start between two anodes. This short-circuit is called an *arc-back* or *flash-back,* and can be very destructive unless high-speed protective equipment is used. Baffles, shields, and increased spacing between anodes is used to reduce the possibility of arc-backs. But such measures tend to reduce efficiency. One other disadvantage of these units is that damage to any part renders the complete rectifier inoperative. For these reasons, multi-anode units are being replaced by multiple single anode units such as the ignitron.

Review Problems

1. (a) Explain how ionization takes place in a hot-cathode gas tube.

(b) What is meant by "ionizing potential"?

2. Explain briefly three disadvantages of residual gas in a high-vacuum tube.

3. (a) State an application for a gas diode, hot-cathode tube.

(b) What is the main advantage of using a gas diode for such service?

(c) What precaution should be observed in such operation?

4. (a) Draw a diagram showing the potential distribution in the space between the cathode and plate of a gas diode. Label the three regions.

(b) Explain briefly why the gradient is so steep near the cathode.

(c) Why is there little change in gradient in the center region?

5. (a) State an advantage of the heater cathode constructions used in gas tubes.

(b) What is the disadvantage of this type heater and cathode?

6. Explain the purpose and action of the grid in a gas triode.

7. (a) What is the significance of the critical grid voltage characteristic of a thyratron?

(b) Why do commercial curves show this as an area rather than a line?

(c) Why does the value of grid circuit resistor affect control action?

8. (a) Explain briefly how a thyratron rectifier output can be regulated by bias control.

(b) Over what portion of the conduction cycle can this method be used? Explain.

9. State two reasons why phase-shift control is superior to bias control.

10. (a) Draw a phase-shift circuit suitable for producing a phase shift of from zero to 180 degrees, at constant output amplitude.

(b) Explain how this circuit functions.

11. For what applications are hydrogen thyratrons preferable to mercury vapor types? Why?

12. State two advantages of the shield grid thyratron over a three-element thyratron.

13. (a) Name the three stages of conduction that exist in gaseous conduction.

(b) Why is a logarithmic scale used for current when plotting the full discharge curve (all three stages)?

14. Explain how gaseous conduction changes from non-self-maintaining to self-maintaining.

15. Explain when and why the drop across a cold-cathode gas tube may remain constant even though the current through it is varied.

16. (a) Why can the arc conduction be dangerous to equipment?

(b) Can any gas diode be used in this region? Explain.

17. (a) What are glow tubes?

(b) How did they get this name?

(c) Give three distinctive types of applications in which these tubes are used.

18. (a) Explain the operation of a voltage regulator tube.

(b) Why do they have minimum and maximum current ratings?

19. (a) What is an ignitron?

(b) In what gaseous conduction region does it operate?

(c) Why is it suited to this type of operation?

20. Explain how conduction is started in an ignitron.

21. Explain how an ignitron can be used as a controlled output rectifier.

22. In what respect are ignitrons superior to multianode mercury pool tubes?

CHAPTER 5

Cathode-Ray Tube

In recent years, the rapid strides and remarkable advances in the electronic field have been partly due to improvements in the design of cathode-ray tubes. The modern cathode-ray tube is undoubtedly the most versatile indicating and measuring device ever developed. The "moving element" in this indicating device is a beam of electrons. Since electrons have practically no mass, this moving element is not limited by the inertia effects common to all mechanical indicators. As a result, the cathode-ray beam can be deflected at a very rapid rate, and can therefore respond to frequencies in the megacycle range.

There are numerous industrial applications of the cathode-ray tube. One of the most common is the cathode-ray oscilloscope used widely in schools, laboratories, production plants, and service stations to observe and analyse the waveshapes fed to or obtained from electronic equipment. Its application in television receivers should be familiar to everyone. Navigational devices such as radar and racon use cathode-ray tubes as indicating devices. Aircraft landing systems such as Ground Control Approach (GCA) use several of these tubes to guide a plane in a blind landing. In addition since sound, light, and heat can be converted into electrical impulses, cathode-ray tubes are being used more extensively in fields other than electronics, for research study and production control.

Cathode-Ray Tube Construction

The constructional details of cathode-ray tubes vary somewhat with the size of the tubes, the purpose for which they are intended, and the manufacturer of the units. These tubes can be divided into two main categories: electrostatic and electromagnetic. Each type has its special advantages that make it more adaptable in certain applications. Most cathode-ray oscilloscopes use electrostatic tubes. Television receivers are mainly designed with electromagnetic tubes. Radar units employ the electromagnetic type exclusively.

A typical cathode-ray tube of the electrostatic type is shown in Fig. 5-1. The tube consists essentially of five major components: the envelope, the tube base, the electron gun assembly, the deflection plate assembly, and the fluorescent screen. Let us consider each of these components in detail.

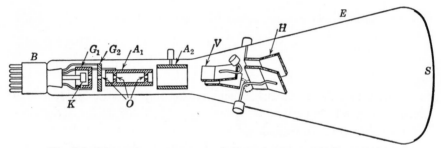

Fig. 5-1. Schematic arrangement of electrodes in a cathode-ray tube:

B : tube base	A_2: high voltage electrode
K : cathode	(anode No. 2)
G_1: control electrode	V : vertical deflection plates
G_2: accelerating electrode	H : horizontal deflection
A_1: focusing electrode	plates
(anode No. 1)	E : envelope
	S : fluorescent screen

(Note: Electrodes K, G_1, G_2, A_1 and A_2 constitute an electron gun.)

1. Envelope. For proper operation and control of the electron beam, the tube must be evacuated. Most cathode-ray tubes are enclosed in a glass envelope to maintain this vacuum. In addition, the envelope also serves as a housing and support for the other components of the tube. Although the glass envelope is purely a mechanical feature, much engineering time has been spent on its design. The problem of designing the tube with sufficient mechanical strength is made more difficult by the desired flatness of the face of the tube. The large surface area of the glass and the vacuum inside the envelope both contribute to develop terrific air pressure strains. As a result, tubes (particularly the larger television tubes) must be handled with care. Jarring and banging must be avoided. Manufacturers often recommend that gloves and protective goggles be worn when handling these tubes.

The inner walls of the tube, between the neck and screen, are usually coated with a conducting material known as *aquadag*. This coating is electrically connected to the accelerating anode, so that electrons striking the walls of the tube are returned to the circuit. In addition this coating acts as a shield against external electrostatic disturbances. The fluorescent coating is applied to the inner face of the tube to form the screen.

Some tubes have a second aquadag coating on the outer surface of the glass envelope. Now we have two conducting layers (inner and outer coatings) separated by a dielectric (the glass envelope). This forms an appreciable capacitance. In many television receivers this capacitance is used as part of the high voltage filtering system. When a double coated tube is used, care must be taken to replace it with a similar type tube—otherwise it will be necessary to add a capacitor to take the place of the tube aquadag-to-glass capacitance.

As long as cathode-ray tubes were small (5- or 7-inch face), it was simple to produce suitable glass envelopes at reasonable cost. With the progress made in the television field, larger diameter tubes became in great demand. And so cathode-ray tubes were made in 10-, 12-, 15- and 20-inch sizes. But the problems of providing a suitable glass envelope, particularly for the 15- and 20-inch tubes were numerous. The manufacturing of large glass envelopes to accurate dimensions was found to be extremely difficult. Mass production was practically impossible and costs zoomed.

One solution to this problem was the development of a metal-glass envelope. Certain advantages are claimed for this type of construction:

(a) *Better optical qualities.* A relatively thin high quality plate glass can be used for the face. This also makes possible the use of a flatter screen.

(b) *Reduction of weight.* Heavy glass masses are no longer needed.

(c) *Greater mechanical strength.*

(d) *Improved safety in handling.* Impact against the envelope may cause radial cracking of the glass face, but no shattering.

(e) *Greater accuracy of dimensions.* Metal is easier to handle.

(f) *Lower cost.* This type is relatively easy to manufacture.

The construction of the "metal" envelope can be seen in Fig. 5-2. It consists of three main sections: a glass neck with flared section; a metal truncated cone; and a glass face plate.

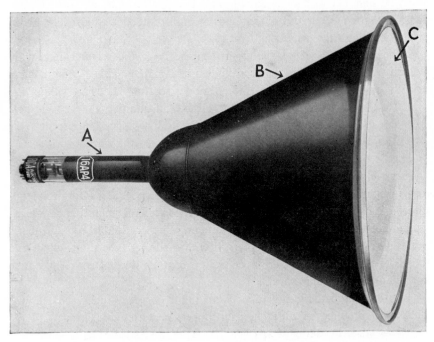

Fig. 5-2. Construction of a metal kinescope: (*A*) glass neck, (*B*) metal cone, (*C*) glass faceplate.

The metal cone is fused to the glass neck and to the face plate. A high-chromium alloy iron is used in its construction so as to match the coefficient of expansion of the glass, thereby maintaining a perfect seal. The resulting assembly is considerably stronger than an all-glass envelope of equal face area.

The metal construction did not eliminate the glass tube from the market. Progress in glass did not stop, and additional improvements were made. It was not long before 24- and 27-inch all-glass tubes appeared on the market.

2. Tube base. The internal elements of the tube are terminated in prongs at the tube base. This simplifies the problem of making connections to the external circuit and at the same time makes replacement of the tube comparatively simple.

3. Electron gun assembly. The electron gun assembly performs several functions. First, it provides the source of electrons for the indicating beam. Second, it focuses these electrons into a narrow beam. At the same time it also accelerates the beam and directs the beam toward the face of tube so that it strikes the screen with sufficient energy to cause fluorescence. In addition it also controls the quantity of electrons in the beam, thereby controlling the intensity of the visible glow. These functions are accomplished by the various components of the gun assembly. These components are held together as a unit by ceramic supports which run the full length of the electron gun structure. Referring to Fig. 5-1, the electron gun assembly consists of the elements marked K, G_1, G_2, A_1, and A_2. Let us discuss each element in turn.

(a) *Cathode* (K). Modern cathode-ray tubes use indirectly heated cathodes, which consist of a cylinder of nickel or nickel alloy approximately $\frac{1}{8}$ inch in diameter and $\frac{1}{2}$ inch long. The end of this cylinder facing the screen is capped, the cap being coated with oxide. This insures a copious supply of electrons aimed, in general, in the desired direction. The cathode is raised to emission temperature by a heater wire inserted through the opposite end of the cathode cylinder. To reduce magnetic effects of the heater current, the heater coil is wound in a double spiral so that the magnetic field of half the winding is cancelled by the equal and opposite field of the other half of the winding. The heater wire is made of tungsten or tungsten-alloy wire coated with an insulating material, as a protective covering for the wire.

(b) *Control grid* (G_1). The control grid in cathode-ray tubes is a metal cylinder which completely encloses the cathode. The end of this cylinder facing the screen is capped by a disc with a small aperture in its center. Electrons emitted by the cathode must pass through this opening to reach the screen. The "effective" size of this aperture is controlled by variation of the grid bias.

(c) *Preaccelerator grid* (G_2). The purpose of the preaccelerator grid is to supply a strong fixed positive potential to pull the electrons emitted by the cathode through the grid aperture at high velocity. In general, this electrode is also a metal cylinder with a small aperture. The size and shape of this structure varies with tube model and manufacturer's design. In fact, in many of the simpler tubes this structure is eliminated and the function of acceleration is taken over by the next electrode.

(d) *Focusing anode* (A_1). This structure is another metal cylinder. Its length will vary in design depending on whether a preaccelerator grid is, or is not, used and on the size of the preaccelerator grid, if it is used.

For example, if the preaccelerator grid is not used, or if this grid is made very short, then the focusing anode is comparatively long and has two discs with small apertures inside the cylinder. Other manufacturers may reverse the design, using a longer preaccelerator grid with small aperture discs and a comparatively short hollow cylinder for the focusing anode. In either case the operating principles are similar. The electron beam can be made to focus on the fluorescent screen by varying the potential applied to the focusing anode.

(e) *Accelerating anode* (A_2). The purpose of this anode is to supply additional accelerating force to the electron beam. It is therefore operated at a high positive potential compared to the cathode. This structure is another metal cylinder with a disc and aperture.

4. Deflection plate assembly. The beam produced by the electron gun must now pass through the deflection system before it hits the screen. This deflection plate assembly provides a means for moving the point at which the electron beam strikes the screen. It consists of two pairs of plates, the plane of one pair being at right angles to the plane of the other pair. The *vertical deflection plates* are mounted horizontally in the tube. By applying proper potentials to these plates the electron beam can be made to move up and down, or vertically on the face of the tube. Notice that the nomenclature of the plates applies not to their physical mounting position but rather to the direction of the deflection they will produce. The *horizontal deflection plates* are mounted in a vertical plane—but they will cause the electron beam to be deflected left and right, or horizontally across the face of the tube. The deflection plate assembly is located in the neck of the tube between the accelerating anode (A_2) and the fluorescent screen. The trailing edges of the plates are flared outward so that the electron beam will not strike the plates when high deflection forces are applied.

5. Fluorescent screen. The screen material is applied to the inner face of the glass envelope. The purpose of the screen material is to convert the kinetic energy of the electron beam into visible light. Certain chemical compounds have been found to emit light when bombarded with electrons. This property is known as *fluorescence*. All fluorescent materials have some afterglow, that is they will continue to emit light for some time after the original excitation by bombardment has passed. This second property is distinguished from fluorescence and is called *phosphorescence*. The duration of phosphorescence varies with the type of material used for the screen. Commercially, the phosphorescence or *persistence* characteristics of a screen material are classified into three groups as short, medium, or long. Each type has its special advantages. For example, if a tube is to be used to observe a waveshape of short duration and that is not repeated (such as a transient), a long-persistence screen will cause the image to linger. The waveshape can be studied even after the original impulse has passed on. Again, when studying waveshapes of very low frequency, a long-persistence screen will reduce flicker of the image. On the other hand, where the image viewed changes rapidly in character, a short-persistence screen is necessary. Otherwise, the afterglow of the previous image will interfere with the new image.

Typical fluorescent materials used in commercial tubes are:

(a) willemite (zinc orthosilicate) for predominantly green light,
(b) zinc oxide for predominantly blue light,
(c) zinc beryllium silicate for predominantly yellow light,
(d) zinc sulphide mixed with cadmium zinc sulphide or zinc beryllium sulphide for nearly white light.

Characteristics of various types of screen materials available can be obtained from the manufacturers of cathode-ray tubes. Standard cathode-ray tubes are usually classified with a phosphor code designation. Some of the more common types are:

(a) *Type P1 screen:* green trace, medium persistence, suitable for general oscilloscope use.
(b) *Type P2 screen:* bluish-green trace, long persistence, suitable for observation of transient signals or low frequency recurrent signals.
(c) *Type P4 screen:* white trace, suitable for television application. Its persistence is well balanced, to minimize flicker and still give clear pictures of rapidly changing images.
(d) *Type P5 screen:* blue trace of high photographic actinity, short persistence, particularly suitable where photographic records of waveshapes are desired.

Effect of Control Grid Potential

The intensity or brilliance of the spot produced on the screen depends (among other factors) on the number of electrons in the beam. Since the grid structure is closest to the cathode, variation of the grid potential is the most effective way of controlling the strength of the beam. This action of the grid is similar to the controlling effect of a conventional grid on the plate current of a vacuum tube. Cathode-ray tubes are normally operated with the grid structure at some negative potential compared to cathode. A potentiometer, connected so as to vary this grid bias, serves as *intensity control.*

In addition, the electrostatic field between the cylindrical grid and the cathode accomplishes another important function. The field acts similar to an optical lens in that it concentrates the electrons into a small beam. This action is illustrated by Fig. 5-3.

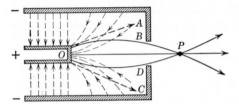

Fig. 5-3. Electron lens action of grid-cathode field.

An electron travelling along a horizontal axis will not be affected by the electrostatic field and will continue to travel in a straight line. However, consider electrons that are emitted at some vertical angle, such as along paths *OA* or *OC*. As these electrons cross the electrostatic field, they will be repelled in the direction of each line of force that they cross. The resultant forces will cause these electrons to follow a curved path, such as *OBP* and *ODP*. Notice that the paths of these electrons cross over at point *P*. This will be true for all electrons whose paths allow them to pass through the aperture. Point *P* can therefore be considered as the focal point or *cross-over point* for the grid-cathode "electronic lens." Any electrons whose original paths are too divergent will hit the walls of the grid cylinder and will be removed automatically from the beam.

Thus we see that the action of the grid is twofold: it concentrates the electrons into a point source for good focusing, and it controls the number of electrons in the beam thereby controlling the intensity of the spot on the tube face. A precaution concerning the setting of the intensity control should be emphasized at this point. When electrons strike the screen, most of the kinetic energy of these electrons is dissipated as heat at the point of impact. *If a small, very bright spot is kept stationary too long in one place a hole will be burned in the screen.* Therefore keep the intensity down as low as permissible for good observation, particularly if the spot is stationary.

Electrostatic Focusing

We have seen that the grid action focuses the beam at the cross-over point. However this point is just outside the grid cylinder itself. Beyond this point the beam diverges again. Additional focusing is needed to make the beam focus at the screen. This effect is produced by the electrostatic field between the focusing anode (A_1) and the accelerating anode (A_2). Both of these anodes are operated at positive potentials with respect to cathode. However the accelerating anode is operated at a higher positive potential, so that it is positive compared to the focusing anode. Figure 5-4 shows the electrostatic field between these two anodes.

The focusing action of this electrostatic field can be explained by reference to Fig. 5-4. Electrons travelling along the radial axis of the tube do

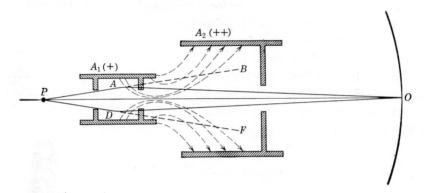

Fig. 5-4. Focusing action of electrostatic field.

not cross the lines of force and are not affected by the field. They will continue to travel along the axis and hit the screen at point O. However, starting from the cross-over point (P), some electrons will tend to take diverging paths, such as PAB or PDF. As these electrons cross the electrostatic field in the region of the focusing anode, they will be repelled by the field in the direction of the lines of force, or *toward the central axis of the tube*. The resultant motion will be along the curved lines PAO and PDO. But the lines of force toward the end of the accelerating anode are outward! Why doesn't the beam diverge again? The explanation is simple. First, the field strength is getting much weaker. (Notice how far apart the lines are.) Second, the beam is now moving at such high velocity due to the acceleration caused by the positive anodes, that the pull of the field at this point has very little effect. Furthermore any electrons that are too divergent to pass through the apertures are intercepted and removed from the beam by the discs in the focusing and accelerating anodes. By varying the potential of the focusing anode, the shape of the electrostatic field can be altered so as to converge the beam till the smallest possible spot is produced on the screen. This action is accomplished by connecting the focusing anode to another potentiometer, which acts as the *focus control*.

From the above discussion, it should be obvious that there will be some interaction between the intensity and focusing controls. For example, variation of the intensity control will change the field between grid and cathode and cause the cross-over point to shift slightly. But this shift will affect the focus. It will be necessary to alter the focus control with change in intensity. In addition, since the potential of the focusing anode is the first positive potential near the cathode, any change in this voltage will vary the attractive force pulling electrons from the cathode through the grid aperture. Therefore resetting of the focus control will also vary the intensity of the beam to some extent. This situation was avoided by the addition of the preaccelerator grid between the grid structure and the focusing anode. The preaccelerator grid is electrically connected to the accelerating anode and both of these structures are operated at a high *fixed* positive potential. The insertion of this preaccelerator grid reduces interaction between the intensity and focus control but does not alter the manner in which each control functions.

Electrostatic Deflection System

So far we have shown that the electron gun system is capable of producing a finely focused spot on the screen. But we stated earlier that the cathode-ray tube is an indicating or measuring device. Therefore, the spot must be made to move in accordance with some applied signal. This is the function of the deflection system. We have seen that the deflection system in an electrostatic type tube consists of two pairs of plates, the vertical and horizontal deflection plates.

Let us consider the action of the vertical deflection plates, shown in Fig. 5-5. Remember that the vertical plates are mounted horizontally in the tube but that they produce an up and down deflection of the beam.

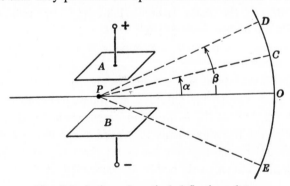

Fig. 5-5. Action of vertical deflection plates.

For the first example, we will assume that there is no difference in potential between plates *A* and *B,* and that the beam will travel along the axis of the tube striking the screen at point *O.* Now let us apply a voltage across the deflection plates, so as to make plate *A* positive compared to plate *B.* An electrostatic field will be set up between the plates. The direction of the lines of force will be upward, from *B* to *A.* Under this condition, as the beam passes through the deflection plate area, it will be deflected upward by the force of the field, striking the screen at some point *C.* The voltage applied across the deflection plates has caused the spot on the screen to move from *O* to *C.*

If the voltage applied across the plates is doubled, the strength of the electrostatic field is also doubled. The angle (β) through which the beam is deflected is doubled and the beam strikes the screen at *D.* The distance that the spot moves on the face of the beam is proportional to the deflection angle of the beam, which in turn is proportional to the voltage applied across the deflection plates. Now if this same voltage is applied to the deflection plates with reversed polarity (plate *A* negative and plate *B* positive), the direction of the electrostatic field will be downward. But the strength of the field will be the same as before. The beam will be deflected downward by an equal amount, and will strike the screen at *E.* The direction of motion of the spot will therefore indicate the polarity of the applied signal voltage.

What would happen if a sine wave of voltage were applied across the deflection plates? The spot would move up and down above and below point *O,* an amount proportional to the *peak* value of the sine wave. Due to the persistence of the screen material, you would see a vertical line.

In exactly the same manner, d-c voltages applied to the horizontal deflection plates would produce motion of the spot in a horizontal direction. If voltages were applied to both sets of plates simultaneously, the electron beam would be acted upon by both the horizontal and vertical fields of force. The spot would move at some angle across the face of the tube, depending on the relative field strengths. For example, if the voltages applied to each set of plates were equal, the spot would move along a 45-degree line. This effect is shown in Fig. 5-6(a). If the voltage applied to the vertical plates is stronger than on the horizontal plates, the spot will move as shown in Fig. 5-6(b). On the other hand, if we reverse the polarity of the signal on the horizontal plates and also make it stronger than the voltage applied to the vertical plates, the spot will move as shown in Fig. 5-6(c). It should be obvious from this discussion that by application of suitable voltages of correct polarities, the spot can be made to move to any location on the face of the screen. Remember that the amount of horizontal motion depends only on the horizontal deflection voltage and is independent of the vertical deflection voltage. The same applies to the amount of vertical motion.

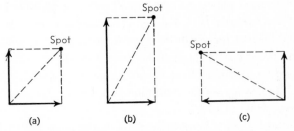

Fig. 5-6. Deflection of spot by combined vertical and horizontal deflection plate fields.

Deflection Sensitivity

The cathode-ray tube, by itself, is relatively insensitive. It may be necessary to apply several hundred volts across the deflection plates to produce full-scale deflection of the spot. *Deflection sensitivity* is the term used to compare the merits of various types of tubes. It is a measure of the deflection voltage required to produce a given spot deflection on the screen.

Several factors affect the sensitivity of the deflection system. A little thought should make these factors obvious. In the preceding section, we saw that a given voltage applied to the plates produced a definite *angle* of deflection. Therefore, the further we place the screen from the deflection plates, the greater will be the spot deflection produced by a given voltage. In construction of cathode-ray tubes, it is common practice to put the vertical plates next to the accelerating anode and follow with the horizontal deflection plates. Obviously the vertical deflection system will have a higher deflection sensitivity than the horizontal deflection system. To increase sensitivity by increasing the distance from plates to screen requires a longer tube structure. On the other hand, with a longer tube, the electrons would tend to slow down, reducing the intensity of the spot. Also, due to the mutual repelling action among the electrons, the beam would tend to diverge resulting in poor focusing. These effects, in addition to mechanical considerations, limit the maximum practical length of a tube.

If we lower the potentials applied to the anodes (A_1 and A_2), the acceleration of the electrons in the beam will be reduced. Because of the lower velocity, the beam will remain under the influence of the deflecting plates' field for a longer time interval. The deflection obtained from a given deflection voltage is increased. But such a method of increasing the sensitivity is not desirable. We just saw that reduction of the beam velocity results in loss of intensity and definition (i.e., poor focus). When selecting the operating anode potentials a compromise must be made between higher potentials for strong intensity and good focus, and lower potentials for higher deflection sensitivity.

For any given tube, the first of these two factors—distance between deflection plates and screen—is fixed by the manufacturer. On the other hand, the potential applied to the accelerating anode may vary over reasonably wide limits as chosen by the user of the tube. But this will affect the amount of spot deflection for a given deflection voltage, even for the same tube, and should not be charged against the merits of the tube. To eliminate this variable, manufacturers specify deflection sensitivities in terms of one kilovolt on the accelerating anode. Typical units used are: *volts per inch per kilovolt, volts per centimeter per kilovolt,* or *volts per millimeter per kilovolt.* Each of the above units specifies the amount of deflection voltage needed for a given spot deflection when the anode voltage is one kilovolt. Sometimes the sensitivity is expressed as the amount of deflection produced when one volt is applied to the deflection plates— i.e., *millimeters per volt per kilovolt.* Either method gives the same information. This second form should be recognized as the reciprocal of the first. An average sensitivity value for commonly used tubes is approximately 30 volts per inch per kilovolt. An example will illustrate the use of this deflection sensitivity factor.

Example 1:

What value of deflection voltage will be needed to produce a three-inch deflection on a cathode-ray tube having a sensitivity of 30 v/in./kv if the anode voltage is 5000 v?

Solution:

1. At 30 v/in., three inches would require 90 v.
2. Since the anode voltage is greater than one kilovolt, the deflection would be reduced. For 5000 v, 5 $\times$ 90, or **450 v** would be needed across the deflection plates.

Intensifier Bands

The need for compromise between low potentials for high sensitivity or high potentials for good definition and intensity is remedied to a great extent by use of *post-deflection acceleration.* The beam travels at moderate velocities until it passes the deflection plate system. Then it is further accelerated to give high intensity. This method requires an additional electrode known as an intensifier band. This electrode is actually a ring of conducting material placed between the aquadag coating and the screen. Connection to the band is made by a contact directly on the body of the tube. The potential applied to the intensifier electrode may be several times that of the normal accelerating anode (A_2). By this means deflection sensitivities from 3 to 5 times higher than in previous models can be obtained.

In certain applications such as observation or photography of transients, or where enlargement by a projection lens system is desired, very high spot intensities are necessary. To produce such high intensities without materially affecting the spot size or deflection sensitivity, tubes using several intensifier bands were developed. One typical model (Fig. 5-7) uses

Fig. 5-7. High-voltage cathode-ray tube with intensifier bands.

three intensifier bands located near the screen end of the cathode-ray tube. The potentials for these high voltage electrodes are obtained from a high voltage power supply. These bands apply increased accelerating voltages to the electron beam in three equal steps. An additional band, operated at ground potential, is located between the normal accelerating anode (A_2) and the three intensifier rings. The purpose of this band is to shield the deflection plates from the intensifier field and from external electrostatic fields.

Positioning Controls

In the discussion of the deflection system, we assumed that the beam would travel along the axis of the tube and strike the screen at the center, when there was no difference in potential across the deflection plates. This may or may not be true, depending upon constructional tolerances in the manufacturing and assembling processes. In addition, it is sometimes desirable that the beam start from some point other than the center—such as top, bottom, left or right edge of the screen. To adjust the starting point of the beam, it is necessary to use a vertical and a horizontal positioning control.

To illustrate the action of these controls let us examine the schematic diagram of a typical cathode-ray tube connected to suitable operating voltages. (See Fig. 5-8.) Two separate positioning controls are used, one for the vertical and another for the horizontal plates [see Fig. 5-8(b)].

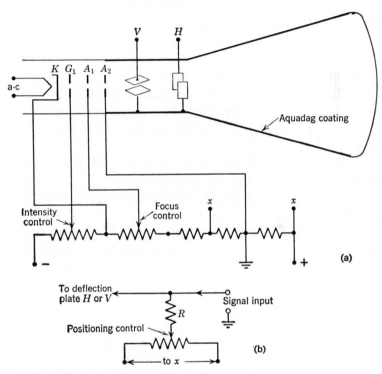

Fig. 5-8. Schematic diagram of cathode-ray tube connected to operating potentials.

In studying this diagram, you may be puzzled by the voltage divider connections. Why are the accelerating anode and one plate of each deflection pair operated at ground potential? Why is the ground connection made near the positive end of the divider? The reason for this is merely as a safety measure. In the use of equipment containing a cathode-ray tube, the operator is most likely to come in contact with the high voltage applied to the screen, the deflection plates, and the positioning controls. It is therefore of definite advantage to operate these components at or near ground potential.

Now let us check the action of the positioning controls. You will notice from Fig. 5-8(b) that the positioning control potentiometer is connected across the voltage divider so that while one end is *slightly* positive compared to ground the other end is negative by an equal amount. What is the deflection plate potential when the potentiometer is set at mid-point? It is at ground or zero potential. But this is also the potential of the opposite deflection plate. Since there is no difference in potential between the plates, the electron beam is not affected and should strike the screen at the center.

If the potentiometer is moved to the right, the upper vertical deflection plate (or right horizontal deflection plate, facing the screen) is made positive. The electron beam will be attracted by this positive plate, and will be deflected upward (or to the right). The magnitude of this displacement will depend on how far the potentiometer is advanced to the right. In a similar manner, movement of the potentiometer to the left will make the upper (or right) plate negative, causing the beam to be displaced in the opposite direction.

What is the purpose of resistor R in Fig. 5-8(b)? Will it reduce the positioning voltage applied to the deflection plates? Since the deflection plates draw no current, the answer is no! Then what is it there for? Remember, we have been discussing only the positioning of the beam on the screen. The signal to be examined on the screen is fed to the deflection plates through the right-hand input leads. If resistor R is eliminated, this signal may very well be "short-circuited" through the voltage divider to ground. This resistor is used to isolate or *decouple* the positioning voltage from the signal voltage.

Balanced Deflection System

The circuit described above for positioning and for deflection by the signal voltage is called an unbalanced deflection system, since voltages are applied only to one plate, the opposite plate being at ground potential. Such a system causes a slight defocusing action, known as deflection distortion. The distortion is negligible with small-screen oscilloscopes since the anode voltage is low and the deflection voltage needed for full-scale deflection is also low. But the distortion increases with the magnitude of the deflection voltage and may be objectionable on larger screen tubes or higher anode voltage tubes, such as projection tubes. The cause for this defocusing action can be understood from the following discussion. Earlier in this chapter, you saw how the electrostatic field created by the difference in potential between the focusing anode and the accelerating anode caused the electrons in the beam to focus at the screen. The spot was well defined —small and round—because this field was symmetrical with respect to the axial length of the tube. (See Fig. 5-4.) Naturally if the beam is to focus at the screen, it still has appreciable width while passing through the deflection plate assembly. We can also see from Fig. 5-8 that one deflection plate of an unbalanced deflection system is always at the same potential as the accelerating anode (A_2), i.e., ground potential. Now if a high deflection voltage is applied to the other deflection plate, a new electrostatic field will be created between the accelerating anode and only this deflection plate. The field is definitely unsymmetrical around the tube axis, and since the beam has appreciable width at this section, the amount of deflection for each electron will vary depending on its location with respect to the tube axis. So—although the spot is deflected, it has lost definition and now appears larger in diameter. If a sine-wave voltage is applied to the vertical plate, the beam will move up and down on the face of the screen, producing a vertical line. But if the focusing is adjusted for smallest spot size at the center of the screen, the spot will widen at the top and bottom of the beam travel. This type of distortion is shown in Fig. 5-9.

Fig. 5-9. Defocusing action due to unbalanced deflection system.

To overcome this defect, the better type of circuits use a balanced deflection system, employing a "paraphase amplifier" (sometimes called push-pull amplifier). Discussion of such systems must be delayed until amplifier circuits have been explained. However a simple explanation can be given. If a deflection voltage of 200 volts is to be viewed, it is applied as +100 to one plate and −100 on the opposite plate. Obviously in this system neither plate of the horizontal or vertical deflection pair is grounded. An electrostatic field is now created between the accelerating anode and *each* plate of the deflection system. This field will be symmetrical. In fact the field potential at the central axis will be zero—just as if the deflection voltage were zero. By this means, defocusing action is almost completely eliminated.

Electron-Beam Path

If you refer back to Fig. 5-8 for a moment, you will see that the beam starts at the cathode and by the action of the gun is shot toward the screen. In its path, the beam is affected by the action of the various controls and by the deflection system and finally hits the screen. What happens now to the electrons in the beam? Do they stay on the screen, or how do they complete a path? If they accumulated on the screen, we would have trouble. The accumulated electron charge on the screen would soon repel the beam.

When the beam hits the screen, it produces secondary emission electrons. These bounce back to the aquadag coating surrounding the walls of the tube near the screen. Since the aquadag coating is electrically conductive, the electrons return through this coating to the second anode and back to the power supply voltage divider. The electron circuit is therefore completed through the action of the secondary emission electrons and the aquadag coating.

Electromagnetic Focusing

In the study of magnetism and d-c motor action * you learned that an electron in motion is surrounded by a magnetic field, and that when a conductor carrying current is located in a magnetic field, a force is produced which pushes the wire in a direction at right angles to both the direction of current flow and the magnetic field (Fleming's rule). Since the electron beam in a cathode-ray tube is actually a current flow (through space), this same principle can be utilized for electromagnetic focusing and electromagnetic deflection of the beam.

For focusing action, a coil is placed axially on the neck of the tube. The focusing anode used in the electrostatic system is eliminated. Direct current is passed through the coil. The magnetic field produced is shown in Fig. 5-10. The strength of the magnetic field can be varied by controlling the amount of current in the coil.

An electron travelling axially through the tube travels in the same direction as the lines of force and is not affected by the magnetic field. However, any divergent electrons tending to follow a path such as *ABC* have a component of motion that is at right angles to the magnetic field, i.e., upward. By motor action, the force produced will act to push such electrons out of the page (at right angles to both the direction of the field and

---

* DeFrance, *Direct Current Fundamentals*, Chaps. 14 and 22.

the component motion of the electron). The combined effect of all these forces produced while the electron is passing through the magnetic field is to cause the electron to move in a spiral path, like the thread on a wood

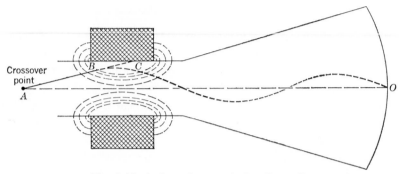

Fig. 5-10. Action of magnetic focusing coil.

screw. The further the divergence of any electron entering the magnetic field, the greater this spiralling force. By proper adjustment of the focus coil current, the electron beam can be made to focus at the screen. In practice, positioning of the coil itself is used for coarse focus adjustment. Once this position is fixed, additional fine adjustment is made by varying the current through the coil.

The electromagnetic focusing system has several advantages. First, the electron gun system is simplified, reducing the cost of the tube. Secondly, the defocusing action from change in beam current (variation of intensity control) is not as apparent as in electrostatic tubes. Finally, if the field produced by the focusing system is not symmetrical with respect to the tube axis (due to improper alignment of the tube components), the electrons in the beam will not converge in the same plane. The spot produced on the screen will not be small and round, but will spread out into an elliptical shape. Adjustment of the focus coil current (magnetic systems) or focus electrode potential (electrostatic systems) cannot correct this distortion. This loss of focus—as in any lens system—is known as *astigmatism*. In an electromagnetic tube, astigmatism of the focus system is readily corrected by adjustment of the focus coil. Where such a condition exists in electrostatic tubes, nothing can be done, since the focusing anode is inside the tube and cannot be adjusted.

On the other hand the focusing anode in the electrostatic system draws negligible power, and the control voltage required is readily supplied from a simple voltage divider. The focus coil consumes power; current for the coil is more difficult to supply and unless this current is steady or regulated the focusing action will vary. In other words the circuit requirements for magnetic focusing are more involved.

Electromagnetic Deflection

An external electromagnetic system can also be used for deflection purposes, eliminating the need for including horizontal and vertical deflection plates within the tube itself. Again the principle involved is the motor principle as stated in the previous section. This time, however, two pairs of coils are used. The horizontal deflection pair is mounted vertically one above and one below the tube, the vertical deflection pair is mounted horizontally on either side of the tube. All four coils are in the same plane around the neck of the envelope. The coils are mounted on a yoke assembly shown in Fig. 5-11.

Fig. 5-11. Commercial electromagnetic deflection yoke assembly.

The magnetic field of either pair of coils pierces transversely across the tube. This magnetic force, in combination with the axial motion of the electrons, will cause deflection of the beam. The action can best be understood by reference to Fig. 5-12. The magnetic field due to the horizontal deflection coils is downward. We are looking at the tube from the back. Therefore the electron motion is away from us or into the page, as indicated by the X sign. The magnetic field around the electron (or electron beam) is counterclockwise. By Lenz's law the force produced by these magnetic conditions will push the beam to the right.

If the current in the deflecting coils is reduced, the magnetic field is weakened and the amount of deflection of the beam is reduced. Also, if the direction of current flow through the coils is reversed, the magnetic polarity of the coils is reversed and the reaction will now cause the beam to be deflected to the left.

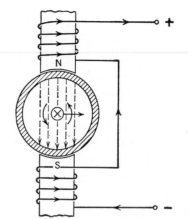

Fig. 5-12. Principle of electromagnetic deflection.

In a similar fashion, current flow through the vertical deflection coils will cause the beam to be deflected up or down across the face of the tube. If current is applied to both sets of coils simultaneously, two magnetic fields will be produced. The resultant force of these two magnetic fields will cause the beam to be deflected at some angle across the screen. This action is analogous to the effect explained under the electrostatic deflection system. For example, if the magnetic fields of the H and V coils are equal in strength, the beam will be deflected at a 45-degree angle.

Use of electromagnetic deflection system simplifies the construction of the cathode-ray tube. The cost of the tube is decreased. Also by eliminating the plates used for electrostatic deflection, the tube can be made shorter, which in turn results in more compact equipment. Yet electromagnetic systems cannot be used in oscilloscopes where it is desired to study the waveform of signals of various frequencies, particularly of complex waves of unknown frequency components. The deflection coils have inductance and their reactance will vary with the frequency of the applied signal. The current in the coils, the strength of the magnetic field produced, and the amount of deflection of the beam will therefore vary with the *frequency* of the applied signal as well as the amplitude of the applied signal. This dual effect will cause undesirable distortion of the screen pattern. In addition, the variation in the phase shift of each component of a complex wave will add to the distortion of the resulting pattern. For this reason use of magnetic deflection systems is limited to such applications as radar, racon, and television, where the deflection frequency is constant.

Ion Spots

In our discussion so far, we have assumed that the beam from the electron gun to the screen contains only electrons. This is not true. Positive and negative ions also exist in a cathode-ray tube. Where do they come from? We can explain their origin in several ways:

1. Positive and negative ions can be emitted from the hot cathode by thermionic emission.

2. Positive and negative ions can be created by ionization when the normally emitted electrons collide with the residual gas molecules in the tube. (You will recall that no vacuum process is complete.)

3. Ions can be produced by secondary emission from the cathode. The positive ions created by collisions are attracted back to the cathode. Bombardment of the cathode by these positive ions "knocks off" additional ions.

These ions have approximately the same magnitude of electric charge as an electron but they are many times heavier—as much as a few hundred thousand times the mass of an electron. The positive ions, as we mentioned above, are drawn back to the cathode. The negative ions join with the electrons to form the so-called "electron" beam.

What is the effect of these negative ions in the beam? In an electrostatic deflection tube it is nothing. Since these ions have the same charge as electrons, they are deflected in exactly the same manner as electrons, and we can forget that they exist. In electromagnetic deflection tubes, we are not so fortunate. The ions are practically unaffected by the magnetic deflection system and will hit in a concentrated area at the center of the screen. The constant bombardment at one spot will "burn" the screen phosphor and produce a brown stain at this area. This ion stain will be apparent even when the tube is not energized.

To explain why the ions are or are not deflected would require a mathematical development of the deflection forces produced in each system. Such an analysis would show that the deflecting force in an electrostatic system is independent of the mass of the particle being deflected, while in the magnetic system the force is inversely proportional to the square root of the particle mass. Since the ions are thousands of times heavier their deflection by magnetic fields is insignificant compared to the electron deflection.

Without resorting to the mathematical proof we can show the truth of the above statements as follows:

1. In the 1780's Charles A. Coulomb proved by experiments that the force acting between two charged bodies in air is proportional to the product of their charges. (This is known as *Coulomb's law.*) In an electrostatic deflection system these two charges are the charge on the moving particle (electron or ion) and the charge on deflection plates. Since the electrons and negative ions have charges of the same general magnitude, the amount of deflection for either particle will be approximately the same.

2. To analyze the deflecting force in the magnetic deflection system, let us first consider the deflection forces in the D'Arsonval meter movement, with which you are more familiar. Here, the torque or deflecting force is due to the interaction of the permanent magnet field and the electromagnetic field of the moving coil. For any given instrument structure, the needle deflection is proportional to the *amount of current* in the moving coil. A similar situation exists in the cathode-ray tube; the interaction between two magnetic fields produces the deflection of the beam. The "amount of current" in this case is the "speed of the particles" as they travel from cathode towards screen. Herein lies the difference. The electrons having little mass travel very rapidly. This is equivalent to a relatively high current and therefore strong magnetic interaction and large deflection. The ions, because of their much larger mass, travel much slower. This corresponds to a much lower equivalent current, very weak magnetic interaction, and insignificant deflection.

Ion Traps and Magnets

The condition described above for magnetic deflection tubes cannot be tolerated. Some means must be used to prevent these ion spots. One such technique is to use an ion trapping system.

The first step is to direct the entire beam (electrons and ions) against the neck wall of the tube. This can be done by mounting the electron gun structure at a slant, so that the beam is aimed at the side wall instead of along the central axis. Such a tube is known as a *bent-gun* tube. The same effect is also achieved with the gun in normal position if the faces between the preaccelerator grid (G_2) and the first anode (A_1) are cut at an angle. This type of gun structure—*the diagonal cut* gun—is shown in Fig. 5-13(b). The electrostatic field between these two faces is no longer parallel to the central axis of the tube. It is now at downward angle as shown. The beam particles, electrons and ions, will follow along the direction of the lines of force, and would strike the neck of the tube at some point such as *p*. The ions actually strike the wall of the tube, and through the aquadag coating of the tube are returned to the power supply and back to the cathode.

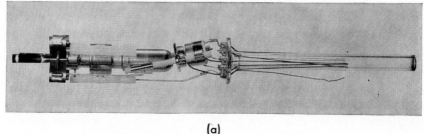

(a)

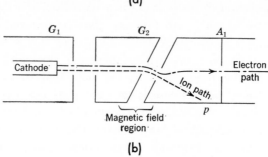

(b)

Fig. 5-13. (a) Bent gun and (b) diagonal cut gun structures.

The second step is to redirect the *electrons* back to the central axis of the tube, without affecting the ions. This is done by the *ion trap magnet*. It is a permanent magnet with springs or clamps so that it can be attached around the neck of the cathode-ray tube. Its action is similar to that of the magnetic deflection coils—the electrons in the beam are deflected but the ions are unaffected. In practice, the ion trap magnet is moved back and forth along the neck of the tube and also rotated around the neck till maximum brightness is obtained on the screen. This indicates that the electrons have been properly redirected through the apertures in the anodes. Improper location of the magnet may cause over-correction or under-correction of the beam path. If the beam strikes the edges of the apertures it can wear these edges and enlarge the apertures, causing widening of the beam and poor focus. Adjustment of focus control will not remedy this condition. The tube has been damaged. Remember this if you have occasion to make adjustments on television receivers or other electromagnetic deflection systems—*always adjust the ion trap magnet for maximum brilliance on the screen.*

Aluminized Tubes

In the previously described cathode-ray tubes, when the screen phosphor is excited light is emitted in all directions. Obviously some of the light is directed backward into the bulb. To make matters worse, a backward ray of light in striking the side walls of the tube can be reflected back to another area on the screen. This places light where there should be none and reduces over-all contrast. The aluminized tube was developed to remedy the above situation. The increase in brightness achieved by this means ranges from 80 to 100%—with only insignificant increase in high voltage.

The aluminized tube differs from a non-aluminized tube in that a very thin coating of aluminum is deposited on the back of the phosphors after the phosphors have been deposited on the glass face. The aluminum coating is held to a thickness small enough so that the electrons can get through to activate the phosphors. However, this aluminum backing acts as a mirror and reflects forward the light output which is generated on the backside of the phosphors. The addition of this "back light" to the normal forward light results in an over-all increase in brightness. Aluminum backing is not used for tubes designed for operation at low accelerating voltages. In such tubes the electron velocity is too low, and the loss of energy by the electron in penetrating the aluminum coating results in poor activation of the phosphors.

The aluminum backing produces two other advantages. One is improved contrast due to the elimination of back lighting. The difference between bright and dark images is enhanced. In addition aluminizing is helpful in preventing the negative ions from hitting the screen phosphors. The effectiveness of "ion trapping" depends on the thickness of the coating. On the other hand, too thick a coating would slow down the electrons and reduce screen brightness. The early models of aluminized tubes used bent-gun construction and ion trap magnets. This was merely a carry-over from the days when non-aluminized tubes were prevalent. By 1957, with superior production control in maintaining proper aluminum thickness, the trend was toward using straight-gun tubes without ion trap magnets and depending on the aluminum coating to prevent screen damage from ion bombardment.

Review Problems

1. Draw a sketch of a typical electrostatic type cathode-ray tube and name all the elements.
2. Why must cathode-ray tubes be handled with extreme care?
3. (a) What is an "aquadag" coating, and where is it located?
   (b) Name two uses for this coating.
4. (a) What elements of the cathode-ray tube are part of the electron gun?
   (b) Name four functions of the electron gun.
5. What is the specific function of each electrode of the electron gun?
6. (a) What is the purpose of the deflection plate assembly?
   (b) How many plates are used and where are they located?
   (c) Does the physical placement of the plates correspond to their designation as horizontal or vertical? Explain.
7. Explain the difference between fluorescence and phosphorescence.
8. Name four common types of screens and give the distinguishing characteristics of each.
9. State two functions of the control grid in the cathode-ray tube and describe how it accomplishes these results.
10. What is meant by the "cross-over" point?
11. Explain the action of the focusing electrode.
12. (a) Why may there be interaction between the focus and intensity controls?
    (b) How is this prevented in more recent tubes?
13. Explain the action of the electrostatic deflection system.
14. (a) State three ways of expressing the deflection sensitivity of a cathode-ray tube.
    (b) What is the average deflection sensitivity of commonly used tubes?
15. Explain briefly two factors that affect deflection sensitivity.
16. Explain how high sensitivity is obtained without sacrificing focusing ability or intensity.
17. Draw a schematic diagram of a cathode-ray tube connected to proper operating potentials. Show intensity, focus, and positioning controls.
18. When used with a cathode-ray tube, why is the positive terminal of the power supply commonly grounded?
19. Explain the operation of the positioning control.
20. (a) What is the difference between a balanced and an unbalanced deflection system?

(b) State briefly the advantage or disadvantage of each.

21. Describe briefly the operation of an electromagnetic system for focusing.

22. State three advantages and one disadvantage of this system compared to electrostatic focusing.

23. Describe briefly the operation of an electromagnetic deflection system.

24. (a) Name three applications of the electromagnetic type of cathode-ray tube.

(b) Why isn't this type suitable for use in oscilloscopes?

25. (a) What type of tube may develop ion spots?

(b) Explain the cause of these stains.

26. (a) Name two types of gun constructions used to prevent ion burns.

(b) What other device is needed in addition to change in gun structure?

27. Explain briefly the two steps involved in preventing ion spots.

28. (a) What was the original goal that led to the development of the aluminized tube?

(b) Explain how an aluminized tube realized this aim.

29. State two other advantages of the aluminized tube.

CHAPTER 6

Cathode-Ray Oscilloscope

Probably the most familiar application of the cathode-ray tube is in the cathode-ray oscilloscope. This versatile instrument has gained wide popularity in laboratories, production lines, schools, and even on the service bench. The oscilloscope is used primarily for the observation of the shape of the voltage waveforms in various types of electrical circuits. Its use has spread to many other industrial fields. Pressure changes, vibrations, light, and sound can be converted to electrical voltages which can be studied by use of the oscilloscope. The application of this instrument to industrial fields are limitless.

There are two other uses of the cathode-ray oscilloscope that are not too well known. These are to measure frequency of an unknown voltage and phase shift caused by electrical components. Before discussing the uses of the oscilloscope in detail, let us study the component sections of this unit. A block diagram (Fig. 6-1) will simplify this analysis.

Block Diagram of the Oscilloscope

Attenuator. When we desire to study the shape of a given voltage waveform, it is fed to the vertical input terminals. Frequently the signal to be observed has a high amplitude and may cause damage to the oscilloscope. An attenuator is therefore required to reduce the amplitude of the signal to a value that can be handled safely. Several factors must be carefully considered in the design of suitable attenuators.

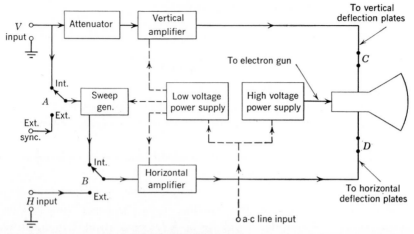

To vertical
deflection plates

To electron gun

To horizontal
deflection plates

a-c line input

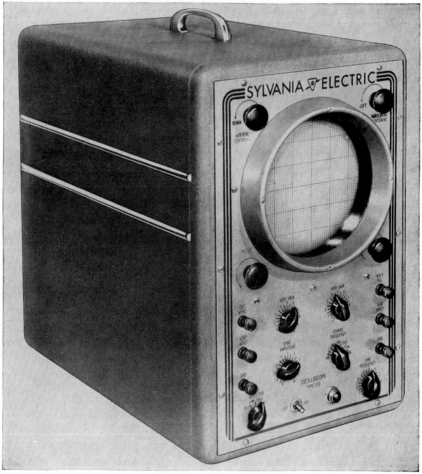

Fig. 6-1. Functional block diagram and external view of cathode-ray oscilloscope.

135

1. The input impedance must be as high as possible to prevent or reduce loading of the circuit under test.

2. The amount of attenuation should be variable so as to handle signals of various amplitudes.

3. For any setting of the attenuation control, the amount of attenuation should be constant regardless of the frequency of the voltage under test.

4. Stray capacitances should be avoided, otherwise high frequency signals may be bypassed to ground.

Amplifiers. In an earlier section, we saw that a common value of deflection sensitivity is approximately 30 volts per inch per kilovolt. Using an oscilloscope with an anode voltage of only one kilovolt, how much deflection would we get if the signal under observation had an amplitude of 0.1 volt? Need I say more as to why amplifiers are needed? With suitable amplifiers, an oscilloscope can be used to investigate waveshapes of very weak amplitudes. The deflection sensitivity with amplifiers may be as high as 0.01 volt per inch, depending on the number of stages used in the amplifier. The amplifier must include a variable gain control for adjusting the amplitude of the deflections on the screen to some convenient level. The gain control may be in addition to a step attenuator, or in cheaper designs the gain control itself may be used as the attenuator.

The use of amplifiers solves one problem—making the oscilloscope suitable for observation of low signal levels—but it creates a new one. Unless these amplifiers are properly designed for wide-band frequency response and minimum phase shift, they will introduce serious distortion in the screen pattern for signals of low or high frequencies, thereby limiting the usefulness of the oscilloscope. Because of price limitations, the amplifiers in the average oscilloscope are seldom suitable for frequencies below 20 cycles or above 200 kilocycles. In the more expensive models, frequency ranges as low as 5 cycles and as high as 6 megacycles can be obtained. In addition, oscilloscopes with d-c amplifiers are available for use when it is desired to study very low frequency effects, complex waves with d-c components, or where a d-c reference must be indicated.

On the other hand, the cathode-ray tube, without amplifiers, will give true reproduction of waveforms even at very high frequencies (approximately 200 megacycles maximum). This requires that the signal be fed directly to the deflection plates. Such a connection can be made in Fig. 6-1 by removing link C and applying the signal to the vertical deflection plates. Many commercial units have this provision. You must remember however, that direct connection can be used only when the signal to be observed has sufficient amplitude.

Time base—sweep generator. So far we have been discussing the application of a signal voltage to the vertical deflection plates. This will cause the electron beam to move up and down at the same rate as the frequency of the applied signal. But under these conditions all we will see on the screen is a vertical line! While the beam is moving up and down, if we could also cause the beam to move horizontally from left to right *at a uniform rate of speed,* the pattern on the screen will show the full variation of signal voltage with time. As soon as a full cycle of the signal voltage has been traced, the beam should be returned *quickly* back to the left-hand side of the screen so that it can start to trace out a second cycle.

How can this timing action be effected? Since timing is a horizontal motion, a suitable voltage should be applied to the horizontal plates. But what constitutes a suitable voltage? If we apply a voltage across the horizontal deflection plates, so as to make the right-hand plate positive with respect to the grounded left-hand plate, the beam will be deflected to the right. If we increase the potential of this plate at a steady rate, the beam will be pulled more and more to the right at a uniform speed. Once the beam reaches the right-hand side of the screen, we will want it to return quickly back to the left. This can be done by rapidly reducing the potential of the right-hand plate. But this is an exact description of the "voltage versus time" variation of a sawtooth wave! Our problem is solved. By applying a sawtooth voltage to the horizontal plates, we can view the exact pattern of the signal on the vertical plates. In the block diagram (Fig. 6-1) this sawtooth voltage is produced by the sweep generator, amplified by the horizontal amplifier, and applied to the horizontal deflection plates. Circuits for sweep generators will be covered later in this chapter.

Let us see how the application of a sine wave to the vertical plates and a sawtooth to the horizontal plates gives us the desired screen pattern. Referring to Fig. 6-2, at time = 0, the sine-wave voltage amplitude is zero and the sawtooth voltage amplitude is also zero. The beam strikes the screen at point *A*. At time = 1, both the sine-wave voltage and the sawtooth voltage have increased. The beam is deflected upward by the sine-wave voltage and to the right by the sawtooth voltage, striking the screen at *B*. At time = 2, the sine wave has reached its maximum value; the sawtooth voltage has increased slightly. The beam is deflected to its highest point and slightly more to the right causing the spot at *C* on the screen. At time = 3, the sine-wave voltage has decreased, but the sawtooth voltage is still increasing. The beam drops down but still moves to the right, hitting the screen at *D*. Finally at time = 8, the sawtooth voltage is at its maximum, causing the spot to appear on the screen at point *I*. The time interval 0-8 represents the forward sweep time. During the time interval 8-9 the beam returns back to the starting point. This time interval 8-9 is often called the *retrace time* or *flyback time*. Since the retrace interferes with the pattern to be observed, most circuits cut off the electron beam current by

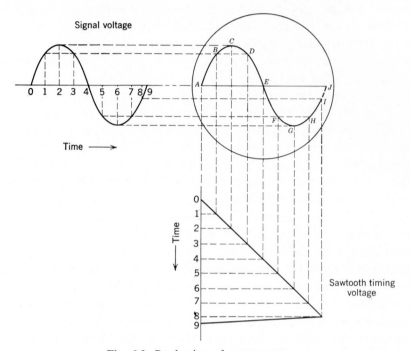

Fig. 6-2. Production of screen pattern.

biasing the cathode-ray tube grid and "blanking out" the screen. Obviously the section of the sine wave from *I* to *J* is lost. For this reason, it is important that the retrace time be as short as possible—in other words the sawtooth voltage should drop to zero as rapidly as possible.

If the frequency of the sine-wave signal were doubled, two cycles of sine wave would correspond, in time, to one cycle of sawtooth. Obviously using the same analysis as above, two cycles would appear on the screen. Also, if the frequency of the sawtooth wave were reduced so that the time for one sawtooth cycle corresponded to the time for three sine-wave cycles, three cycles of the signal would be seen on the screen. If a one cycle pattern is desired on the screen, the sawtooth frequency and signal frequency must be the same.

Synchronization. When the sweep frequency is equal to (or a submultiple of) the signal frequency, we have seen that the desired pattern is traced on the screen. Also, with each cycle of the sawtooth voltage the pattern retraced on the screen is identical with the previous one, and the resulting image, due to the retentivity of the eye and the persistence of the screen, is stationary. Figure 6-3 shows what happens if the sawtooth frequency is slightly faster than the signal frequency. Obviously each cycle

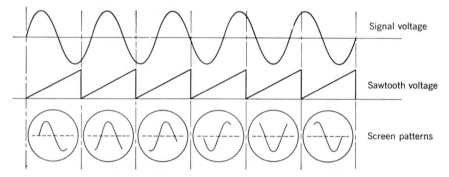

Fig. 6-3. Apparent motion of screen pattern owing to slightly higher sweep frequency.

of the sawtooth wave corresponds to less than one cycle of the signal. Successive patterns on the screen appear to have been shifted to the right. As a result the image is not stationary but appears to drift to the right. The speed with which the pattern moves will increase if the difference between the two frequencies is increased. On the other hand if the sweep frequency is slightly too slow, the pattern will drift to the left.

Although sweep circuits are designed with fine control of frequency, no simple sweep circuit will hold its frequency exactly constant. The resulting drift of the screen pattern is annoying. To remedy this, a synchronizing voltage is fed into the internal sweep generator circuit to lock the sweep frequency to the desired conditions. The synchronizing voltage can be taken internally from the signal being fed to the vertical amplifier, or from any desired external source. When internal synchronization is used, each signal viewed on the screen is synchronized (in phase relation) with respect to itself. Therefore all patterns will appear to have identical phasing. Where each signal is of individual interest only, this apparent phasing is of no objection. But quite often we are examining two waves and we are particularly interested in the phase relation of one compared to the other. In this case *external* synchronization is necessary, using the same "sync" signal as the reference for both observations. This reference signal could be some third voltage wave—or better yet—one of the two signals under observation. The sync voltage is applied across the Ext. Sync input terminals and switch *A* (block diagram Fig. 6-1) is set to Ext. Details of how synchronization is effected will be seen in a later section.

External horizontal input. When using the sweep voltage to view waveforms on the screen, switch *B* on the block diagram is set so as to connect the sawtooth voltage through the horizontal amplifier to the "scope" plates. The gain of the horizontal amplifier is set so as to give the desired horizontal spread to the pattern on the screen. For example, if a section of the full pattern needs careful analysis, increasing the gain of the horizontal amplifier will spread the wave out.

But you will recall that the oscilloscope can also be used for frequency comparison measurements or phase shift measurements. Under these conditions, the internal sweep circuit is not desired. Switch *B* (block diagram Fig. 6-1) is set so as to connect the horizontal amplifier to the horizontal input terminals. Now the two signals to be compared for frequency or phase shift are connected one to the vertical input and the second to the horizontal input. The details of how these measurements are made will be given later in the chapter.

Power supplies. We saw earlier in this chapter that proper potentials must be supplied to the cathode-ray tube to produce and position the electron beam. Common oscilloscopes require at least 1000 volts for the electron gun system. However the current drawn by the tube elements is very low—less than one milliampere.

In addition the amplifiers and sweep generator circuits require approximately 300 volts at much higher current values (approximately 50 milliamperes) for proper operation. Because of the difference in current requirements it has been found more economical to use two separate power supplies, one for the cathode-ray tube and a second unit for the auxiliary circuits.

Simple Sweep Circuit

In the study of the action of a capacitive circuit on direct currents * you learned that if a resistor and capacitor are connected in series across a d-c supply, the capacitor will charge to the full supply voltage along a logarithmic curve. However the lower portion of this curve—before the capacitor is charged to half the line voltage—is essentially a straight line. Therefore, if we discharge the capacitor rapidly before it reaches half charge, we have obtained a good sawtooth wave! This can be done by add-

---

* DeFrance, *Direct Current Fundamentals*, Chap. 20.

ing a cold-cathode gas diode (glow tube) to the *R-C* circuit. Such a circuit is shown in Fig. 6-4. It is often called a *relaxation oscillator.*

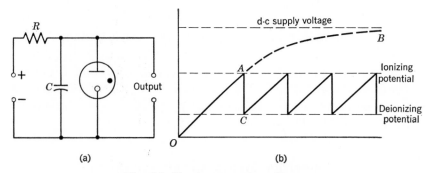

Fig. 6-4. Simple sawtooth oscillator.

Let us analyze the action of this circuit. The supply voltage should be at least twice the ionizing potential. A higher supply potential is preferable for linearity. The capacitor begins to charge up toward the full supply voltage following the logarithmic curve *OAB.* At point *A,* the voltage across the capacitor reaches the ionizing potential for the gas tube. The tube ionizes. Under this condition, its internal resistance is very low and it acts practically as a short-circuit across the capacitor. The capacitor discharges very rapidly along line *AC.* At point *C,* the voltage across the capacitor is so low that the glow tube deionizes—becoming an "open circuit." This series of events completes one cycle of the sawtooth wave. Now the capacitor starts to charge again until it reaches the ionizing potential of the gas tube. The sawtooth cycle is repeated over and over again.

How long will it take to complete one cycle of the sawtooth wave? The discharge time is practically negligible (except at very high frequencies). The length of time required to charge the capacitor to the ionizing potential depends on three factors:

1. *Supply voltage.* If the supply voltage is increased, the ionizing potential will become a lower percentage of the total voltage. Therefore the capacitor will reach the ionizing potential in a shorter period of time.

2. *Series resistance value.* The smaller the resistor *R,* the higher the charging current and the shorter the time required for the capacitor to reach the ionizing potential.

3. *Capacitance value.* The smaller the capacitor *C,* again the shorter the time required to charge it to the required value.

Since in any practical circuit, the supply voltage is usually fixed, we have two methods available for changing the sawtooth frequency—variation of R or C. In practical circuits a switching arrangement to change the capacitance value is used for large frequency variations, and is called the *coarse frequency control*. To get frequencies between the "steps" obtained by changing capacitors, the resistor R is made variable and acts as a *fine frequency control*. In many oscilloscopes this variable resistor is called the *vernier control*.

However the gas diode is not used in commercial circuits because its action is somewhat unstable. We also pointed out, previously, that synchronization is desirable to lock the pattern on the screen. The diode is not well adapted to this purpose.

Commercial Sweep Circuit—Thyratron

Sweep circuits employed in nearly all oscilloscope circuits use a thyratron tube in place of the gas diode. The exception to this is for extremely high frequency sweeps where hard vacuum tube circuits are employed. Thyratron tube circuits are more stable than the diode circuit previously discussed. With this type tube, synchronization is very readily applied to the grid. The circuit is shown in Fig. 6-5.

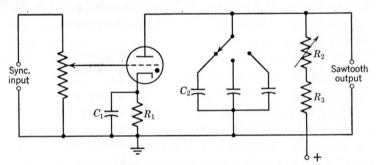

Fig. 6-5. Typical thyratron sweep circuit.

The action of this circuit is essentially the same as for the gas diode circuit described above. The only question now is how is synchronization effected? This can be explained by reference to Fig. 6-5. When the thyratron conducts, current flows through the cathode resistor R_1 making the cathode positive with respect to ground, and charging the capacitor C_1 so that the upper plate is positive. The values of C_1 and R_1 are chosen so that their time constant is quite long compared to any desired sweep time interval. As a result, even when the tube is not conducting the cathode is maintained at the desired positive potential. Meanwhile, assuming no signal is connected to the "sync input" terminals, the grid of the tube is at ground potential or negative compared to the cathode. Under this condition, the sweep frequency is determined by the time constant of the plate circuit ($C_2R_2R_3$) values and the ionizing potential of the thyratron tube with the normal cathode bias. The value of C_2 and R_3 should be adjusted for a sweep frequency that corresponds as closely as possible to the signal frequency we wish to observe (or a submultiple of this frequency). The pattern on the screen will then be practically stationary. However, any variation of circuit constants will cause the sweep frequency to vary and the pattern will drift to left or right on the screen.

To prevent this drift, a portion of the input voltage is fed to the "sync input" terminals of the sawtooth oscillator. The effect of such a connection can be seen in Fig. 6-6.

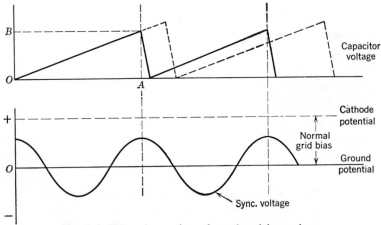

Fig. 6-6. Triggering action of synchronizing voltage.

Remember that the synchronizing voltage is the same as the signal frequency. If the sweep frequency is too low compared to signal frequency, the sawtooth voltage would appear as shown by the dotted line of the capacitor voltage curve. The screen pattern will not be stationary. At time interval *OA,* one cycle of the signal voltage has been completed, yet the capacitor voltage *OB*—with normal grid bias condition—has not reached the ionizing potential of the thyratron. But now, due to the synchronizing voltage, the grid bias is not the normal value. The grid has become less negative. The ionizing potential of the thyratron will decrease as the grid bias is made less negative. So—if we vary the setting of the grid potentiometer we can adjust the grid bias at point *A* so as to cause the thyratron to fire at this instant. The sawtooth wave will then follow the solid curve. Since the sawtooth wave and the signal are at the same frequency, the pattern is "locked" in a stationary condition. *Caution:* using too high a synchronizing potential may cause distortion of the pattern even though it is stationary.

Applications of the Cathode-Ray Oscilloscope

We have already seen one application of the oscilloscope—examination of waveshapes. This is probably the most important use of this piece of equipment. For this purpose, the signal voltage is connected to the vertical input terminals of the oscilloscope and the gain of the vertical amplifier is adjusted to give sufficient vertical deflection on the screen. The sweep circuit is set for internal sweep and adjusted for a stationary pattern. The horizontal amplifier gain is adjusted so that the pattern sweeps the full width of the screen.

In addition there are four other valuable applications of the oscilloscope which are not too widely used, probably because they are not too well understood. Let us consider each of these applications in turn.

Voltage measurement. Since the oscilloscope has a very high input impedance, it can readily be used in place of a vacuum-tube voltmeter for measurement of voltage amplitudes, within the frequency limitation of the vertical amplifier. For this application, it is preferable to turn the sweep circuit off. The pattern on the screen will be a vertical line. The height of this line is proportional to the peak-to-peak value of the applied voltage. All that is necessary is to calibrate the deflection against a known voltage. For purpose of calibration, the simplest procedure is to use a 60-cycle supply voltage, measure the voltage with the usual a-c voltmeter, and adjust the gain control of the oscilloscope to give a suitable deflection. The calibration can be made in terms of rms or peak values. For example, if a 60-cycle voltage of 10 volts rms (as measured by voltmeter) is applied to the oscilloscope and the gain is adjusted for a deflection of 10 divisions, the calibration is 1 volt rms per division. On the other hand, this same voltage (10 volts rms) has a maximum value of 14.14 volts or 28.28 volts peak-to-peak. Therefore, with a gain setting that gives a deflection of 28¼ divisions, the calibration is 1 volt peak-to-peak per division. If the signal voltage to be measured on a calibrated oscilloscope is also a sine wave, the calibration can be made either in terms of rms or peak values. However, when the signal voltage is a complex wave, the calibration should be in terms of peak-to-peak values. To facilitate the use of the oscilloscope as a voltmeter, commercial units have "built-in" calibrating voltages. These are usually square-wave voltages having some specific stabilized peak-to-peak value. One manufacturer, for example, supplies four calibrating voltages: 500 millivolts, 5 volts, 50 volts, and 500 volts peak-to-peak. It is also possible to obtain separate *voltage calibrators* for use with oscilloscopes that do not incorporate this built-in feature.

When the oscilloscope has been calibrated for a given gain setting, this dial setting should not be changed. The calibration would not apply for any other position of the control. Furthermore, since these dials are not precision adjustments, trying to readjust for the same setting may or may not give the original gain. Also, since the amplifier in the oscilloscope is not stabilized for gain, it is wise to recalibrate the unit whenever it is to be used for voltage measurements.

Now let us assume that we have calibrated the oscilloscope so that a deflection of 1 division is equal to 1 volt RMS. When we apply a signal voltage, the deflection is 25 divisions. Obviously the signal voltage is 25 volts RMS. If it becomes necessary to measure a high-level signal voltage, the resulting deflection may exceed the tube screen diameter. What can we do to measure this new voltage? Of course we could recalibrate the oscilloscope for a lower gain setting, using the method outlined above. But there is a simpler method. First adjust the *signal* voltage so that the deflection is exactly 25 divisions. Then change the *gain* setting so as to reduce the deflection to 5 divisions. Now, 5 divisions on the oscilloscope correspond to a signal of 25 volts—or the calibration of our oscilloscope has been simply and accurately changed to 5 volts per division. We are ready to measure signal voltages of much higher amplitudes. Obviously a similar method can be used if we wish to calibrate the oscilloscope to measure weaker signal voltages.

If d-c voltages are to be measured, the amplifiers in the oscilloscope cannot be used. However if the voltage is high enough, direct connection can be made to the vertical deflection plates. Naturally the oscilloscope must be calibrated again for such use. Direct connection to the plates can also be used for frequencies above the range of the amplifiers.

Phase shift measurements. One of the most important applications of the oscilloscope, next to observation of waveshapes, lies in its ability to indicate various degrees of phase shift. You will recall from your studies of a-c circuits * that phase shift may occur when a signal is passed through an *R-C* or *R-L* circuit. Since electronic equipment contains such components, it is often desirable to know how much phase shift, if any, is introduced by such units. For example, in television amplifiers and in oscillo-

---

* DeFrance, *Alternating Current Fundamentals*, Chap. 9.

scope amplifiers, phase shift should be reduced to a negligible value or compensating circuits must be included to make the effects of phase shift constant for signals of all frequencies. It should be obvious that any discussion of phase shift is limited to only one frequency at a time. If a signal of 1000 cycles is fed into a unit, the output frequency is naturally also 1000 cycles—but what is the phase relation of the output voltage compared to the input voltage? The phase shift of this same unit (between input and output) can also be checked at any other frequency. Discussion of phase relation between two signals not of the same frequency has no meaning, since the phase relation is continuously changing.

To measure the phase shift caused by any piece of electronic equipment is a simple matter. Merely connect one input of the oscilloscope (horizontal or vertical) to the input voltage being fed to the unit under test and connect the other input of the oscilloscope to the output of the unit under test. Obviously, the internal sawtooth sweep circuit should be disconnected, and the horizontal deflection plates and amplifier should be connected to the external signal source. This is done by setting switch B (Fig. 6-1 block diagram, page 135) to "Ext." position. The pattern obtained on the screen will not be a reproduction of the waveshape of the input (or output) voltage signal, but rather a peculiar shaped figure. This pattern is called a *Lissajous figure* (named after a French scientist who developed this type of measurement). The particular pattern obtained will vary depending on the phase relation and relative amplitudes of the two signals being compared.

First, let us make the assumption that the signals which are reaching the horizontal and vertical plates are of equal amplitude. This does not mean that the original signals being compared must have the same amplitude. Any difference in their signal strengths can be made up by using compensatingly greater oscilloscope amplifier gain for the weaker signal. A legitimate question at this time is how do we adjust the H and V gain for equal voltages on the horizontal and vertical deflection plates. The method is very simple. Set the horizontal gain to zero. With no signal on the horizontal deflection plate, the pattern on the screen is a vertical line. Adjust the vertical gain for a good size deflection. After noting the vertical amplifier gain setting, turn this control to zero and increase the gain of horizontal amplifier until the resulting horizontal line is equal in length to the vertical line previously obtained. Now merely adjust the gain of the vertical amplifier to the setting recorded above. Q.E.D., the signals reaching the horizontal and vertical deflection plates are equal in amplitude.

Figure 6-7 shows a point-by-point development of the Lissajous figures

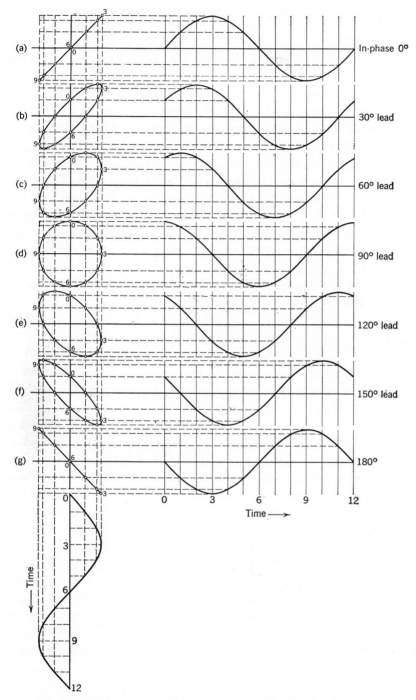

Fig. 6-7. Effect of phase shift on Lissajous figures (1:1 frequency ratio).

147

that are obtained for various angles of phase shift between zero and 180 degrees. In each of these diagrams, the signal fed to the vertical input terminals of the oscilloscope is leading the signal fed to the horizontal input terminals. Using similar point-by-point developments it can be shown that the patterns obtained for vertical input signals lagging by the same angle of phase shift would be identical. In other words, a 30-degree (or any other angle) phase shift between the two signals—regardless of which signal is leading (or lagging)—produces identical screen patterns. Since this is so, is it necessary to develop Lissajous figures for phase shifts greater than 180 degrees? Obviously not—one signal leading by some angle, θ, greater than 180 degrees, is the same as that signal lagging by $(360 - \theta)$ degrees. For example, a signal that leads by 300 degrees can equally well be considered as lagging by 60 degrees, and the Lissajous figure would be the same as shown in Fig. 6-7(c).

This coincidence simplifies the pattern structures that must be understood when making phase shift measurements. But—and there usually is a fly in the ointment—it adds a complication. Let us suppose that we have checked an amplifier for phase shift and found that a 15-degree phase shift exists between the input voltage (E_i) and output voltage (E_o) of the amplifier at a certain frequency. Now we would like to know, does the output voltage lead or lag the input voltage? From the pattern analysis, we cannot tell. It would seem that our measurements were of no avail. But there is a solution. Let us insert an R-C circuit between the E_o signal and the oscilloscope, with the constants (R and C) deliberately selected to add approximately 15 degrees *lead* to the E_o signal. If the Lissajous elliptical pattern now widens, indicating an *increase* in phase toward 30 degrees, the original output voltage (E_o) must have been leading! On the other hand, if the pattern collapses toward a slant line, the original output voltage must have been lagging.

Now that this ambiguity of lead or lag has been cleared, let us get back to Fig. 6-7. Remember that these patterns are obtained only when the two signals are of equal amplitude. Referring to Fig. 6-7(a), notice that a straight line at a 45-degree angle is obtained when the two signals are in phase and of equal amplitude. If the amplitudes were unequal, the pattern would still be a straight line but the slope of the line would change. If the vertical signal amplitude were greater, the vertical deflection would be greater, and the slope of the line would increase toward the vertical. In other words, the zero-degree phase shift is determined *not by the slant of the line but by the fact that it is only a line*!

Now examine Fig. 6-7(d). Notice the perfect circular pattern. How will this pattern be affected if the two signals are not equal in amplitude—or if the vertical and horizontal gain settings do not produce equal amplitudes at the deflection plates? A little thought should make this obvious. For example, let us assume that the signal fed to the horizontal plates is 50% lower in amplitude than the signal applied to the vertical plates. The horizontal deflection will be only half as much as the vertical deflection. The pattern will become elliptical, with the major axis vertical. Similarly, an ellipse would also be obtained if the vertical deflection signal were of lower amplitude. Only this time, the major axis of the ellipse would be horizontal. So—a 90-degree phase shift may produce a circular or an elliptical pattern, depending on signal level proportions. Won't this cause confusion with the ellipses produced by other phase shift angles—such as Fig. 6-7(b) and (c)? Yes, it could—if you forget that *for a 90-degree pattern, the axes of the ellipse must be vertical and horizontal.*

Evaluating the degree of phase shift for intermediate angles is more confusing—if the two signal levels are not equal. The elliptical patterns shown in Fig. 6-7 will vary in thickness and also in the slant of the major axis of the ellipse.

It would seem that except for zero- and 90-degree phase shifts, evaluation of phase shift by this method is only a good guess. However the oscilloscope is capable of much better accuracy. The system explained below will give a high degree of accuracy. In addition, when using this second method, it will not be necessary to have both signals of equal amplitude. Reference to Fig. 6-8 will make the procedure clear. Merely measure the maximum

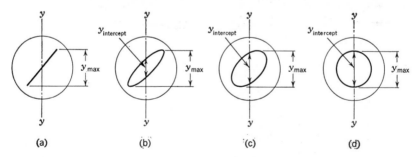

Fig. 6-8. Evaluation of phase shift angle from y maximum and y intercept.

vertical deflection of the pattern (y maximum) and the vertical distance intercepted by the pattern as it crosses the y axis (y intercept). The position of the y axis can be determined either by estimating the center line of the pattern or by temporarily turning the horizontal gain to zero. The vertical line left on the screen will coincide with the y axis. (For convenience the location of the y axis can be made to coincide exactly with the center of the screen by using the horizontal centering control.) When this axis is determined, the horizontal gain should be adjusted to a suitable value.

The phase shift angle (θ) between the two signals is obtained from the following relation:

$$\sin \theta = \frac{y_{\text{intercept}}}{y_{\text{maximum}}}$$

Once the sine of the phase shift angle is calculated, the angle itself can be found from trigonometric tables or slide rule scales. From Fig. 6-8, we can readily see that when the phase shift is zero, as in (a), the y intercept is zero; as the phase shift increases, the y intercept increases and $\sin \theta$ from our formula also increases; while in the extreme case of 90° phase shift, as in (d), the y intercept equals y maximum and $\sin \theta =$ unity.

A more rigorous proof of the above formula can be made from Fig. 6-9. Here the signal applied to the vertical plates leads the horizontal voltage by an angle θ. If both signals were in phase, the projection on the oscilloscope axis for time $= 0$ would be at the center of the coordinate

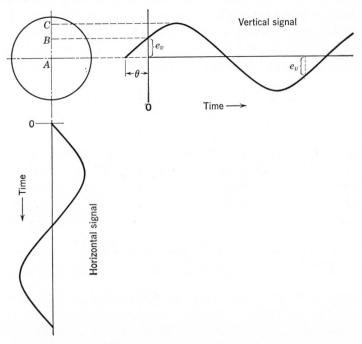

Fig. 6-9. Relation between phase shift and y intercept.

axis, A. However, due to the lead of the vertical signal voltage, the projection of this point is at B. Since the amplitude of the horizontal voltage is zero at time $= 0$, the y intercept, A-B, on the screen is caused by the instantaneous voltage value of the signal on the vertical plates at time $= 0$. Expressed mathematically,

$$y_{\text{intercept}} = e_v$$

But the instantaneous value of this voltage depends on its own maximum value and the degree of phase shift, θ, or

$$e_v = E_{v\,\text{max}} \sin \theta$$

Where $E_{v\text{max}}$ is the maximum vertical deflection, (y_{max} or A-C). Substituting this value, we get

$$e_v = y_{\text{intercept}} = y_{\text{max}} \sin \theta$$

Solving for $\sin \theta$,

$$\sin \theta = \frac{y_{\text{intercept}}}{y_{\text{max}}}$$

So far we have discussed the y intercept and y maximum values obtained from the positive half cycle of the signal applied to the vertical deflection plates. If we repeat the analysis for the negative part of the cycle, we would get equal but negative values for the y intercept and y maximum. Therefore in calculating the phase shift between the signal applied to the vertical and horizontal deflection plates we can use either the half-values (positive or negative) as proved from Fig. 6-9 or the total values as shown in Fig. 6-8; doubling both the y intercept and y maximum gives the same result for $\sin \theta$. In practice it is usually easier to measure the total values.

A word of caution must be added at this point. Remember that the amplifiers in the oscilloscope (horizontal and vertical) may not be identical. It may be possible, at certain frequencies, that these amplifiers may introduce phase shifts of their own. If the phase shift is not equal for the horizontal and vertical amplifiers, then the phase shift as measured from the scope pattern may be due not only to phase difference between the original signals, but also to phase shift introduced by the H and V amplifiers.

The solution to this seeming vicious circle is quite simple. First check the H and V amplifiers by feeding the *same* signal to both the H and V inputs. If the amplifiers are identical, the pattern seen will be a straight line. If any other pattern is seen, calculate the phase difference between the H and V amplifiers and whether the horizontal or vertical amplifier output is leading (or lagging). Now feed the signals to be tested one each to the H and V inputs. Again calculate the phase difference from the scope pattern. Correct this value by the phase difference between the horizontal and vertical scope amplifiers, found previously. The remaining phase difference must be due to shift between the test signals.

Since the phase shift difference between the vertical and horizontal oscilloscope amplifiers may also vary with the input signal frequency, this precaution must be made separately for all frequencies above and below the limitations of these amplifiers.

Phase measurements using external synchronization. The above method for measurement of phase shift seems rather involved. Actually the difficulty lies in the verbal explanation of the procedure rather than in the technique itself. It is harder to explain than it is to show. There is another method sometimes used which avoids the necessity of checking the oscilloscope amplifiers and is somewhat simpler to understand and to apply. The accuracy of this second method may not be as good, but it is often sufficient. Let us assume we wish to determine the phase shift (if any) introduced between input and output of some electronic unit.

1. Feed the input voltage (E_i) of the unit under test, to the vertical input terminals of the oscilloscope. Adjust the vertical gain of the oscilloscope amplifier to give maximum usable deflection on the screen.

2. Using the internal sawtooth generator, adjust the coarse and fine frequency control so as to produce a one-cycle pattern as stationary as possible. Also adjust the horizontal gain to give a large but convenient horizontal sweep across the screen face. (Since one cycle is 360 degrees, convenient deflections would be 12, 18, or 36 spaces; i.e., one space equals 30, 20, or 10 degrees respectively.)

3. Using *external synchronization* apply the minimum synchronizing voltage needed to lock the screen pattern. As a source of this external synchronizing voltage, we can use the same input voltage (E_i) that is being fed to the unit under test (and at present, also to the vertical input terminals of the oscilloscope).

4. Draw the pattern seen on the screen (preferably trace) showing the exact starting point and zero axis of the wave.

5. Now disconnect the signal voltage (E_i) from the oscilloscope and reconnect the vertical input terminals of the oscilloscope to the output of the unit under test. Adjust the vertical gain for the same vertical deflection as in step 1.

6. Since the frequency of this output voltage (E_o) is the same as the input voltage (E_i), no change need be made to any other control.

7. Repeat step 4 above. Since the synchronizing signal is the same for step 4 and step 7, the two waveshapes (E_i and E_o) are drawn with respect to a common reference. Their phase relation can now be identified as follows:

(a) If the two waves are in coincidence (they both start at zero and rise in a positive direction) they are in-phase.

(b) If the E_o wave starts at some positive value, while E_i starts at zero and rises in a positive direction, then E_o leads E_i. The amount of lead can be calculated by noting the spacing between some identical point on each wave. For example, with the horizontal gain adjusted for 36 spaces equal to 360 degrees, if the zero (and going positive) point for E_o occurs two spaces to the left of the zero (and going positive) point of E_i, E_o leads by 20 degrees.

(c) If the E_o wave appears shifted to the right of the E_i wave, then E_o is lagging and the amount of lag can be calculated from the number of spaces difference, as above.

Frequency measurements. Another basic application of the oscilloscope is in the measurement of frequency. In addition to an oscilloscope, it is necessary to have a source of known frequencies as a standard for comparison. (A calibrated audio or r-f oscillator is suitable as the standard.) The signal of unknown frequency is fed to the vertical input terminals of the oscilloscope, while the standard frequency source is connected to the horizontal input terminals. Obviously the internal sawtooth sweep circuit is not used. (Switch B in the block diagram of Fig. 6-1 is set to Ext. This connects the horizontal input terminals through the horizontal amplifier to the horizontal deflection plates.) Again, as for phase shift measurement, the patterns developed on the screen will be Lissajous figures. Analysis of these patterns will give the frequency ratio between the two signals.

Let us analyze the pattern that is formed when the unknown frequency is twice the standard frequency. In other words two cycles of the unknown frequency will correspond in time to one cycle of the standard frequency. Figure 6-10 shows a point-by-point development of the pattern. The method used is the same as in Fig. 6-2 (page 138).

In stating frequency ratios, it is common practice to state the horizontal frequency first and then the vertical frequency. In Fig. 6-10, the frequency ratio would be 1:2, that is one horizontal to two vertical. Let us add two tangent lines to the oscilloscope pattern of Fig. 6-10. Notice that the *horizontal motion* of the electron beam would cause the beam to touch the *vertical tangent line AB* only once, at point 6. On the other hand, the *vertical motion* of the beam causes it to touch the *horizontal tangent line* twice, at points 5 and 1. By this method, the frequency ratio of any Lissajous figure can be determined. Merely count the number of times the beam

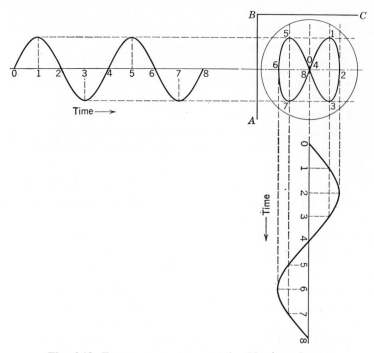

Fig. 6-10. Frequency measurement by Lissajous figure.

sweeps horizontally to vertically. If you prefer formulas, then this relation can be given by:

$$\frac{\text{Frequency on horizontal axis}}{\text{Frequency on vertical axis}} = \frac{\text{Number of loops touching the vertical line}}{\text{Number of loops touching the horizontal line}}$$

The pattern shown here, (Fig. 6-10), applies only if the two signals are starting with an in-phase relationship—starting at zero and increasing in a positive direction. It should be obvious from our previous discussion on phase shift that with any other starting phase relation, the pattern would be different. However, regardless of the exact shape of the pattern, the beam would still make one horizontal sweep to two vertical sweeps. In terms of the formula, the pattern would approach the vertical tangent line once and the horizontal tangent line twice. The frequency ratio can still be readily identified as 1:2. To illustrate this point, a problem is included at the end of this chapter, for a different starting phase angle between the two signals.

If the two frequencies are not exactly in a 1:2 ratio, the starting phase relation will vary continuously. If they start in-phase, the angle will gradually increase to 360 degrees (or back to zero degrees). As a result, the pattern seen on the screen will change continuously from the horizontal figure eight shown in Fig. 6-10 to an upright (or inverted) U and back again. In any case, the pattern will always retain the 1:2 relationship.

Let us use a problem to illustrate frequency measurement by Lissajous figures.

Example 1:

What is the frequency of each of the unknown signals (Fig. 6-11) if the frequency applied to the horizontal plates is 1000 cycles?

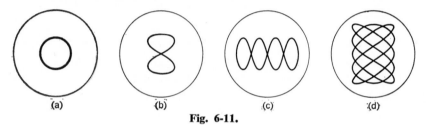

(a)   (b)   (c)   (d)

Fig. 6-11.

Solution:

(a) Since the beam sweeps vertically once and horizontally once, the ratio is 1:1. Therefore the unknown frequency is also 1000 cycles.

(b) The beam sweeps horizontally twice but only once in the vertical direction. The ratio is 2:1. This time the unknown frequency is only half of the standard frequency or 500 cycles.

(c) The frequency ratio is 1:4. The unknown frequency must be 4000 cycles.

(d) Five horizontal sweeps are made while the vertical motion makes three sweeps. The vertical frequency is at a slower rate (three-fifths of 1000, or 600 cycles).

When the standard frequency is fixed in value, the size of the oscilloscope screen will limit the frequency range of the unknown signals that can be measured. For example, if the difference between known and unknown frequencies is too great (10:1 or 1:10), the number of tangent loops may be too difficult to evaluate. Also if the frequency difference is too small, such as 10:9 or vice-versa, again the number of tangent loops may be too many to count.

The 1:1 ratio (since it has the least number of loops) is the easiest to identify and most accurate in its indication. Therefore, the simplest method of measuring the frequency of an unknown signal is to compare it to the output from a calibrated variable frequency oscillator. Vary the frequency of this standard oscillator until a 1:1 pattern is obtained. [Although Fig. 6-11(a) shows a circle for the 1:1 pattern, remember that this pattern may also vary from a straight line to an ellipse or circle—depending on phase shift.] Then, merely read the frequency indicated on the dial of the variable frequency oscillator. The accuracy of the determination is obviously limited to the accuracy of the oscillator used as the standard.

Frequency response by square-wave testing. You will recall from your studies of complex waves,* that a square wave has many harmonics and that the amplitude of these harmonics is fairly strong. For example, the fifteenth harmonic has an amplitude equal to one-fifteenth of the fundamental frequency amplitude. Also from an analysis of this wave, you will recall that the steepness of the wave front is due to the high order harmonics. These characteristics of a square wave give us a very quick method of checking the frequency response of an amplifier, using a square-wave generator and an oscilloscope. A square wave is fed into the amplifier, and the output wave is examined on the oscilloscope for distortion of the square-wave pattern. Since we are examining the waveshape, the signal is fed to the vertical input, and the internal sawtooth generator is used for horizontal sweep.

For checking the low frequency response, the square-wave frequency should be as low as the lowest frequency limit desired. If the amplifier has good response at this low frequency, the screen pattern will be undistorted [Fig. 6-12(a)]. If the gain of the amplifier falls off at this low frequency,

(a)   (b)   (c)   (d)

Fig. 6-12. Effect of amplifier low-frequency response on square-wave pattern.

the pattern will show a dip in the center [Fig. 6-12(b)]. Usually low gain at low frequencies is accompanied with a high degree of phase shift. The combined effect of low gain and phase shift are seen in Fig. 6-12(c) and (d). Figure 6-12(d) is obtained when the response drops off to 10% and the phase shift is 80%. Notice that this waveshape looks like the output

---

* DeFrance, *Alternating Current Fundamentals,* Chap. 4.

from a differentiating circuit. This is exactly what happens. *R-C* circuits in a poorly designed amplifier will cause differentiation of the square-wave input.

To test the high frequency response of an amplifier, the square-wave signal should have a frequency of approximately one-tenth of the maximum frequency desired. If the output as seen on the screen is a good square wave, the amplifier has good response up to at least the fifteenth harmonic of the square-wave frequency. Figure 6-13 shows the effects of poor high frequency response. The rounding of both edges of the square

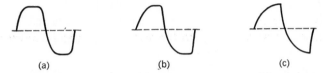

| (a) | (b) | (c) |

Fig. 6-13. Effect of poor amplifier high frequency response on square-wave pattern.

wave represented in (a) is due to poor high frequency response without phase shift. This pattern represents a loss of gain of approximately 30% at 10 times the square-wave frequency. Figure 6-13(b) represents a similar loss of gain but with attending phase shift. The curve of Fig. 6-13(c) results from very poor gain and high phase shift. It represents a loss of 30% gain at a frequency of approximately twice the square-wave frequency.

So far we have discussed four basic uses of the oscilloscope. To summarize, they are:

1. Viewing of waveshapes—for analysis.
2. Measurement of voltage.
3. Measurement of phase shift.
4. Measurement of frequency.

In addition we included a fifth use—checking of frequency response by square-wave testing. Actually this last application is not a basic use, but rather a *specific* application of viewing a waveshape for analysis. Similarly, the oscilloscope can be used for many other specific applications of the above four basic functions. For example, the oscilloscope is used for calibration of signal generators; alignment of AM, FM, and T.V. receivers; "trouble shooting" and servicing of the above receivers; and modulation checks of percentage and linearity in transmitters. Again, these are not new uses, but applications of the four basic techniques. Specific applications will not be covered at this time. They will be understood much better when studying the individual circuits.

Review Problems

1. Draw a block diagram for a cathode-ray oscilloscope.

2. State four desirable characteristics for attenuators used in oscilloscopes.

3. (a) Why are amplifiers used in oscilloscopes?
(b) State two desirable characteristics for these amplifiers.
(c) Why are these characteristics desirable?

4. (a) Why is a "time base" needed in an oscilloscope?
(b) Draw a waveshape suitable for a time base.

5. Show by diagram how a screen pattern is obtained by applying a square-wave voltage to the vertical plates and a sawtooth voltage to the horizontal plates.

6. How can three cycles of the signal voltage be produced as the screen pattern?

7. (a) Why is a synchronizing circuit used in oscilloscopes?
(b) Explain the screen pattern obtained when the sawtooth frequency is slightly higher than the signal frequency.

8. State two applications requiring the use of the external horizontal input in place of the internal sweep circuit.

9. (a) How many power supplies are used in oscilloscopes?
(b) Give the approximate rating of each.

10. Explain the operation of a simple relaxation oscillator circuit.

11. (a) How is good linearity obtained from such a circuit?
(b) State three factors that affect the frequency of the output voltage and how the frequency varies with each.

12. (a) Draw the circuit diagram of a commercial thyratron sweep circuit.
(b) State the function of each of the three variable controls in this circuit.

13. Explain how synchronization is obtained in the thyratron sweep generator.

14. (a) Describe how the oscilloscope can be used to measure voltages.
(b) How would you measure voltages above or below the frequency range of the amplifiers?

15. Draw a block diagram showing a CRO (cathode-ray oscilloscope) connected for phase shift measurement.

16. Develop the Lissajous figure obtained when the vertical signal leads the horizontal signal by 90 degrees, and the vertical amplitude is only one-half the horizontal amplitude.

17. The pattern generally shown for a 90-degree phase shift is a perfect circle. Explain why the results of Problem 16 do not conform.

18. Show by aid of a diagram how accurate phase shift measurements can be made.

19. Using the method of Problem 18, how can you tell if the phase shift is between 90 and 180 degrees?

20. In checking an amplifier for phase shift, it is found that a 20-degree phase shift exists between the input voltage to the amplifier and the output voltage from the amplifier. Explain, with the aid of a suitable circuit diagram, how we can determine whether the output leads or lags the input.

21. (a) When checking for phase shift by separate observation of the *waveshapes* of the input and output voltage, why is external synchronization necessary?
    (b) What source can be used for the external synchronizing signal?
    (c) Explain how to determine which wave is leading, and by how much.

22. Using the phase shift evaluation method of Problem 21, explain whether you can readjust between observations (a) vertical amplifier gain; (b) horizontal amplifier gain.

23. Draw a block diagram showing a CRO connected for frequency measurement.

24. Develop the Lissajous figure for a frequency ratio of 1:2 with both signals starting at their positive maximum values.

25. Develop the Lissajous figure for a frequency ratio of 2:3 with both signals starting in-phase.

26. Sketch the Lissajous figures that may be obtained for frequency ratios of 2:1 and 1:3.

27. (a) Explain a simple way of judging the low-frequency response of an amplifier.
    (b) Repeat (a) for high-frequency response.

CHAPTER 7

Semiconductor Fundamentals

The tiny transistor emerged into public view when the Bell Telephone laboratories announced the development of the point contact transistor in June of 1948. Much excitement was created because this speck of solid matter could control the flow of electrons in much the same manner as an electron tube. Voltage, current, and power amplification could all be achieved with this simple device consisting of a small crystal of the element germanium and two pointed wires making contact to it. The transistor required no heating power, and it operated effectively on only a few volts of power supply. The space and weight saving advantages of this midget device were tremendous. However these early transistors had their drawbacks. They produced high noise levels; they had serious frequency limitations; and they were unreliable, as it was impossible to produce two units with identical characteristics. Would the transistor replace the electron tube, or would it remain a laboratory curiosity?

Research continued. Manufacturing techniques were improved, and within a few years many of the limitations of the early transistor were sufficiently overcome. Meanwhile a new type, the *junction* transistor, was developed. By 1953 commercial applications of transistorized equipment began to appear on the market. Their small size and low power requirements made the transistor ideal for such uses as hearing aids and miniature portable radios. The transistor was here to stay—not as a replacement—but as a companion to the electron tube.

Semiconductors

Before we can discuss the characteristics of a transistor it is necessary to study the basic fundamentals that make its operaton possible. We have already mentioned that transistors are made from a small crystal of germanium. Other materials, such as silicon can be used. What is it about these materials that leads to devices which function like electron tubes? Electrically, these materials are classified as *semiconductors,* that is, they are neither good conductors like copper nor good insulators like glass. Germanium, for example, offers a resistivity of 60 ohms per cubic centimeter as compared to 1.7×10^{-6} for copper and 9×10^{13} for glass. You might wonder, if germanium is not a good conductor nor a good insulator, why not classify it as a resistance material? To answer this let us first check the resistance of nichrome, one of the highest resistance materials. The resistance of nichrome is approximately 60 times that of copper, or 1×10^{-4} ($1.7 \times 10^{-6} \times 60$) ohm per cubic centimeter. Compare this value with germanium and you will see that as a conductor germanium is 600,000 times poorer. In other words, resistance materials (with regards to the general classifications of insulators, semiconductors and conductors), fall under the category of conductors. Germanium and silicon are not the only semiconductor materials. Other materials in this class are elements such as selenium, sulphur, cesium, boron, and most oxides and carbides.

It is interesting to note that some peculiar properties of semiconductors were discovered many years ago. For example, around 1880, it was found that current would flow only in one direction through a junction of selenium and a conductor. Yet the commercial application of this discovery was not made till 1930 when the selenium rectifier was developed. Even more interesting is the example of the crystal detector used in the early 1900's when radio was in its infancy. It consisted of a lump of semiconductor crystal such as lead sulphide (galena), silicon or silicon carbide with a pointed wire, *the catswhisker* bearing on it under a slight spring pressure. This combination also had the property of allowing current flow in only one direction. Unfortunately this early crystal detector had an annoying defect. The crystal had sensitive spots that were destroyed by overload or could be readily lost by a slight displacement of the catswhisker. The early radio operators were always fiddling with this contact trying to find a more sensitive spot. So, with the invention of the vacuum-tube diode, the crystal detector became obsolete. Then as electronic applications went to higher and higher frequencies, the diode performance was impaired. Research on crystals as diodes was resumed, and during World War II silicon and germanium crystal diodes were in extensive use as mixers and detectors in radar and other UHF equipment.

Valence Electrons

As a first step in explaining semiconductor action let us first review the structure of the atom. Any student of chemistry, physics, or electricity is probably familiar with the theory of the planetary structure of the atom —a compact nucleus in the center and electrons revolving around it. We are primarily interested in the electrons. The chemical and electrical characteristics of each element is closely related to the quantity and arrangement of these electrons.

In the Periodic Table of elements,* all the elements are given an *atomic weight* and an *atomic number*. The atomic weight corresponds to the number of neutrons and protons in the nucleus, and the atomic number to the number of electrons revolving around the nucleus. An electron as it revolves around the nucleus may be considered as having a definite orbit. However, unlike the motion of the planets in our solar system, the plane of the electron orbit keeps shifting, so that in time, the electron will have traversed the surface of a sphere, or shell. This is similar to the way a ball of cotton is made. As you wind each turn at a different angle from the previous turn, the end result is a ball rather than flat loops. Now to complete the picture for *any one electron,* also imagine that the radius of motion changes slightly from time to time so that instead of a thin line orbit we have a band and eventually a thick shell, as the total surface traversed. The distance of this "pathway" from the nucleus depends on the *energy level* of the electron. Such a pathway is common to all electrons having this energy level.

The electrons of an atom do not all travel at the same energy level. Some are at a second and higher energy level, others at a third and still higher energy level, etc. There is a definite pattern to their arrangement as the atomic number and atomic weight of the element increase. Each energy level has a specific quota or maximum number of electrons as follows:

$$1st \quad 2 \times 1^2 = 2$$
$$2nd \quad 2 \times 2^2 = 8$$
$$3rd \quad 2 \times 3^2 = 18$$
$$4th \quad 2 \times 4^2 = 32$$

* Consult a general chemistry text.

$$\text{5th} \qquad 2 \times 5^2 = 50$$
$$\text{6th} \qquad 2 \times 6^2 = 72$$

Furthermore, whenever the outermost level (other than the first) contains 8 electrons, the next electron starts at a higher level.

You might be wondering by now—why all this lecture on atomic theory? Well, we have just about reached the end for our immediate needs. The electrical (and chemical) characteristics of each element depend on the number (and arrangement) of the electrons at the outermost level. These electrons are known as *valence electrons*. Table I shows the distribution of electrons for several elements that we will discuss later.

Table I. Distribution of Electrons at Various Energy Levels

Element	Atomic number	First level	Second level	Third level	Fourth level
Boron	5	2	3 *		
Carbon	6	2	4 *		
Silicon	14	2	8	4 *	
Copper	29	2	8	18	1 *
Gallium	31	2	8	18	3 *
Germanium	32	2	8	18	4 *
Arsenic	33	2	8	18	5 *
Selenium	34	2	8	18	6 *

* Valence electrons.

Semiconductor Crystal Lattice

From Table I, we see that copper has only one valence electron, whereas germanium has four and selenium six. Yet copper is a good conductor while the other elements are not. To explain this we must now analyze the interatomic structure of each type of element. Any element is held together by the bonding action of the valence electrons. In copper, and other conductors, the valence electrons comprising these bonds are not specifically associated with any particular atom, but exist as a communal group. They are therefore relatively free to move, and as one electron moves away another moves in to maintain the bonding structure. That is why these electrons are often referred to as *free electrons*.

With semiconductors we have a slightly different interatomic structure. Each valence electron of one atom forms a direct bond with a valence electron from an adjacent atom. These bonds are called *covalent pairs*, and the individual electrons are not free to move away from their associated atom. Figure 7-1 shows this type of structure diagrammatically. In this diagram the circle represents the nucleus *and all the electrons in the inner shells*. Four valence electrons are shown around each circle. The

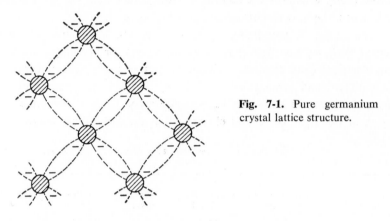

Fig. 7-1. Pure germanium crystal lattice structure.

dashed lines between circles represent the covalent pair bond between atoms. Although the diagram is for a germanium crystal, it can just as well represent the crystal structure for carbon or silicon since each of these also have four valence electrons. Unfortunately the diagram (Fig. 7-1) has a drawback, which cannot be avoided. The crystal structure should be shown in three dimensions, with some of the atoms coming up from the paper and others down. With this picture in mind, we can then visualize the selenium crystal structure (valence 6) with two more valence electrons making covalent pair bonds with two other adjacent atoms.

Based on this crystal lattice structure with covalent pair bonds, a pure semiconductor should have no conductivity whatever and therefore theoretically it should be an insulator. There are two factors that create the semiconductor characteristics. Impurities in the crystal structure will produce an excess or deficiency of valence electrons, or absorption of energy from light or heat can break the covalent bonds. For example, in the case of germanium, thermal agitation even at room temperature will create one free electron for every ten million germanium atoms. This may seem a ridiculously small value, but when you consider the number of atoms even in a tiny bit of matter, germanium is not an insulator.

Donors and Acceptors

Conduction caused by impurities is the basic principle underlying semiconductor diodes and transistors. In the preparation of germanium for use in transistors, first it is refined to a purity of not more than one foreign atom for each hundred million (10^8) germanium atoms. Then carefully controlled impurities are introduced in a ratio of one millionth of a gram of impurity to sixteen hundred grams of crystal. Still using germanium as an example, let us see the effect of adding impurities. Since germanium has four valence electrons, atoms having five valence electrons such as arsenic, antimony, or phosphorous are often used as impurities. Four of their five electrons will enter the interatomic bonds of the crystal lattice structure. The fifth electron will be bound only by the relatively weaker electric charge on the nucleus. This is more in the nature of the communal bond found in conductors. These extra electrons are therefore sufficiently free to wander through the crystal lattice structure and conduct electricity. This effect is shown in Fig. 7-2. A semiconductor having such excess electrons is known as *N-type* because the conduction is by negative carriers. The impurities used to produce this type of semiconductor are called *donors* since they provide the excess or conduction electrons.

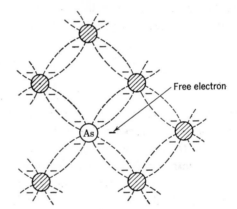

Fig. 7-2. Electron released by donor (arsenic) impurity.

Free electron

Semiconductor properties can also be obtained by using, as impurities, elements having one less valance electron. With reference to germanium, suitable impurities would be boron, aluminum, gallium, or indium, each of which have only three valence electrons. As an impurity atom enters into the crystal lattice structure, there will be a deficiency of one electron leaving a vacancy or *hole* in the covalent pair bonds. This is shown in Fig. 7-3. Since the hole is an absence of an electron it acts as a positive charge. An electron from a nearby bond can jump into this hole leaving a hole behind. Still another electron can be attracted into the newly formed hole creating a new hole. This process can continue so that the hole wanders throughout the crystal lattice structure, and in so doing conducts elec-

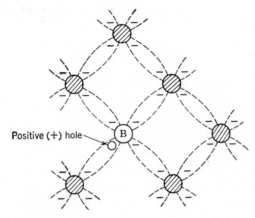

Fig. 7-3. Hole produced by acceptor (boron) impurity.

tricity. A semiconductor having such properties is known as *P-type* because conduction by holes is similar to conduction by positive carriers. The impurities used to produce this type of semiconductor are called *acceptors* in that the holes they produce can accept electrons.

Electrical Charge of N- and P-type Semiconductors

So far we have seen that in an N-type semiconductor conduction is due to excess electrons, while in a P-type semiconductor, conduction is by holes or positive carriers and is due to a deficiency of electrons. This might lead you to conclude that the N-type material has a negative charge, and the P-type a positive charge. Such a conclusion is fallacious, erroneous— in fact it is absolutely wrong! Let us analyze the situation more carefully. We have said that the N-type semiconductor has excess electrons. True— but these extra electrons were supplied by atoms of the donor impurity, and each atom of the donor impurity is electrically balanced. The number of negative electron charges equal the positive charges in the nucleus; the total charge is zero. The pure semiconductor was also electrically neutral, and so the *N-type semiconductor is still electrically neutral.* When the impurity atom is added, the term "excess electron" refers to an excess with regard to the number of electrons needed to fill the covalent crystal lattice structure. The extra electron is a free electron and increases the conductivity of the semiconductor. Remember that free electrons in a copper wire do not give the wire a negative charge.

The situation with regard to P-type semiconductors is quite similar. The crystal lattice structure has a deficiency in electrons—or holes. Conduction is by means of these holes. Acceptor impurity atoms created these holes because they were shy one electron (compared to the semiconductor atom), but remember that each acceptor atom also has one less positive charge in its nucleus and is electrically netural. So—what is the charge of a piece of P-type semiconductor? Zero!

Majority and Minority Carriers

The above picture of N-type and P-type semiconductors is oversimplified. It may create the impression that in an N-type semiconductor there are no holes or positive current carriers and also that there are no free electrons or negative current carriers in a P-type. This is not the actual case. You will recall that even in a pure semiconductor heat or light energy can break the covalent bonds, releasing some electrons and creating holes. This effect also happens when a semiconductor has been doped with acceptor or donor impurities. Therefore *both* holes and free electrons are present regardless of the type of impurity added. In an N-type semiconductor some holes and electrons are present due to the breaking of covalent bonds, and in addition a much greater number of electrons are produced by the donor impurity. Therefore electrons are considered as the *majority carriers* and the holes are *minority carriers*. Using a similar line of reasoning, it follows that in a P-type semiconductor the holes form the majority carriers and electrons are the minority carriers.

P-N Junction

If a piece of P-type semiconductor makes intimate contact with another piece of N-type, a P-N junction is formed. Such a junction has the characteristic that it will allow relatively easy passage to electric current flow in one direction but offers high opposition to current flow in the opposite direction. This is the "peculiar" property of semiconductors mentioned earlier in this chapter. To explain this property of the semiconductor junction, first let us recall that the current carriers in semiconductors are the holes (positive carriers) in the P-region and excess electrons (negative carriers) in the N-region. Now let us apply a direct voltage across this junction, with a polarity such as to make the N-region negative and the P-region positive. This is shown in Fig. 7-4(a). The negative potential applied to the N-region will repel the excess electrons toward the junction and through the junction. As a result of the interchange of positive and negative current carriers through the semiconductor junction, an easy flow of current (or low resistance path) is established for the entire circuit. This is called the *forward* direction. Notice that the semiconductor must be biased with the N-type negative polarity and the P-type positive polarity.

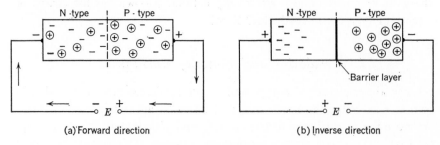

(a) Forward direction   (b) Inverse direction

Fig. 7-4. Unilateral current flow of a P-N junction.

Now let us reverse the power supply polarity so as to apply a negative potential to the P-region and a positive potential to the N-region. This time the excess electrons in the N-region will be attracted toward the positive terminal of the power supply and *away from the junction*. In addition the hole carriers of the P-region will be attracted toward the negative terminal of the power supply and again *away from the junction*. The area immediately adjacent to the junction is now devoid of current carriers (holes or electrons) thereby becoming an insulator. A so-called *barrier layer* is formed at the junction and current cannot flow. A P-N junction so connected is said to be biased in the *inverse* direction. This effect is shown in Fig. 7-4(b).

From the above discussion for a P-N junction with inverse bias, it may be inferred that absolutely no current will flow, or that the resistance in the inverse direction is infinite. This is not completely true. Earlier in the chapter it was mentioned that even in a pure semiconductor, the inter-atomic bonds can be broken by heat or light energy and therefore some conduction carriers will always be present. As a result, a small current will flow even with inverse bias, and the resistance to current flow will be high, but not infinite.

Review Problems

1. What is meant by a semiconductor?
2. How does a resistance material compare with a semiconductor with regard to conduction properties?
3. Name six elements that may be classified as semiconductors.

4. Describe how the electrons of an atom are arranged around its nucleus.

5. What is meant by energy level with regard to this arrangement?

6. What is meant by valence electrons?

7. Why are there theoretically no conduction electrons in a semiconductor?

8. Give two reasons why a semiconductor is not a perfect insulator.

9. What is meant by donor impurities?

10. Explain how free electrons are created in a semiconductor. What is this type of semiconductor called?

11. (a) How are holes created in a semiconductor?
    (b) How do these holes contribute to conduction?
    (c) What is this type of semiconductor called?
    (d) What type of impurity is used to create this effect?

12. Explain why electron current carriers are present in a P-type semiconductor.

13. What are the majority and minority current carriers in: (a) N-type semiconductor; (b) P-type semiconductor?

14. (a) What is a P-N junction?
    (b) What important electrical property does such a junction exhibit?

15. (a) How is a P-N junction biased in the forward direction?
    (b) What is its electrical property when so connected?

16. (a) What is meant by a barrier layer in reference to a P-N junction?
    (b) What causes this action?
    (c) Under what operating condition does this effect occur?
    (d) What is this type of connection called?

CHAPTER **8**

Crystal Diodes

▗▄▖▄▖▄▄

In the previous chapter it was shown that a semiconductor P-N junction had the property of allowing easy current flow in one direction and practically no current flow if the applied voltage is reversed. This unilateral current flow is similar to the action that takes place in a vacuum diode. It is therefore not surprising to find that semiconductors are used as diodes or rectifiers, in place of tubes. Depending on construction these semiconductor devices may be divided into two general categories as point contact rectifiers and junction or area rectifiers.

Point Contact Rectifier Action

Figure 8-1 shows a slab of N-type semiconductor connected in the forward or conductive direction. Notice that the point contact is made posi-

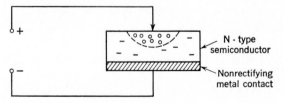

Fig. 8-1. Rectifying action of point contact.

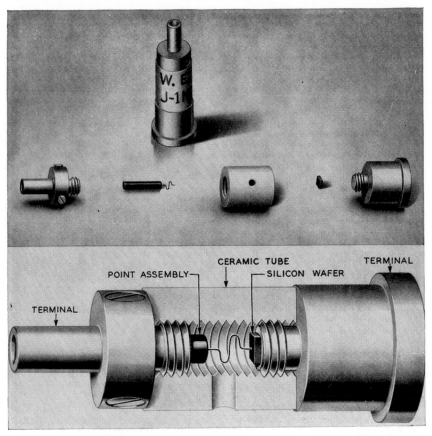

(a)

(b)

Fig. 8-2. Point-contact silicon crystal diodes: (a) external, exploded, and interior view of W.E. J-1N23; (b) external view of Sylvania 1N358.

tive with respect to the semiconductor. Conduction can be accounted for in two ways. First, since the semiconductor is N-type, it has excess electrons. These excess electrons are attracted to the positive point contact and current flows. However, since there are relatively few such free electrons, conduction by this means is very low. The second explanation for current flow is that the high potential gradient at the point contact is sufficient to tear electrons out of the covalent pair bonds. Holes are created in the atoms of the semiconductor adjacent to the point contact. These holes are repelled by the positive charge on the point contact and move deeper into the semiconductor. In effect we have created a P-region around the point contact and a P-N junction further in. Conduction is increased by these holes or positive carriers. In the manufacturing of point contact diodes a special "forming" process is used to produce an effective P-type area around the point contact. As we saw in the previous chapter, if the polarity of the applied voltage is reversed a barrier layer is formed and conduction is reduced to a negligible value.

Types of Crystal Diodes

The term *crystal diode* is generally used for semiconductor diodes primarily intended for operation at radio frequencies (as contrasted with power-line frequency). These units may be of the point contact or junction variety. Silicon or germanium is used as the semiconductor material. They are the modern counterpart of the crystal detector used in the early days of radio. Figure 8-2(a) shows the construction and external view of one type of crystal diode. This unit is suitable for operation at ultra high frequencies (above 300 megacycles). In fact its peculiar external construction is ideally adapted for use with waveguide elements.* Another silicon point contact diode suitable for operation in the microwave region (above 3000 megacycles) is shown in Fig. 8-2(b).

Two typical germanium point contact diodes are shown in Fig. 8-3. An appreciation of the smallness of these crystal diodes can be obtained from the dimensions shown on the one unit, or the comparison of the diode against the ordinary playing card as background. A junction-type silicon diode is shown in Fig. 8-4. This type is more commonly referred to as a *bonded* diode. Bonded diodes are available with germanium as a semiconductor as well as silicon.

---

* Waveguide elements look like rectangular or round pipe sections and are used in place of inductors and capacitors at ultra high frequencies.

Crystal Diode Characteristic Curve

In Chapter 1, the characteristic curve for the electron tube diode was shown as a plot between plate voltage and plate current. Plate voltage was taken only in the positive direction (compared to cathode). This is quite normal for the electron tube since current does not flow *in either direction* when the plate is negative. The situation with semiconductor diodes is some-

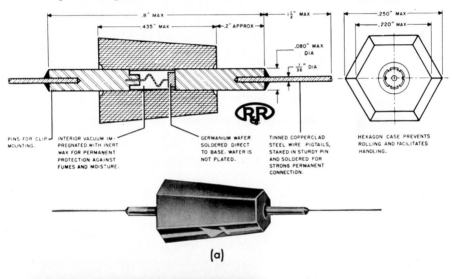

(a)

(b)

Fig. 8-3. Two types of germanium crystal diodes.

what different. Current will flow regardless of the polarity of the applied voltage. With one polarity—*forward voltage*—a relatively high forward current will flow; the forward resistance is low. If we reverse the polarity—

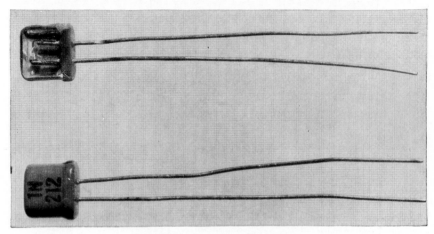

Fig. 8-4. Silicon junction diodes.

reverse voltage—a small current will flow in the reversed direction; the reverse resistance is comparatively high. Characteristic curves for semiconductor diodes must show both forward and reverse magnitudes. Since the reverse conduction is very much lower than the forward conduction, it is common practice to employ different scale magnitudes for each direction. A typical characteristic curve of a germanium diode is shown in Fig. 8-5.

From such curves it is possible to find the d-c resistance and a-c (or dynamic) resistance of a diode. These quantities have the same significance as the d-c and a-c plate resistance discussed earlier for vacuum-tube diodes. Since the method for calculating diode resistance is identical to the calculations for plate resistance (see page 12) no illustrative example need be shown. With crystal diodes however, since current also flows with reversed polarity, it is necessary to consider two resistance values—the forward resistance and the reverse resistance. Notice in Fig. 8-5 that the forward current is in milliamperes while the reverse current is in *micro*amperes. Also notice the difference in voltage scales. From these scales it should be obvious that the d-c resistance of the diode is much higher with reverse polarity than with forward polarity.

But we also learned, when discussing vacuum tubes, that the a-c resistance of the tube varied with the slope of the characteristic curve: a flat curve, approaching the horizontal meant very high resistance; a steep curve meant low resistance. With this in mind, re-examine Fig. 8-5. In the forward direction, the curve, in general, is quite steep, indicating low a-c resistance. This is desirable. In the reverse direction, *at low voltages* (below 40 volts), the slope is nearly horizontal, indicating very high a-c resist-

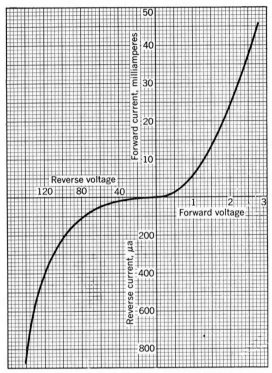

Fig. 8-5. Static characteristics of germanium diode 1N63 (25 °C).

ance. Again, this is desirable. Efficiency of rectification is good. Now notice the slope of the characteristic at reverse voltages above 120 volts. The slope of the curve is approaching the vertical and the a-c resistance is decreasing rapidly. At some still higher inverse voltage, a point of zero dynamic resistance will be reached. The peak inverse voltage rating of a diode is below this critical value by a safe design margin.

Beyond the point of zero dynamic resistance, the reverse current can continue to increase even though the reverse voltage remains constant. This condition is the result of increased conduction in the semiconductor. The electric field at this inverse voltage is strong enough to break the covalent pair bonds producing additional current carriers. The effect is analogous to conduction in a gas diode after the ionizing potential is reached. The voltage at which this breakdown occurs is called the *Zener* voltage.

Diode Specification Data

One of the most serious bottlenecks to the application of semiconductor devices by industry has been the high price and lack of uniformity of the products. Owing to uncontrolled impurities in the crystal and to imperfections in the crystal structure, the characteristics of the units, even from the same production batch, may vary widely. As a result, it has been necessary to grade and separate the products into various classifications at the end of the production line. The only other alternative would be to reject the products that did not come up to specifications, within acceptable tolerance limits. This latter technique would skyrocket prices. Luckily such drastic action is not necessary. A semiconductor unit which would be a "production reject" may be perfectly satisfactory in some other application with less stringent requirements.

Newer techniques and better control of the manufacturing processes have reduced the amount of variation in the product. However, sorting into various type ratings is still necessary. This selection process yields certain types in greater quantities than others and accounts for the wide difference in price of semiconductor diodes and transistors.

Each diode type has certain specific electrical characteristics that define that type. These characteristics are listed by the manufacturers in their manuals or data sheets. Typical data will usually include:

1. *Reverse voltage ratings.* These may be given as peak, continuous (or both), and minimum value for zero dynamic resistance. Reverse voltage ratings of crystal diodes vary drastically for the various types, ranging from as low as 1.5 volts for the 1N299 to as high as 260 volts maximum continuous working voltage for the 1N59.
2. *Reverse current ratings.* These are generally shown for two values of reverse voltages; one low and one near the maximum operating value.
3. *Forward current ratings.* These ratings will show minimum current at +1 volt, maximum average current, maximum peak current, and may also include surge current for one second.

Such a typical data sheet is shown in Table I. Other characteristics which may be listed are: upper frequency limit; noise figure; operating temperature range; and reverse recovery time. (This last characteristic,—reverse recovery time, is defined as the time required for the diode to recover to a given reverse current when the voltage is switched from the positive

GERMANIUM AND SILICON DIODES

Table 8-I

PHYSICAL TYPES AVAILABLE

GLASS-INCASED DIODE

GLASS-FILLED PLASTIC CASE DIODE

GLASS-FILLED PLASTIC CASE DIODE ... CLIP-IN TYPE

QUAD WITH STANDARD OCTAL BASE WILL BE SUPPLIED FOR ANY CBS DIODE

Type	Outline Drawing	Peak Reverse Voltage	Operating Reverse Voltage	Forward Current, ma – Average	Recurrent Peak	Surge 1 sec.	Min. Forward Current at +1V, ma	Rev. Volts	Rev. μa	Rev. Volts	Rev. μa	Description
1N34	A & B	75	60	40	150	500	5.0	-10	50	-50	500	General Purpose
1N34A	A & B	75	60	50	150	500	5.0	-10	30	-50	500	General Purpose
1N35	*	75	60	50	150	500	7.5	-10	10			Matched Pair 1N34A
1N38/1N38A	A & B	120	100	50	150	500	4.0	-3	6	-100	500	High Reverse Voltage
1N39/1N39A	B	225	200	50	150	200	5.0	-100	200	-200	800	High Reverse Voltage
1N40	D	75	70	40	150	500	5.0	-10	100	-50	850	Quad (4 1N34's)
1N48	A & B	85	70	50	150	400	4.0	-50	833			General Purpose Detector
1N51	A & B	50	40	25	100	300	2.5	-50	1660			General Purpose
1N52	A & B	85	70	50	150	300	4.0	-50	150			General Purpose
1N54	A & B	50	35	40	150	500	5.0	-10	10			General Purpose
1N54A	A & B	75	50	50	150	500	5.0	-10	7	-50	60	General Purpose
1N55/1N55A	A & B	170	150	50	150	500	4.0	-100	300	-150	500	Gen. Purpose High Reverse Voltage
1N55B	B	190	150	60	150	500	5.0	-150	500			Gen. Purpose High Reverse Voltage
1N56/1N56A	A & B	50	40	60	200	1000	15.0	-30	300			High Conduction
1N58/1N58A	A & B	120	100	50	150	500	5.0	-100	600			High Reverse Voltage
1N60	A	30	25	50	150	500	3.0	-10	67			Video Detector
1N63	A & B	125	100	50	150	400	4.0	-50	50			General Purpose
1N64	A & B	20	15					-10	200			Video Detector
1N65	A & B	85	70	50	150	400	2.5	-10	200			General Purpose
1N67	B	100	80	35	100	500	4.0	-5	5	-50	50	General Purpose
1N67A	A	100	80	35	100	500	4.0	-5	5	-50	50	General Purpose
1N69	A & B	75	60	40	125	400	5.0	-10	30	-50	500	General Purpose, JAN
1N70	A & B	125	100	30	90	350	3.0	-10	25	-50	200	General Purpose, JAN
1N71	D	50	40	60	200	1000	15.0	-30	300			Quad (4 1N56's)
1N73	D	75	60	22.5	60	100	15 at 1.3 to 1.7V	-10	50			Quad (4 general purpose)
1N74	D	75	60	22.5	60	100	15 at 1.2 to 1.8V	-10	50			Quad (4 general purpose)
1N75	A & B	125	100	50	150	400	2.5	-50	50			General Purpose
1N81	B	50	40	30	90	350	3.0	-10	10			General Purpose, JAN
1N82†	B & C		5				Designed for efficient low-noise mixer operation from 470 to 890 mc					Silicon — UHF Mixer
1N82A†	B & C		5				Designed for efficient low-noise mixer operation from 470 to 890 mc					Silicon — UHF Mixer
1N126	A	75	60	30	90	350	5.0	-10	50	-50	300	General Purpose, JAN
1N127	A	125	100	30	90	300	3.0	-10	25	-50	200	General Purpose, JAN
1N128	A	50	40	30	90	300	3.0	-10	10			General Purpose
1N198 at 25°C	A	100	80	30	90	300	4.0	-10	10	-50	40	High Temperature
at 75°C		100	60	30	90	300	5.0	-10	75	-50	250	
ND-416	A	45					100	-20	100			Gold Bonded Diode
ND-417	A	90					100	-40	100			Gold Bonded Diode
ND-418	A	110					100	-50	100			Gold Bonded Diode
ND-419	A	120					100	-60	80			Gold Bonded Diode
ND-420	A	150					100	-80	60			Gold Bonded Diode

*Special package
†Units are tested for noise figure in instruments designed to correlate with customer applications.

177

value necessary to give 30 milliamperes forward conduction, to —35 volts.) With regard to temperature range, it should be noted that the characteristics shown in Table I are for 25°C. In general the temperature range for crystal diodes is given as —50 to +90°C. Silicon diodes are available that will operate at ambient temperatures of from —55 to +150°C. However, it should be realized that ambient temperature deviations from 25°C may cause drastic changes in the electrical characteristics. For example the IN63 is described as a "high back-resistance diode." Its reverse current is only 50 microamperes at —50 volts. However at 50°C the reverse current is doubled, and at 75°C the reverse current rises to 250 microamperes! This diode can no longer be considered as a high back-resistance diode.

Crystal Diode Advantages and Applications

Compared to electron-tube diodes, the crystal diodes have inherently longer life, greater ruggedness, lighter weight, smaller size, lower shunt capacitance, produce less noise, and do not require heater power. They are used in low-power circuits where rectification, unilateral or non-linear current flow is required, at frequencies up into thousands of megacycles. (The 1N53 has a design frequency of 35,000 megacycles.) Typical applications of crystal diodes are as clippers, clampers, limiters, discriminators, detectors, mixers, and switching gates. They are found in home receivers (AM, FM, and T.V.) and in military and industrial equipment. Typical circuits cannot be covered at this time but will be discussed when the individual circuit application is covered in a later volume.

Polarity and Graphic Symbol

Semiconductor diodes whether they are the small crystal diode variety or the larger power rectifiers (to be discussed later) are represented in schematic diagrams by the graphic symbol shown in Fig. 8-6. The arrow in this symbol was used to indicate the direction of easier *conventional* current flow.* Electron flow is in the direction opposite to the arrow. Compared to the vacuum-tube diode, the arrow of this symbol corresponds to the plate and the bar of the symbol to the cathode of the diode.

When using a semiconductor diode it is often necessary to know which

---

* The unilateral current flow action of semiconductor materials was discovered as early as 1883. At this time the electron theory had not been developed and conventional current flow was in use.

end is which. For this purpose, manufacturers generally code the cathode end (bar of graphic symbol) with a "k," "+," or "cath" marking. In some cases RETMA (Radio, Electronics and Television Manufacturers Associa-

Fig. 8-6. Graphic symbol for semiconductor diodes.

tion) standard color code bands are placed on the cathode end of the diode. This not only identifies the cathode end but also serves to classify the diode number. For example, the 1N163 would use brown, blue, and orange bands to indicate the 1, 6, and 3, respectively. One manufacturer actually prints the graphic symbol directly on the body in the direction of the arrow of the graphic symbol.

Review Problems

1. Name two types of semiconductor diodes based on basic constructional differences.
2. Explain the rectifying action of a point-contact diode.
3. (a) To what is the term crystal diode generally applied?
   (b) Name two types of semiconductor materials used in these devices.
4. What is meant by forward polarity and forward direction with reference to a semiconductor diode?
5. How does the resistance of a crystal diode compare between forward and reverse voltage?
6. Find the d-c and a-c forward resistance of the IN63 (Fig. 8-5) at forward voltages of: (a) 0.6 volts; (b) 2.6 volts.
7. Find the d-c and a-c resistance of the IN63 at reverse voltages of: (a) 40 volts; (b) 120 volts.
8. What is meant by the Zener voltage?
9. State 5 advantages of the crystal diode over its tube counterpart.
10. (a) Draw the graphic symbol used to designate a semiconductor diode.
    (b) Below this symbol, show by an arrow the direction of easy electron flow.
    (c) Compared to vacuum-tube elements, which part of this graphic symbol corresponds to which tube element?
11. (a) Which end of a semiconductor diode is identified by markings?
    (b) Name 3 methods used for such marking.

CHAPTER 9

Semiconductor Power
Rectifiers

▀▄

Power rectifiers are of the area contact variety. The earlier types used copper oxide, copper sulphide, and selenium as the semiconductor, and were generally known as *dry rectifiers* or *metallic rectifiers*. Since 1951, power rectifiers using silicon and germanium have become quite popular. The terms dry rectifier and metallic rectifier have also been used with germanium and silicon rectifiers, but use of these terms is decreasing. Each of these semiconductor materials will be discussed in more detail later.

Chronologically, the first large area rectifier was produced in 1883 by C. E. Fritts while working on selenium. However, commercial application was not made till 1930. Meanwhile in the 1920's L. O. Grondahl and P. H. Geiger developed the copper-oxide rectifier and photo cell. Early commercial application of these devices were made in battery chargers and photographic exposure meters. Within a few years a third type, the magnesium-copper sulphide rectifier was invented.

From 1930 till approximately 1950 these were the only commercially used area rectifiers. However, further studies with germanium and silicon since the invention of the transistor led to the development of the germanium and silicon power rectifier. Meanwhile further research is continuing with these and other semiconductor materials.

Basic Principle of Area Rectifiers

The construction of an area rectifier can be graphically represented as shown in Fig. 9-1. The materials used for active plate, semiconductor, and back plate are different for each type but the action in each case is the same. When connected with polarity as shown, current (electrons) flows easily from the active metal plate through the semiconductor, to the back metal plate. If the polarity of the applied voltage is reversed, only a small *leakage* current flows in the reverse direction.

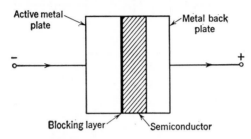

Fig. 9-1. Basic area-rectifier cell.

For many years, the underlying principles of this unilateral conduction of current were not understood. The construction of these rectifiers has been more of an "art" than a scientific development. It was not till about 1940 that scientists realized that rectification was a surface property and that any contact between a semiconductor and a metal would show some rectifying properties. The degree of unilateral conduction varied with choice of materials and method of processing. Referring to Fig. 9-1, the rectifying action takes place at the interface between the active metal plate and the semiconductor and is represented by the blocking layer.

What is the scientific explanation of rectification at this surface? Why is there no rectification at the other surface of the semiconductor? These answers were not yet known. The "art" in the manufacturing process was to make the contact to one side of the semiconductor as non-linear or rectifying as possible and the other contact a simple ohmic contact with as low a resistance as possible. The above questions have since been answered. However a thorough discussion of these theories is complicated. Deeper studies into the physics and chemistry of matter, particularly work functions and energy levels, would be necessary. Such an analysis is considered above the technician level and is therefore beyond the scope of this text. However from the semiconductor principles of the previous chapter the following points of explanation can be made:

1. The semiconductor material in each case has been proven to be a defect or P-type semiconductor having a deficiency of electrons, or excess holes.

2. Temporarily let us insert a piece of N-type semiconductor between the active metal plate and the semiconductor—in place of the barrier layer. (See Fig. 9-2.)

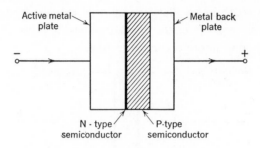

Fig. 9-2. P-N junction effect in area rectifier.

3. We now have a P-N junction, and as explained in Chapter 7, with the polarity as shown holes from the P-side will move toward the center; excess electrons from the N-side will also move toward center; no barrier is formed, and we have easy current flow.

4. With reversed polarity, holes and electrons move in opposite direction leaving no current carriers at the junction, thereby forming a barrier layer and allowing very little current flow.

The explanation becomes easy once we postulate the N-type layer at one end of the semiconductor material. The formation of this N layer depends on the material used in contact with the semiconductor; the work functions and energy levels of the electrons in the two materials; and in some cases on a special *forming* process in manufacturing the unit.

Power Rectifier Cell Characteristics

The term rectifier *cell* is often used to denote a basic semiconductor rectifier device containing only one junction, one positive, and one negative electrode. The use of the term "cell" is necessary to distinguish this basic device from a "rectifier" or "rectifier unit" which may consist of more than one cell connected in series, parallel or series-parallel. Such combinations will be discussed below. Certain characteristics are common to all types of semiconductor rectifiers. These can be discussed in general before each specific type of rectifier is covered in more detail.

Static characteristic. The voltage-current static characteristic curve of all semiconductor power rectifiers is quite similar to the typical crystal diode characteristic curve shown in Fig. 8-5. In the forward direction, the current is high for a correspondingly small voltage drop. With reverse polarity the leakage current is low. The amount of leakage current for a given reverse voltage will differ for each type of rectifier. Similarly the forward resistance or forward current for a given voltage will not be the same for each type. Typical curves for each semiconductor will be shown later.

Forward current rating. The rating is generally expressed in three ways: the average rectified current (or direct current); the peak rectified current; and the rms rectified current. (Since current waveforms may not always be of sine-wave nature, all three specifications are needed.) Each semiconductor has a rated current per unit area or *current density*. Exceeding this rating will cause excessive I^2R losses. The heat developed cannot be dissipated and the temperature of the cell will rise, ruining the semiconductor action. The permissive current density varies with the type of semiconductor and with effectiveness of cooling. Wider spacing, addition of cooling fins, and forced air cooling are effective means of increasing the current density rating. For a given density, the total current rating of a cell can be increased by increasing the area of its junction. A similar effect can be achieved by using a *rectifier unit* consisting of two or more cells in parallel. This technique also increases the effective area of the junction.

Peak inverse voltage rating. In a vacuum tube this rating denotes a breakdown voltage. This is not necessarily true in a semiconductor rectifier. A temperature limitation may be reached before the actual voltage breakdown point. Leakage current rises rapidly as the reverse voltage is increased. I^2R losses due to this leakage current may cause failure as a result of temperature. The peak inverse voltage rating will depend on the type of semiconductor used and its degree of purity. For a given type of cell, if a higher inverse voltage rating is needed, cells can be connected in series.

Temperature. Semiconductor devices are in general quite critical with regard to ambient temperature and temperature rise. In the previous chapter we saw that thermal energy was one method of breaking the covalent electron bonds of a semiconductor. The holes and electrons so produced would greatly increase the conductivity (forward and reverse) of the semiconductor, and since the effect is cumulative (more current more heat losses; more heat, more current, etc.) the semiconductor would fail. Some semiconductor materials can withstand higher temperatures better than others. Also the degree of purity will affect the maximum temperature limit.

When selecting the type of cell, careful consideration should be given to its ambient temperature rating. Where operation above its ambient temperature is necessary the standard cell can be used with a sacrifice in its current and/or voltage rating, or in some cases special cells are available that can still be operated at full rating but with reduced life expectancy.

Aging. Aging is defined as "any persisting change (except failure) which takes place (for any reason) in either the forward or reverse resistance characteristic." The most important change in this respect is the gradual increase in forward resistance. Depending on the type of semiconductor, manufacturing process, and conditions of operation, aging may continue and end the useful life of the rectifier or may stabilize after approximately six months to one year of operation. The severity and rapidity of aging is directly affected by ambient temperature or any factor which tends to cause undue temperature rise.

Self-capacitance. In one respect, the semiconductor rectifier cell is similar in construction to a capacitor. It also has two plates separated by a dielectric. It is therefore not surprising to find that these rectifiers exhibit some self-capacitance. Obviously, the larger the plate area, the higher this capacitance value. Since increase in operating frequency causes a reduction in capacitive reactance, leakage current increases appreciably with increase in frequency. This places an upper frequency limit on these rectifiers. On the other hand crystal diodes, because of their smaller area or point contact construction, have much higher upper frequency limits.

Copper-Oxide Rectifier

The construction of the copper-oxide rectifier cell follows the basic design shown in Fig. 9-1. The active metal plate is a specially selected and processed copper. By heating the copper to a high temperature and then quenching it in water, a thin film of cuprous oxide with an outer layer of cupric oxide is produced on the surface. The cupric oxide is removed. The remaining cuprous oxide is the semiconductor. The blocking layer or P-N junction is formed at the interface between the copper and the cuprous oxide. Contact with the outer surface of the oxide is made in either of two ways to form the disc-type cell or the plate-type cell shown in Fig. 9-3.

The disc-type uses a lead disc which is held against the oxide surface at a definite pressure. In the second method, a metallic conductor such as nickel is deposited on the free oxide surface by electroplating action. From this technique the cell is named the plate type. The disc in the one case and the plated surface in the second case act as the metal back plate of the basic cell in Fig. 9-1.

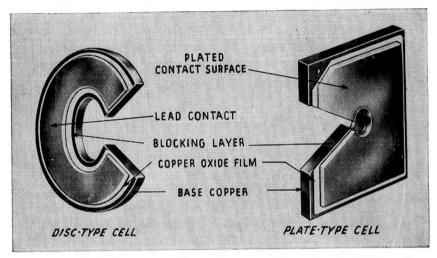

Fig. 9-3. Cross section of copper-oxide rectifier cell.

The rated current density for the copper-oxide cell is fairly low—only 0.16 amperes per square inch. With forced cooling this figure can be approximately doubled. As a result, the disc-type cell which ranges in diameter from $\frac{3}{16}$ inch to $1\frac{1}{2}$ inch, have low forward current ratings. For higher currents the plate-type cells are used. They are available with plates as large as $4\frac{3}{8}$ by $6\frac{1}{2}$ inches, and can be used to deliver up to 25 amperes in three-phase circuits with forced cooling.

The current-voltage characteristics of this rectifier cell, as shown in Fig. 9-4, follow the general pattern for all semiconductor diodes. In order to keep the reverse or leakage current within desirable limits, the peak inverse voltage should be restricted to from 8 to 11.5 volts depending on other design factors. For this reason, use of this type cell is limited to low voltage applications, where line voltages do not exceed 6 volts (RMS). As mentioned under general characteristics, cells can be stacked in series for operation at higher line voltages. Cutaway view of a typical stack assembly is shown in Fig. 9-5 (see page 187). However other types of semiconductor rectifiers are better suited for higher voltage operation.

Examine Fig. 9-4 again; this time with regard to the effect of temperature. Notice how higher temperatures result in higher reverse or leakage currents—for the same inverse voltage. These cells are rated for an ambient temperature of 35°C and a temperature rise not to exceed 15°C. These specifications will keep the leakage current within tolerable limits. The cell may be operated at above 35°C but at a sacrifice in voltage rating.

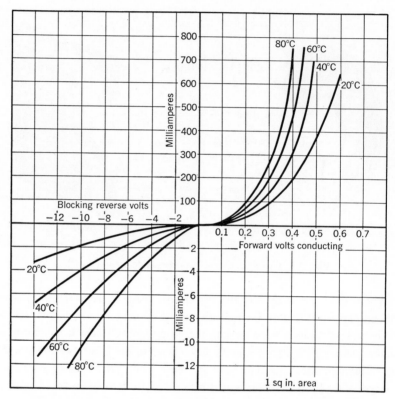

Fig. 9-4. Current-voltage characteristics of plate-type copper-oxide cell.

For example, operation at an ambient temperature of 60°C requires 50% derating, otherwise the life of the cell will be impaired.

Copper-oxide cells are subject to aging. However, according to the manufacturers there is no runaway tendency in the aging process but, rather, the resistance of the cell becomes stable after a period of operation ranging from six months to one year. The rating of rectifier units is based on the aged condition. In other words a new rectifier will have less voltage drop, deliver a higher output, and give better efficiency than its rating would imply.

Remarkable life expectancy claims are made for this type of rectifier. In the manufacture of these cells no special forming process is needed to produce an adequate rectifying junction. So no deterioration takes place due to unforming, even after long periods of disuse. If the units are operated within their rating their life is considered to be unlimited. According

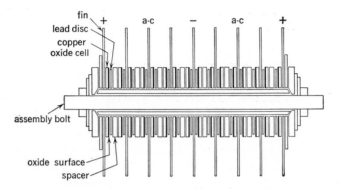

Fig. 9-5. Cutaway view of typical stack assembly.

to one manufacturer, copper-oxide stacks in continuous-life test since 1926 were still delivering their original rated output in 1956.

Magnesium-copper Sulphide Rectifier

This cell is quite similar in construction to the copper-oxide cell. The active metal plate is now a magnesium plate. The semiconductor is cupric sulphide. The rectifying junction is formed between the magnesium plate and the cupric sulphide. A back plate of copper is then used to establish an ohmic (non-rectifying) contact to the opposite surface of the semiconductor material. The forward direction of electron flow is from the magnesium through the semiconductor to the copper back plate.

Several advantages are claimed for this type of cell:

1. It has a high normal current density rating (14 amperes per square inch or approximately one hundred times better than the copper-oxide cell). This makes it adaptable for high current loads.
2. It can withstand temporary heavy current overloads.
3. It will operate satisfactorily over a wide range of temperature (from −70°C to 135°C).

Unfortunately this cell has its limitations or disadvantages. It is the poorest of the semiconductor rectifiers in several aspects:

1. Lowest efficiency.
2. Lowest inverse voltage rating (5-volt peak).

3. Lowest ability to withstand over voltage.
4. Deforms most, when not in use.
5. Shortest life expectancy.

In application this type of rectifier is generally limited to low-voltage, high-current devices.

Selenium Rectifier Cell

Selenium was not applied commercially to rectifier cells till about 1930 in Europe and as late as 1938 in the United States. In spite of its late start its progress was phenomenal. Within a few years, selenium rectifiers were in wide use, in many cases replacing rectifier tubes in electronic applications and replacing motor-generator sets in power applications. These rectifiers are available for currents of a few microamperes to over 100,000 amperes and for voltage outputs as high as 500,000 volts.

The construction of a selenium rectifier cell is shown in Fig. 9-6. Com-

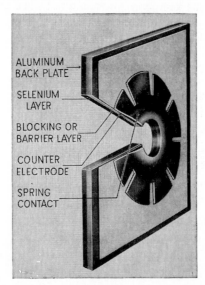

ALUMINUM BACK PLATE

SELENIUM LAYER

BLOCKING OR BARRIER LAYER

COUNTER ELECTRODE

SPRING CONTACT

Fig. 9-6. Cross section of a selenium rectifier cell.

paring this view with the basic area-rectifier cell of Fig. 9-1, we see that the counter electrode is the active metal surface, the selenium the semiconductor material, the rectifying junction or blocking layer is at the interface between the selenium and the counter electrode, and aluminum is used as the back plate to make a direct ohmic contact with the selenium. Steel back plates have also been used. However, because of its lighter weight, aluminum is being used almost exclusively in present-day commercial production.

In the manufacturing process, the aluminum back plate is specially treated to obtain a low contact resistance and to prevent formation of a rectifying barrier layer. Then a thin film of selenium is applied. Some manufacturers spread the selenium in powder form over the supporting plates. The plates are then subjected to high temperatures and pressures. This is known as the *powder-press* method. Another technique of applying the selenium film is by the *evaporation process*. The selenium is heated in an evacuated container and allowed to condense on the aluminum plate. In a third technique, the *molten dip* method, the supporting plates are dipped into the molten selenium for a predetermined time. Regardless of the technique used, the plates are then heat-treated to convert the selenium to crystalline form (or to improve the crystal structure). Now the cell is ready for the counter electrode. This electrode is an alloy of tin, cadmium, and bismuth and is applied by spraying the molten material directly onto the exposed surface of the selenium. The final step is an electroforming process wherein a high d-c voltage is applied in the reverse direction for several hours. During this time the barrier layer is formed.

The static forward and reverse voltage-current characteristics for a typical selenium rectifier cell are shown in Fig. 9-7. As you can see, this

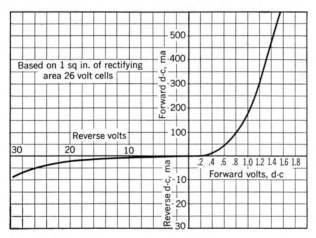

Fig. 9-7. Static current-voltage characteristics of a selenium rectifier cell.

curve follows the general trend that we have noticed earlier for semiconductor diodes. Notice that the reverse voltage scale has been carried out to 30 volts (as compared to 12 volts for the copper-oxide cell of Fig. 9-4), and that the reverse current is not excessive. This indicates that the selenium cell has a higher inverse voltage rating. The original selenium cell had a rating of 14 volts (RMS). Improvements in the manufacturing process particularly in the purity of the selenium and the crystalline structure have resulted in higher inverse voltage ratings. Cells with a 26-volt (RMS) rating were available around 1946, while 40- and 45-volt cells were produced around 1952 and 52-volt cells in 1957. Since the higher voltage cells are more expensive to manufacture, 26-volt cells are still available.

The ambient temperature rating of the standard selenium cell is 35°C, and it is recommended that the temperature rise should not exceed 20°C. Under these conditions some manufacturers consider the life expectancy to be indefinite. More conservative claims give the rectifier a life expectancy of 60,000 hours when operated within its ratings. These standard cells may be operated above these temperature limits if proper current and voltage derating factors are observed, but with a reduction in life expectancy. Special high temperature cells are available that can be operated at ambient temperatures up to 130°C without derating and providing 1000 hours of life.

Selenium cells can be arranged in series stacks for various voltages and applications. Such rectifier units are available in many forms. Figure 9-8 shows some of the more common types. They are also available in metal-clad housings and as oil-filled hermetically sealed units.

Germanium Power Rectifiers

The development of the germanium (and silicon) power rectifier was rather roundabout. Research started with the diode—the point-contact crystal rectifier of low power capacity. This led to the point-contact transistor. Further studies in the rectifying action of germanium and silicon led to the P-N junction and junction transistor. These units were still low power devices. Improvements in manufacturing techniques led to the diffused junction transistors, and then this technique was applied to the diode to produce the power rectifier. One technique for producing a diffused P-N junction starts with a slab of N-type germanium. In the center of one face a dot of indium is applied. Indium is an element with a valence of three—or an acceptor impurity. In a special heating process, the indium alloys into the germanium producing a "doped" region with a deficiency of electrons—or excess holes. This section has become P-type and a P-N junction exists between it and the remaining N-type slab.

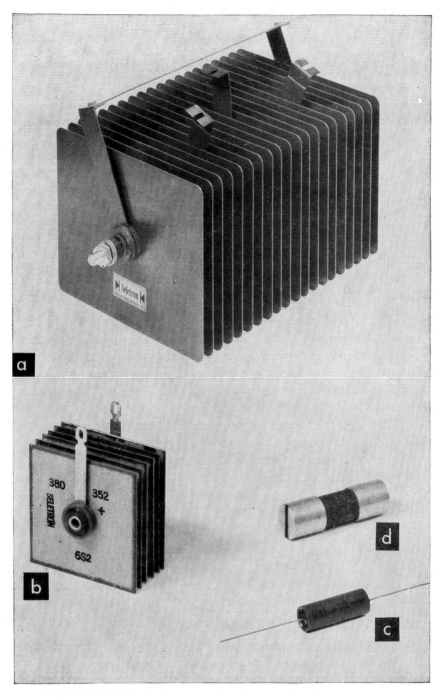

Fig. 9-8. Typical selenium rectifier stacks: (a) industrial open stack; (b) radio and TV open stack; (c) cartridge type; (d) ferrule type.

The germanium power rectifier appeared on the market during 1951. Many advantages are claimed for this unit as compared to the semiconductor rectifiers previously covered:

1. Higher voltage rating, up to 300 volts peak per junction.
2. Lower forward resistance, therefore lower voltage drop and higher efficiency.
3. Much higher current density rating, 300 amperes per square inch. Compare this to 0.16 ampere per square inch for selenium and copper-oxide cells (half-wave air-cooled) and 14 amperes per square inch for the magnesium cell. This feature, in combination with item 1 above, leads to smaller size units, for the same rating.
4. Lower leakage current, about one-fifth that of the best selenium cells.
5. Aging, negligible or zero.

Unfortunately, the germanium cell is not a cure-all. It, too, has its drawbacks, mainly due to temperature. Although they are rated for an ambient temperature of 55°C, they are very sensitive to increase in temperature. One manufacturer specifies that the junction temperature must never exceed 65 to 75°C, as higher junction temperatures will alter the diffusion and damage or destroy the rectifier. However, germanium cells are available for ambient temperatures up to 85°C but with drastic reduction in rating. Due to this temperature sensitivity, heavy overloads, even for a very short duration, or short-circuits will destroy the rectifier. For this reason, fast-acting circuit breakers or overload relays are required to provide over-current protection.

Germanium cells are available in various sizes and combinations. Some of these are shown in Fig. 9-9. The first one (a) is a low power cell (IN93) rated at 300-volts peak inverse voltage and 75 milliamperes d-c output current. By adding a cooling fin, better heat dissipation is obtained and this cell [IN151, Fig. 9-9(b)] now has a current rating of 500 milliamperes. Still higher rating is obtained by adding a second fin [Fig. 9-9(c)] to the same single cell. For higher current and voltage ratings cells can then be combined in series or parallel to form a stack. Figure 9-9(d) shows a typical stack assembly consisting of cells each with two fins.

Another type of cell and fin construction can be seen in Fig. 9-10. This is a medium power cell rated at 5 amperes d-c output current and 200-volts peak inverse. By connecting junctions and assemblies in series or parallel, germanium rectifiers are available for voltage ranges from 10

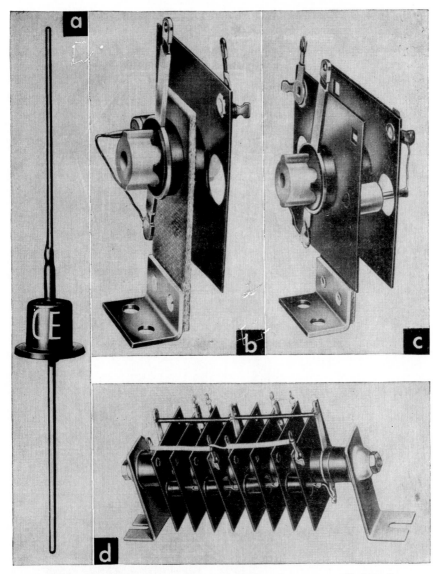

Fig. 9-9. Low power germanium rectifiers: (a) low power cell; (b) cell with single fin; (c) two-fin cell; (d) stacked cells.

volts to 100 kilovolts and for currents of from milliamperes to 100,000 amperes. The largest single installation in 1955 supplied 1950 kilowatts at 3000 amperes and 650 volts, and another unit 5850 kilowatts at 90,000 amperes and 65 volts was on order.

Silicon Power Rectifiers

The development of the silicon junction rectifier paralleled the progress of the germanium cell. A typical medium power cell, together with its current-voltage characteristic, is shown in Fig. 9-11. This cell has a rating of 200-volts peak inverse and 15-amperes d-c output (with heat radiator)

(a)

Fig. 9-10. Medium power germanium rectifier: (a) single fin cell; (b) rectifier stack.

(b)

at 30°C, and 5 amperes at 170°C. Here you see immediately one of the big advantages of silicon cells. They will operate at high temperatures—up to 230°C. Cells are also available with peak inverse voltage ratings up to 1500 volts. These cells also have high current density rating. The result again is small size, as compared to other types of rectifiers.

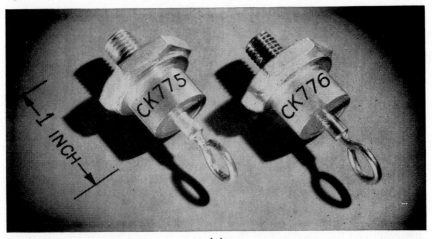

(a)

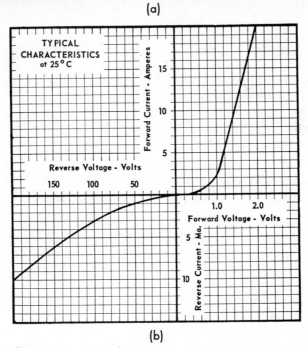

(b)

Fig. 9-11. (a) Typical medium-power silicon junction rectifier; (b) current-voltage characteristics.

An idea of the reduction that is possible in size can be obtained from Fig. 9-12. The six-cell silicon rectifier replaces the bulky selenium rectifier as to current and voltage rating and in addition can operate at higher ambient temperatures.

Fig. 9-12. Comparison between silicon junction rectifier and selenium rectifier for same rating.

Two other advantages of the silicon cells are that they have even less leakage current than germanium cells and that they do not require fast-acting protective devices. Silicon units do not fail suddenly as is possible with germanium. They give sufficient warning of overload or rise in leakage current to permit reducing the input to save the rectifier.

Review Problems

1. Give two other names sometimes used to denote semiconductor power rectifiers.
2. Name 5 semiconductor materials that are used in the manufacture of power rectifiers.
3. (a) What is a rectifier "cell"?
   (b) How may it differ from "rectifier" or "rectifier unit"?

4. (a) What limits the current density rating of a rectifier cell?
   (b) How can higher current densities be carried safely?
   (c) How can the total current rating for a rectifier be increased?
5. Explain how temperature effects limit the inverse voltage rating of a cell.
6. (a) Why do some cells have higher inverse voltage ratings than others?
   (b) How can a semiconductor rectifier be used at above the *cell* inverse voltage rating?
7. Explain why semiconductor devices are comparatively critical with regard to temperature.
8. What is meant by "aging"?
9. Draw a cross-sectional sketch showing the construction and basic elements of a copper-oxide rectifier cell.
10. What is the direction of easy electron flow in this cell?
11. What is the current density rating for a copper-oxide cell?
12. What is the maximum peak inverse voltage limit for the copper-oxide cell?
13. (a) What are the elements of a magnesium-copper sulphide rectifier cell?
    (b) Which is the forward direction of current flow?
14. (a) What is the current density rating of the magnesium-copper sulphide cell?
    (b) What is its inverse voltage rating?
15. Draw a diagram showing the basic construction of a selenium rectifier cell. Label the elements and indicate the location of the rectifying junction.
16. What are the inverse voltage ratings of two commonly available selenium rectifier cells?
17. (a) What is the current density rating of a germanium power rectifier cell?
    (b) At how high an inverse voltage rating is this cell available?
18. Give three other advantages of germanium power rectifiers over previous types.
19. (a) What precautions must be observed when using germanium rectifiers?
    (b) Why?
20. (a) What is the main advantage of silicon power rectifiers over previous types?
    (b) State two other advantages.

CHAPTER 10

Basic Transistors

▄▄▖▄

Although diodes, whether of the vacuum-tube type or semiconductor type, are suitable for many electronic purposes, they cannot perform the essential function of amplification. This great advancement in electronics was not achieved until 1907 when Dr. Lee De Forest invented the triode. By introducing a grid between the cathode and plate of a diode and applying battery power (d-c) between plate and cathode, he found that a small signal applied between grid and cathode could produce enlarged replicas of the original signal in the circuit between plate and cathode. Power supplied by the battery was converted to additional signal power, the result— amplification!

The characteristic curves for vacuum-tube diodes and semiconductor diodes are very similar. Would it not be possible to add a "third electrode" to a crystal diode and get amplification? Research on this idea led to the invention of the *point-contact transistor* in 1948 by Dr. J. Bardeen and Dr. W. Brattain of the Bell Telephone Laboratories.

Point-Contact Transistor

This early transistor is shown in Fig. 10-1. It consists of a small pellet of N-type germanium soldered to a metal plate and two fine wires making pressure contacts against the free surface of the germanium. The combination is enclosed in a metal cylinder $\frac{3}{16}$ inch in diameter and $\frac{5}{8}$ inch long.

One of the catwhisker point contacts is called the *emitter* because when properly biased it injects or emits current carriers into the germanium pellets. The other point contact when properly biased apparently collects

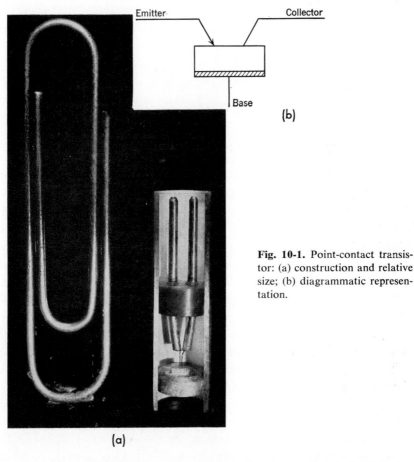

(b)

(a)

Fig. 10-1. Point-contact transistor: (a) construction and relative size; (b) diagrammatic representation.

these current carriers. It is therefore called the *collector*. These point contacts are spaced only a few thousandths of an inch apart on the germanium surface. The germanium pellet, which is no larger than the head of a pin, together with the metal plate is called the *base*. The schematic diagram is shown in Fig. 10-1(b). Notice that the collector is shown without an arrowhead.

In the final stages of manufacturing point-contact transistors, small islands of P-type germanium are produced by an electrical forming process. This effect was described as hole injection when discussing crystal diodes in the previous chapter. Actually then P-N junctions are formed between the emitter and collector contacts and the main body of N-type germanium. This effect is represented in Fig. 10-2 where the transistor is shown connected in a complete circuit. (For subscript nomenclature used for transistors, see Appendix 10, page 283.)

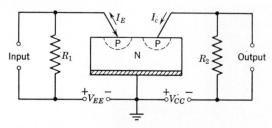

Fig. 10-2. Basic point-contact transistor circuit.

Current relations. Notice from Fig. 10-2 that the emitter-base circuit is biased in the forward direction, whereas the collector-base circuit is biased in the inverse direction. Therefore, considering the collector-base circuit alone, very little current would flow in this circuit. But the emitter circuit has a great effect on the collector circuit action. Since the emitter has a positive potential, electrons are attracted into the emitter and additional holes are produced or injected into this region. These holes are attracted by the negative potential on the collector and travel through the P-N junction surrounding the collector. The presence of these positively charged holes reduces the effect of the P-N barrier layer and increases the collector-base current. The relative mobility of holes and electrons permits a larger number of electrons to enter the germanium under the influence of a smaller number of holes. In other words, a small change in emitter current (I_E) causes a relatively larger change in collector current (I_C). Current amplification factors of from two to three are common for this type of transistor. With a common-base connection as shown in Fig. 10-2, *current amplification factor,* α (the Greek letter *alpha*), is defined as the ratio of the change in collector current to a change in emitter current, for a constant collector voltage, or

$$\alpha = \frac{\Delta I_C}{\Delta I_E} \quad (E_C \text{ constant})$$

Voltage and power gains. The above discussion indicates that the transistor is essentially a current-operated device. Furthermore current amplification factors (α) of from two to three seem very poor compared to the amplification factors (μ) of up to 100 for triode vacuum tubes and over 1000 for pentodes. However, remember that these latter figures are *voltage* amplification factors. Also, as you will learn later when studying amplifier circuits, the actual voltage *gain* in a circuit can never equal the full amplification factor of the tube and may be considerably lower. Voltage and power gain can also be achieved with transistors. This can be shown from the circuit of Fig. 10-2. Since the emitter circuit is biased in the forward direction, the opposition to current flow is low. Therefore the input impedance for this circuit is also low, on the order of 500 ohms. To match this low input impedance, low resistance values are used for resistor R_1. On the other hand, the reverse bias used in the collector-base circuit creates a high opposition to current flow and results in a high output impedance. The load resistance values (R_2 of Fig. 10-2) must be fairly high (10,000 to 20,000 ohms) for good impedance matching and proper operation of the circuit.

Assuming typical values of 500 ohms for R_1, 20,000 ohms for R_2, and 2.5 for α, the voltage gain for this circuit would be

$$\frac{E_o}{E_i} = \frac{\Delta I_C R_2}{\Delta I_E R_1} = \alpha \frac{R_2}{R_1} = \frac{2.5 \times 20,000}{500} = 100$$

This is the actual circuit voltage gain and is better than an amplification factor, μ, of 100.

We can also calculate the power gain of a circuit from the relation between power, current, and resistance:

$$\frac{P_o}{P_i} = \frac{I_C^2 R_2}{I_E^2 R_1} = (\alpha)^2 \frac{R_2}{R_1} = \frac{(2.5)^2 \times 20,000}{500} = 250$$

Limitations of point-contact transistor. The original point-contact transistors shown in Fig. 10-1 were designated as the Type A. Small as they were, it was not long before a smaller and more rugged type was developed. This was known as the "bead transistor." The contact points, the germanium pellet, and the base contact tab were encapsulated in a small plastic bead. The other non-essential parts were eliminated. Mechanically this was an improvement on the earlier construction. However, the point-contact transistor still had several serious shortcomings. Among the more important of these limitations were that they produced high noise levels and that their use was restricted to very low power applications of around 100 milliwatts. The low power handling capacity of the point-contact transistor is directly attributable to its point contacts—particularly the collector point. Even a few milliamperes of current represents extremely high current densities. Considerable heat may be generated in the contact and surrounding germanium. If this heat is not conducted away from the point of contact, the resulting rise in temperature will cause breakdown of the covalent electron bonds. The resistance of the germanium will decrease and the current will increase, causing further rise in temperature. The effect is cumulative and the transistor is permanently damaged.

Junction Transistors

Research to reduce the above limitations led to the development of P-N junctions and the junction transistor. This new addition to the semiconductor family was in many respects superior to the point-contact transistor. Junction transistors were found to produce much lower noise levels, were more stable in operation, had higher power gain, higher power handling capacity, and greater efficiency. The early junction units had a serious frequency limitation that restricted their use mainly to audio fre-

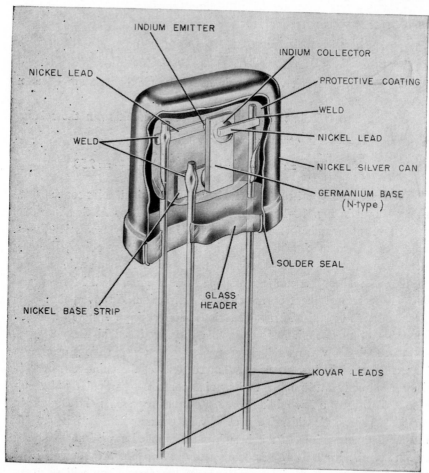

Fig. 10-3. Constructional details of a P-N-P junction transistor.

quencies. In this respect point-contact transistors were appreciably better. However this advantage of the point-contact construction was short lived. By 1956 junction transistors were available as amplifiers with usable gains up to 100 megacycles and as oscillators at over 300 megacycles. As a result many manufacturers stopped production of point-contact transistors.

In its simplest form the junction transistor consists of three layers of alternate type (P or N) semiconductor. This results in two possible configurations: N-P-N or P-N-P. Both types are used. Figure 10-3 shows in pictorial form the details of the internal construction of a typical P-N-P transistor. The transistor is hermetically sealed in a metal case for mechanical strength and protection against atmospheric conditions. An idea of the physical size of the unit can be obtained from Fig. 10-4 where transistors are compared to a dime.

Fig. 10-4. Comparative size of junction transistors.

Current relations. To understand how gain is achieved in the junction transistor, we will show a transistor in diagrammatic form connected to suitable sources of power in an appropriate circuit. Figure 10-5 is such a diagram. For the transistor, since you are more familiar with electrons than with holes as current carriers, we will use an N-P-N unit. Therefore the emitter and collector sections are N-type semiconductor, while the central portion is of P type. Notice that this "sandwich" construction

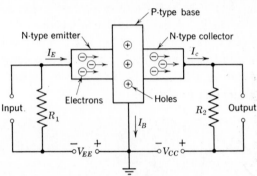

Fig. 10-5. Basic N-P-N junction transistor circuit (grounded base connection).

creates two P-N junctions—one between emitter and base, and the other between collector and base. In a way this is similar to two diodes back-to-back. Now let us examine the power supply polarities. The collector-to-base junction is biased in the reverse or high resistance direction. Considering the action of this half of the transistor by itself (emitter side open circuit), very little current would flow—only a few microamperes. In a semiconductor diode this was referred to as a leakage current due to minority carriers. In transistors this current is called the *collector cutoff current* (I_{C0}), and again is due to minority carriers.

If we turn our attention to the other half of the transistor, we see that the emitter-base sections by themselves again are similar to the junction diode. Will current flow, or is it also biased in the reverse direction? Since power is applied negative to the N-section and positive to the P-section the polarity is in the forward direction and as a diode relatively high current *would* flow from the supply, through the emitter, through the P-N junction, through the base, and back to the power supply. But this ignores the action of the collector and its potential. So, let us see the combined action.

1. The emitter-base is biased in the forward direction—low resistance to current flow.

2. Electrons leave the power supply (V_{EE}), and enter the emitter (cur-

rent I_E). This being N-type semiconductor, electrons are the current carriers.

3. Electrons move through the emitter region and across the P-N junction into the base area (still I_E).

4. Here, in the base, since it is P-type semiconductor, normal conduction is by holes. Due to the field created by the power supply (V_{EE}), a hole is injected into the base region, at the positive terminal of the supply, as an electron is pulled out of its covalent bond. An electron from an adjoining atom fills this hole and a hole "moves" further in. Somewhere, one of the electrons that crossed the P-N junction from the emitter fills this hole. This constitutes the base current I_B. *Were it not for the collector action all of the emitter current electrons would end up as base current I_B.*

5. However, once electrons cross the P-N junction from the emitter side into the base area, they feel the attractive force due to the higher positive potential of the collector. So, instead of combining with holes to create base current, most of these electrons flow on through the base-to-collector junction, through the collector as collector current, I_C to the positive side of the supply voltage, V_{CC}, and back to supply source V_{EE} to complete the circuit. In this way, the collector current rises from the few microamperes of leakage to a much higher value. The greater the emitter current I_E, the greater will be the collector current I_C. Again, as in a point-contact transistor, we find that a change in emitter current will cause a change in collector current.

Current amplification (α). We saw earlier in this chapter that the point contact transistor had a current gain, α, of between two and three. How much current gain can we get with the junction transistor of Fig. 10-5? Don't jump to conclusions. Consider again the current relations discussed above. Emitter electrons (I_E) as they pass the emitter-to-base junction are attracted over and through the second junction and become collector current I_C (*except for a few electrons that combine with holes in the base area to produce the base current I_B*). Consequently, whatever the change made in the emitter current, the change in collector current must be less. Expressed by equation:

$$I_E = I_C + I_B \quad \text{and} \quad \Delta I_E = \Delta I_C + \Delta I_B$$

Obviously, then, the current amplification factor, α, for a junction transistor must be less than unity. In order to achieve as high a value as possible for the current amplification factor, α, it is necessary to reduce the possibility of emitter current electrons combining with base holes. This feature is achieved by making the base region very thin. Practical values for current gains, α, in commercial junction transistors range from 0.85 to as high as 0.999.

Voltage and power gain. At first thought, it might seem that since there is no current gain with a junction transistor, no voltage amplification or power gain could be possible. However, think back to the discussion on point-contact units. You will recall that with a modest current gain of 2.5, we were able to obtain voltage and power gains of 100 and 250 respectively. Why? Because the output circuit resistance was much higher than the input circuit resistance. The same condition exists in the junction transistor circuit, since we again use forward bias in the input circuit and reverse bias in the output circuit. This time we get even higher gains. While the input resistance of the grounded base circuit of Fig. 10-5 is very low, on the order of 100 ohms, the output resistance is around 100,000 ohms. (The point-contact unit had only 20,000 ohms output resistance.) Using an average figure of 0.95 for α, the voltage gain would be

$$\frac{E_o}{E_i} = \frac{\Delta I_C R_2}{\Delta I_E R_1} = \alpha \frac{R_2}{R_1} = 0.95 \times \frac{100,000}{100} = 950$$

Similarly, the power gain would be

$$\frac{P_o}{P_i} = \frac{\Delta I_C{}^2 R_2}{\Delta I_E{}^2 R_1} = (\alpha)^2 \frac{R_2}{R_1} = (0.95)^2 \times \frac{100,000}{100} = 903$$

These gains are definitely superior to the point-contact values.

The P-N-P junction transistor. In explaining the current relations for a junction transistor we used an N-P-N unit. However, we did mention that by reversing the "sandwich" construction P-N-P transistors were also manufactured. Such a transistor and its basic circuitry is shown diagrammatically in Fig. 10-6. Compare the power supply polarities with the previous basic circuit (Fig. 10-5) for an N-P-N unit. Both supplies (V_{EE} and V_{CC}) are reversed. But the P-N junctions between emitter-to-base and collector-to-base are also reversed! In other words, the important fact to remember in any transistor is that the emitter-to-base junction is biased in the forward direction (low resistance) and the collector-to-base junction is biased in the reverse direction (high resistance).

The operation of the P-N-P transistor follows the same basic principles as discussed earlier for the N-P-N type. This time the chief current carriers are holes. When the positive potential is applied to the emitter, holes are injected into this region. These carriers, (current I_E), travel through the first P-N junction into the base region. A few of these holes combine with the electrons found in the N-type base and produce a base current (I_B). But again, since the base region is very thin, most of these holes reach the

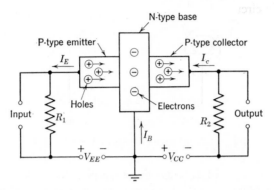

Fig. 10-6. Basic P-N-P junction transistor circuit (grounded base connection).

collector junction. Now the holes are attracted by the strong negative field due to the high negative collector potential and they move toward the collector terminal. Meanwhile electrons from the power source V_{CC} enter the collector to neutralize these excess holes. As a result, the collector current rises from the low leakage or cutoff value (I_{Co}) to a much higher value. However, we saw that some holes do recombine with electrons in the base region. Therefore the alpha (α) for this junction transistor will be less than unity. Practical values of alpha (α) range from 0.85 to 0.999. In this respect P-N-P and N-P-N junction transistors are alike. Voltage and power gain for the P-N-P unit can be explained in the same fashion as was previously done for the N-P-N transistor. The discussion will not be repeated here.

Transistor Graphic Symbols

In the earlier diagrams in the chapter, the transistors have been shown in diagrammatic form. For drafting convenience, schematic diagrams use a simpler representation. Transistor symbols are shown in Fig. 10-7. Notice that the only distinction between the P-N-P and N-P-N types is the direction of the arrowhead on the emitter. If we consider this arrowhead as indicating the direction of current flow in the emitter-base circuit, notice that it is a carry over from the older metallic rectifier symbol and denotes direction of *conventional* current flow.

In specific circuit applications, the transistor symbol may often be seen rotated to simplify interconnection with other circuit components. This however does not alter the basic symbol. At times modified versions of this

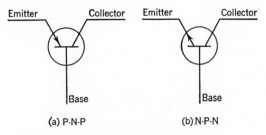

(a) P-N-P   (b) N-P-N

Fig. 10-7. Schematic symbols for transistors.

basic representation will be seen. For example, the circle around the elements may be omitted, or the base may be shown as a heavier line or even with appreciable thickness.

Base Current Amplification Factor (β)

When discussing the current relations in the junction transistor, we saw that most—but not all—of the current carriers (holes or electrons) injected into the emitter reached the collector junction and caused an increase in collector current. As a result, the ratio $\Delta I_C/\Delta I_E$ will approach but can never equal unity. This ratio was called the current amplification factor, α. The smaller the change in base current, the greater the change in collector current and the higher the factor, alpha.

In this same transistor, let us examine the ratio of change in collector current to change in base current. We will designate this new ratio by the Greek letter beta (β). This factor is known as the *base current amplification factor*. What is the relationship between beta and alpha? We can derive this relation by simple algebra.

$$\beta = \frac{\Delta I_C}{\Delta I_B}$$

and since $\Delta I_B = \Delta I_E - \Delta I_C$,

$$\beta = \frac{\Delta I_C}{\Delta I_E - \Delta I_C}$$

Dividing numerator and denominator by ΔI_E

$$\beta = \frac{\Delta I_C/\Delta I_E}{(\Delta I_E - \Delta I_C)/\Delta I_E} = \frac{\alpha}{1 - \alpha}$$

What is the significance of this relationship? We already know that the range of alpha in commercial transistors is from 0.85 to 0.999. Using a common value of 0.95, the base current amplification factor would be 0.95/(1 − 0.95) or 19. As alpha approaches unity, beta approaches infinity. Base current gains of 100 are not uncommon. To utilize this high current gain, the transistor is connected with the emitter as the common or grounded element. This connection will be shown later. (See Fig. 10-10.)

Static Characteristic Curves

When studying vacuum tube triodes, we saw how the plate family (or mutual family) of static characteristic curves could be obtained, and how these static curves in turn could be used in developing the dynamic curves needed for design calculations. Similar families of *E-I* curves can be obtained for transistors. These curves may then be used with superimposed load lines in designing transistor circuits. While various sets of static curves may be plotted, the most important and most commonly used are:

1. Collector to base voltage, V_{CB}, versus collector current, I_C, for various values of constant emitter currents I_E. This representation is most useful for the grounded base connection.

2. Collector to emitter voltage, V_{CE}, versus collector current, I_C, for various values of base currents I_B. When the high current gain, β, of the grounded emitter connection is used, the transistor characteristics are best shown in this form.

Figures 10-8 and 10-9 show typical transistor characteristic curves, the former for the grounded base connection, the latter for the grounded emitter connection. Several "peculiarities" should be noted in these diagrams.

1. The collector voltages are marked as negative. This is to indicate that the collector voltage is of negative polarity, which is normal for any P-N-P transistor. (The 2N68 is a P-N-P unit.) Had the transistor been of the N-P-N type, the collector voltages would have been marked positive. This technique is not used universally, and so an unmarked polarity could be either positive or negative.

2. Notice that collector currents are also marked negative. This is to indicate that the current flowing is a leakage current flowing in the direction of high junction resistance.

3. In Fig. 10-8 notice that collector voltages are also shown with positive polarity. This biases the collector-base junction in the forward direction. The *reverse* current drops *rapidly* to zero. If the collector voltage had

been increased in the positive (forward) direction, the forward (positive) collector current would increase so rapidly due to the much lower forward resistance that the transistor would be instantly damaged.

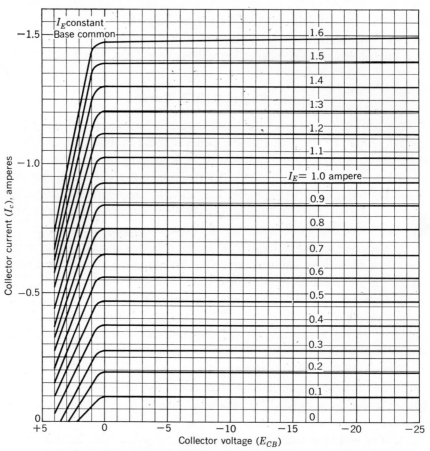

Fig. 10-8. Static characteristic curves for 2N68 junction transistor (common base connection).

This third point brings up a precaution that must be observed when connecting power sources to transistors. If the collector voltage is accidently reversed, the resulting high currents will ruin the transistor. Contrast this with vacuum tube practice. What will happen if the plate voltage is reversed? Nothing—because current cannot flow from plate to cathode!

With triode vacuum tubes we used the characteristic curves to find such tube parameters as μ, r_p, and G_m. However, you may recall that with pentodes we did not evaluate these values from the curves because the curves were too flat (nearly horizontal) and the accuracy of the calculations would have been poor. In this latter case, we pointed out that the tube parameters were determined directly from test data.

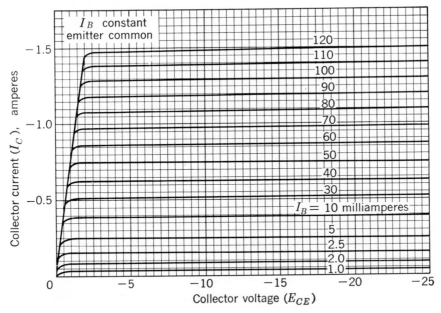

Fig. 10-9. Static characteristic curves for 2N68 junction transistor (common emitter connection).

Now examine the transistor characteristic curves of Figs. 10-8 and 10-9. Notice their resemblance to the pentode curves. These too are almost horizontal, and so although theoretically we could use these curves for finding alpha, beta, and other transistor parameters, the accuracy of such determinations would be poor. These values are therefore generally found by direct measurement or calculated from experimental data. However, the static curves still have value in circuit design as you will see when you study amplifier circuits.

Transistor Configurations

So far in this chapter, we have shown the transistor connected in a common or grounded base circuit. In addition, we mentioned that a common emitter circuit is also used. To complete the picture, the third element could be grounded, or made common, producing what is known as the common or grounded collector circuit. In their simplest forms (without power supply and associated circuitry) the three possible configurations are shown in Fig. 10-10. The details of these circuits will vary with

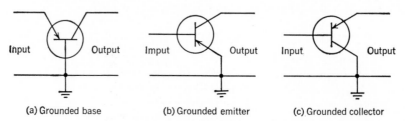

(a) Grounded base   (b) Grounded emitter   (c) Grounded collector

Fig. 10-10. Basic transistor configurations.

the specific application, and so they will not be studied at this time. The main purpose of introducing this topic is so that we can discuss transistor parameters and the effect of circuit configurations on these values.

Transistor Parameters

In our earlier study of vacuum tubes we discussed the parameter plate resistance (r_p), and its effect on the flow of plate current. A similar concept must apply to transistors. But whereas the tube had only one current, plate current, we find that a transistor has three currents: emitter, base, and collector currents. So it should not be surprising to find that we are now concerned about three parameters: emitter resistance r_e; base resistance r_b; and collector resistance r_c. Figure 10-11 is an equivalent diagram for a grounded base configuration, and shows the relative location of these resistances. The values of these parameters can be derived from suitable static characteristic curves (if they are not too flat) or they can be calculated from test data as follows:

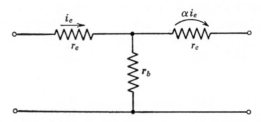

Fig. 10-11. Transistor equivalent circuit, showing resistance parameters.

1. Base resistance (r_b). With a grounded base connection, if the emitter current is kept constant, any change in collector current must cause a corresponding change in base current. This in turn causes a change in the emitter to base voltage, V_{eb}, due to the voltage drop $I_b r_b$. Since the emitter current was constant, emitter resistance has no effect. Therefore

$$r_b = \frac{\Delta V_{eb}}{\Delta I_c} \quad \text{(with } I_e \text{ constant)}$$

For ease in direct test evaluation, the measurements are made with the emitter circuit open ($I_e = 0$). [See Fig. 10-12(a).]

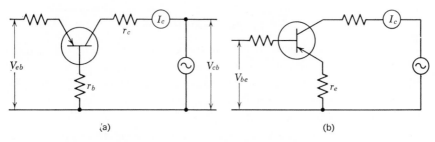

(a)   (b)

Fig. 10-12. Basic measurement circuits for transistor parameters.

2. Emitter resistance (r_e). By changing the configuration to the grounded emitter circuit, and using circuit analysis as above, it follows that:

$$r_e = \frac{\Delta V_{be}}{\Delta I_c} \quad \text{(with } I_b \text{ constant)}$$

Again for simplicity in direct test methods this measurement is made with base circuit open. [See Fig. 10-12(b).]

3. Collector resistance (r_c). For this evaluation, we go back to the grounded base configuration and keep emitter current constant. This time we measure the change in collector current due to change in collector voltage. This change is a function of collector resistance and of base resistance (in series). Therefore,

$$r_c + r_b = \frac{\Delta V_{cb}}{\Delta I_c} \quad \text{(with } I_e \text{ constant)}$$

Since the collector resistance is very much higher than the base resistance, it could be neglected and

$$r_c \cong \frac{\Delta V_{cb}}{\Delta I_c} \quad \text{(with } I_e \text{ constant)}$$

This time again, if the evaluation is made from direct test, the data is taken with the input circuit open, or I_e constant at zero. [See Fig. 10-12(a).]

In addition to the above internal resistances, other parameters of interest to circuit designers are: the input and output impedances; the current amplification factors; maximum ratings; and typical operating conditions. Such information is supplied by the manufacturers' data or technical information sheets. Typical manufacturers' data is shown in Tables I, II, and III, pages 221-223.

Frequency Limitations

Transit time in a vacuum tube (time for electrons to travel from cathode to plate) rendered conventional tubes useless at frequencies of around 300 megacycles and over. Disc seal tubes reduced transit time effects by reducing the *distance* between elements, and operating frequencies up to around 3000 megacycles became possible. With transistors, frequency limitations were much more serious. The early transistors showed poor characteristics even at the higher audio frequencies. Again, transit time was the culprit, but the effect is now detrimental at rather low frequencies. In tubes, the current carriers (electrons) are whisked across from cathode to plate at very high speeds because of the strong electric field between these elements. No such strong field exists in transistors, because they are low voltage devices and also because instead of acting through a vacuum, whatever field there is must act through the "interruptions" created by minority carriers. As a result the travel of current carriers (electrons or holes) in transistors is characterized by a seemingly aimless motion of diffusion or drift.

As with vacuum tubes, if the *distance* of travel could be reduced, transit time would be less and higher frequency limits could be reached. This was achieved by improved manufacturing techniques. One technique produces what are known as *grown junction* transistors. The semiconductor is grown from a single crystal by introducing alternate types of impurities as the crystal is grown. Another technique produces *alloyed junction* or *diffused junction* transistors. In making a P-N-P-type transistor by this latter method, a dot of indium, P-type impurity, is held to each side of an N-type wafer and the combination is heated in a special furnace. By controlling the time and temperature exact degrees of alloying can be achieved, and the distance between the two junctions can be held to no more than a thousandth of an inch. These improvements in manufacturing techniques resulted in transistors usable at broadcast-band (500 to 1700 kilocycles) radio frequencies. Figure 10-13 shows internal views of the grown junction and alloy junction transistors.

As an indication of upper frequency limit of a transistor, manufacturers will often include a term *alpha cutoff frequency* in their data sheets. The current gain, α, of a transistor is measured at various frequencies. The

(a)   (b)

Fig. 10-13. Internal view of grown junction and diffused junction transistors.

frequency at which this gain falls off to 0.7 of its low frequency value is called the alpha cutoff frequency. In general, this is an optimistic value. In order to get power gains that will compare to vacuum tube circuits, the upper frequency limit should be restricted to approximately 50% of the alpha cutoff value.

The development of high frequency transistors has continued. By 1956 improved techniques, a "meltback" process and a "vapor diffusion" process have resulted in central layers only 50 millionths of an inch thick. These new transistors have been reported to reach alpha cutoff between 500 and 600 megacycles.

Power Transistors

The early transistors were definitely low power devices. Their power dissipation rating was on the order of milliwatts. Transistors are essentially low voltage devices. To achieve high power ratings, high currents are required. High currents, in turn, mean higher I^2R losses. If the temperature rise exceeds the maximum rating, transistor action will be ruined. Since most of the heat is developed at the collector junction, commercial designs use some techniques to remove heat from this junction as quickly as possible. These techniques include attaching more massive metal structures (with fins) to the body of the transistor and provision for bolting the transistor case directly to a larger piece of metal, such as the chassis. The chassis would then act as a "heat sink," and would carry heat away from the collector junction more quickly by conduction. Figure 10-14 shows two typical power transistors with heat-radiating fins and provision for bolting to a "heat sink."

Fig. 10-14. Typical power transistors.

By 1956 power transistors were available with power dissipation ratings as high as 60 watts and power output ratings up to 24 watts. Research in this phase is also continuing. Other means for raising power ratings are being investigated. Among these are improvement in emitter design (lower resistance, higher efficiency, and higher current ratings) and improved high temperature operation. In this latter connection, silicon and silicon alloys show promise. A transistor that can operate at higher temperatures can dissipate more heat and would therefore have higher power rating.

With regard to power rating, a distinction between vacuum tube and transistors must be emphasized. It is common practice with vacuum tubes to give power ratings in terms of *average* power. And so a "maximum plate dissipation" of 12 watts means that the *average* power dissipated should not exceed 12 watts. The instantaneous *peak* power for a sine-wave signal can be as high as twice this value, or 24 watts. In pulse operation, such as is used in radar, the instantaneous peak power may run as high as one thousand times the average power. Any temporary overload for a portion of the cycle is balanced by the reduced load in the next portion of the cycle, and the tube can carry this load safely. But a transistor does not have this safety margin. An overload, even for a portion of a cycle, may damage the transistor permanently. Therefore the manufacturers' rating of maximum dissipation must be considered as the instantaneous maximum *peak* power dissipation, and should not be exceeded for any portion of the cycle.

Since power dissipation rating is closely allied to allowable temperature of the junctions, it is not surprising to find that transistors must be derated when operated at higher ambient temperatures. Figure 10-15 shows the effect of ambient temperature on power rating for the 2N68 of Fig. 10-14.

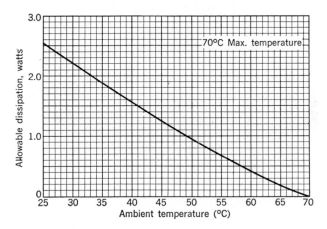

Fig. 10-15. Effect of ambient temperature on power rating, 2N68.

Tetrode Transistor

Another line of attack on extending the high-frequency limit of the transistor led to the development of the tetrode transistor. Basically this unit is the same three-element junction transistor, but with an added fourth connection, this extra connection being made to the base. The base now has two connections—this second connection is made at a point directly opposite to the original base connection. This configuration is shown, with biasing voltages in Fig. 10-16. Since the basic transistor is of the N-P-N type, the emitter is made negative with respect to base and the collector is made positive. The second base connection (b_2) is made negative with respect to lower base (b_1) and *the applied voltage is appreciably higher than the emitter-to-base voltage.* Temporarily let us neglect the effect of the second base connection. Normal transistor action takes place: electrons enter the emitter and travel through the emitter-base junction; a few electrons combine with base holes to form base current, but the majority of the electrons travel on through the base-collector junction to the collector and on through the power supply V_{CC} and V_{EE} to complete the circuit. Remember that the electron motion is not direct but rather a migratory aimless but general drift through the entire area from the emitter toward the collector. This long transit time was one reason for poor high-frequency operation.

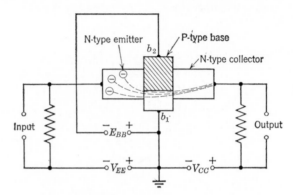

Fig. 10-16. Basic tetrode transistor circuit.

A second restriction on the useful high-frequency limit is created by the capacitance effect between base and collector, with the base and collector each acting as one plate of the capacitor and the junction barrier as the dielectric. This capacitance acts to bypass the output circuit of the transistor. At high frequencies the bypass reactance decreases; the total load impedances decreases, and the output falls off rapidly.

Now let us see how the added connection improves high-frequency operation. First notice in Fig. 10-16 that the upper base connection b_2 is made negative with respect to lower base b_1. Current will flow between these two points—electrons from b_2 to b_1 or holes from b_1 to b_2. Either way a voltage drop will exist between these two points, starting at zero at b_1 and *increasing uniformly to a maximum negative value* at b_2. Now, owing to this current and voltage drop in the base, most of the base region is negative compared to the emitter bias voltage. (Remember that V_{BB} is appreciably higher than V_{EE}.) This base region is represented in Fig. 10-16 by the hatched area.

What effect does this have on our normal transistor action? Current carriers, electrons, from the emitter can no longer migrate over the entire area. They are repelled away from the hatched area and must flow toward the bottom of the base region as shown by the dotted lines in Fig. 10-16. This reduces the drift motion reducing transit time.

A second advantage is achieved in that the effective "plate area" of the collector-base capacitance is reduced to the small bottom section. Smaller plate area, means lower capacitance and higher reactance. This in turn reduces the shunting effect on the load resistance and the transistor has usable gain at higher frequencies.

Life Expectancy

We have become accustomed to considering a vacuum tube as expendable. And so we think very little of changing a tube now and then in a home radio or television receiver. But in military equipment or in aviation, a tube failure at an inopportune time may prove very costly. Aircraft firms discard tubes after only a relatively few hours of operation merely because they cannot trust that certain tubes will last for one more flight. They prefer to gamble on a new tube. Reliability is needed in these and other industrial applications. Tubes can be constructed and operated so that their life expectancy is increased. For example, tubes used for amplifiers (repeaters) in the Trans-Atlantic cable have a life expectancy of 350,000 hours (40 years). This prediction is based on 0.02 per cent failures in 1000 hours. However, such operation is far from normal.

In a vacuum tube, no matter how carefully "husbanded," cathode emission will eventually fall off. The cathode is "worn out" and the tube becomes useless. But in a semiconductor there is no cathode or other source of electrons that may run dry. So, if operating conditions (temperature and current) are properly specified and adhered to, and if the unit is effectively protected from atmospheric effects (corrosion or chemical interaction), and if units are not subjected to excessive shock so as to cause mechanical damage to the crystal structure or contacts, if all these conditions are met transistors should last forever! Theoretically, there is no reason why a perfect transistor should fail under normal operating conditions.

However, there are many practical limitations to the attainment of this ideal. Such factors as crystal defects, possible non-uniformity in the doping of crystals, contamination effects—internal within the crystal or alloying elements, or on the surface subsequent to manufacturing—may cause changes to occur to the component after its manufacture is complete. These factors are all dependent on the manufacturing techniques and processes.

Deterioration of a transistor due to these aging effects will be noticed by an increase in the leakage current, a decrease in current gain, or both.

In addition transistors may be rendered useless because of short-circuits or open circuits. These are purely mechanical defects. One manufacturer claims to have very good control of these mechanical factors and advertises that their life tests "indicate an average of one failure in eight hundred thousand hours for mechanical reasons."

It is generally agreed that life expectancies of several hundred thousand hours are not unrealistic. All manufacturers are expending great effort toward the perfection of manufacturing processes and techniques, in attempts to eliminate all possibilities of contamination of the crystal. As these aging effects are minimized, life expectancies will be further increased.

Table 10-I

RAYTHEON	**TECHNICAL INFORMATION**	**GERMANIUM TRANSISTOR**

Excellence in Electronics

TYPE 2N65

The 2N65 is a hermetically sealed PNP junction transistor intended primarily for use in audio or low radio frequency applications. The tinned flexible leads may be soldered or welded directly to the terminals of circuit components without the use of sockets. Standard inline subminiature sockets may be used by cutting the leads to a suitable length.

MECHANICAL DATA

CASE: Metal and Glass
BASE: None (0.016" tinned flexible leads. Length: 1.5" min.
Spacing: Leads 1-4 0.144" center-to-center;
Other Leads 0.048" center-to-center)

TERMINAL CONNECTIONS:
Lead 1 Collector
Lead 4 Base
Lead 5 Emitter

MOUNTING POSITION: Any

ELECTRICAL DATA

RATINGS - ABSOLUTE MAXIMUM VALUES:

Collector Voltage (V_c)	-12 volts
Peak Collector Voltage (V_c) ♦ ⊕	-24 volts
Collector Current	-10 ma.
Collector Dissipation ★	
Emitter Current	10 ma.
Ambient Temperature ■	85 °C

AVERAGE CHARACTERISTICS: (at 27°C)

Collector Voltage	-6 volts
Emitter Current	1.0 ma.
Collector Resistance	2.0 meg.
Base Resistance	1500 ohms
Emitter Resistance	25 ohms
Base Current Amplification Factor	90
Cut-off Current (approx.)	6 μa.
Noise Factor (max.) ●	20 db

AVERAGE CHARACTERISTICS - COMMON EMITTER: (at 27°C)

Collector Voltage	-1.5	-6 volts
Emitter Current	0.5	1.0 ma.
Input Resistance	4300	2700 ohms
Load Resistance	20,000	20,000 ohms
Power Gain (Matched Input)	40	42 db

AVERAGE CHARACTERISTICS - COMMON COLLECTOR: (at 27°C)

Collector Voltage	-6 volts
Emitter Current	1.0 ma.
Input Resistance ▲	1.0 meg.
Load Resistance	20,000 ohms
Power Gain (Matched Input)	16 db

AVERAGE CHARACTERISTICS - COMMON BASE: (at 27°C)

Collector Voltage	-6 volts
Emitter Current	1.0 ma.
Input Resistance	110 ohms
Load Resistance	0.1 meg.
Power Gain (Matched Input)	30 db.

■ *This is the maximum operating temperature recommended. However, characteristic damage will not result from occasional exposures to storage temperatures up to 100°C.*

● *Measured under conditions for grounded emitter operation at Vcb = 2.5 volts for 1 cycle bandwidth at 1000 cycles.*

▲ *Higher input impedances, without appreciable loss in gain, can be achieved by operating at lowered collector current.*

★ *This is a function of maximum ambient temperature (T A) expected. It is approximately equal to 1.7 (85°C - T A) milliwatts.*

♦ *Collector voltage Vce at which Ic rises to 2 ma. in common emitter circuit with base lead connected directly to emitter lead. Ambient temperature = 25°C.*

⊕ *In circuits stabilized for Ic or Ie and which do not have critical distortion requirements, absolute maximum peak voltage is 45 volts.*

Tentative Data

RAYTHEON MANUFACTURING COMPANY
RECEIVING AND CATHODE RAY TUBE OPERATIONS

0.420" max.

0.230" max.

0.195" max.

0.390" max.

0.460" max.

5 4 1

Table 10-II

 **engineering data service 2N141**

SYLVANIA

MECHANICAL DATA

Dimensions and Basing . . . . See Drawing
Ambient Temperature[1] . . . . 25 °C
Cooling Structure . . . . Anodized Aluminum fin
                         Connected electrically to the Collector.
Mounting Position . . . . Any

ELECTRICAL DATA

MAXIMUM RATINGS (ABSOLUTE)[2]

Collector to Base Voltage	—60 Volts
Collector to Emitter Voltage . . . :	—30 Volts
Collector Current	—0.8 Ampere
Total Dissipation[3]	
Free Air	1.5 Watts
Standard Dissipator	4.0 Watts
External Base to Ground	
Resistance[4] (Recommended Max.)	200 Ohms

TYPICAL SMALL SIGNAL, LOW FREQUENCY PARAMETERS

$V_c = -12V$, $I_e = +50$ ma

Alpha	0.975
Current Gain . . . . : . .	40
Emitter Resistance	1 Ohm
Base Resistance . . . . : . .	75 Ohms
Collector Resistance	250,000 Ohms
Collector Cut-off Current	
At $V_c = 20V$	100 μa
Collector Capacitance	200 μμf
Alpha Cutoff Frequency	400 KC/S

TYPICAL APPLICATIONS DATA[5]

Class A Amplifier, Common Emitter

Collector Supply Voltage	—24 Volts
Collector Current	—75 ma
Base Current	—2.5 ma
Generator Resistance	100 Ohms
Input Resistance[6]	100 Ohms
Load Resistance	400 Ohms
Power Output . . . . . :	600 mw
Power Gain	26 db

Class B Push-pull amplifier, Common Collector[7]

Collector Supply Voltage	—24 Volts
Collector Current	
Maximum Signal	—275 ma
Zero Signal	—1.0 ma
Generator Resistance	100 Ohms
Input Resistance[6]	100 Ohms
Load Resistance	
(Per Collector)	48 Ohms
Power Output	5 Watts
Power Gain	18 db

QUICK REFERENCE DATA

The Sylvania Type 2N141 (PNP) is a hermetically sealed, alloy juction type, germanium transistor designed for use at audio to low r f frequencies where its characteristic high voltage and high power capabilities are required. It is particularly useful in audio output stages operating Class A or Class B push-pull.

This type is of extremely rugged construction and adapted to solder, plug-in, and screw type mounting.

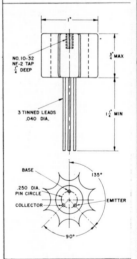

SYLVANIA ELECTRIC
PRODUCTS INC.

ELECTRONICS DIVISION
WOBURN, MASS.

Prepared and Released By The
TECHNICAL PUBLICATIONS SECTION
EMPORIUM, PENNSYLVANIA

APRIL 1956

Table 10-III

PNP JUNCTION TRANSISTOR

ACTUAL SIZE

TYPE 2N44

The General Electric type 2N44 germanium fused junction transistor triode is a P-N-P unit particularly recommended for intermediate-gain, low-to-medium power applications. A hermetic enclosure is provided by use of glass-to-metal seals and resistance-welded seams. This transistor is capable of dissipating 150 mw in 25°C free air.

SPECIFICATIONS

ABSOLUTE MAXIMUM RATINGS:

Collector Voltage (referred to base), V_c	— 45 volts
Collector Current, I_c	— 50 ma
Emitter Current, I_e	50 ma
*Junction Temperature, T_j	100° C

*Junction temperature may be determined by the method outlined in curve number 6. As an alternative method, a small thermocouple may be attached to the transistor shell (allowing 0.2° C/mw temperature drop between junction and shell). Rating may not be exceeded when soldering into circuit or during operation.

AVERAGE CHARACTERISTICS:

	DESIGN CENTER	TYPICAL PRODUCTION SPREAD MAX.	MIN.	
(Common Base, T_j = 30°C, f = 270 cps)				
Collector Voltage	— 5.0			volts
Emitter Current	1.0			ma
Output Admittance (input open circuit), h_{22}	1.0	2.0	0.5	μmhos
Current Amplification (output short circuit), h_{21}	— .955	— .97	— .94	
Input Impedance (output short circuit), h_{11}	40	50	30	ohms
Voltage Feedback Ratio (input open circuit), h_{12}	3×10^{-4}	5×10^{-4}	1×10^{-4}	
Collector Cutoff Current, I_{co}	10	15	1.0	μa
Output Capacitance, C_c	40	50	30	mmf
Noise Figure (V_c, — 1.5V; I_e, 0.5 ma; f, 1kc; BW, 1 $\sim$), NF	22	33	11	db
Maximum Power Gain (Common Emitter)	39	43	34	db
**Frequency Cutoff, f_{co}	1.0	2.5	0.5	mc
Temp. Rise/Unit Collector Dissipation (in free air)	0.5			°C/mw
***Temp. Rise/Unit Collector Dissipation (infinite heat sink)	0.2			°C/mw

**Frequency at which the magnitude of h_{21} is 3 db down from its 270 cps value.

***Temperature rise with transistor clamped to metallic heat sink.

TYPICAL OPERATION (Small Signal Amplifier):

	COMMON BASE	COMMON EMITTER	COMMON COLLECTOR	
(T_j = 30°C, f = 1 KC)				
Collector Voltage	— 5	— 5	— 5	volts
Emitter Current	1.0	1.0	1.0	ma
Input Impedance	55	700	15,000	ohms
Source Impedance	100	600	15,000	ohms
Load Impedance	50,000	30,000	600	ohms
Power Gain (PG)	28	38	12	db

TYPICAL OPERATION (Medium Power Amplifier, Class A):

	COMMON BASE	COMMON EMITTER	COMMON COLLECTOR	
(T_j = 75°C, f = 1 KC)				
Collector Voltage	— 20	— 20	— 20	volts
Emitter Current	5	5	5	ma
Input Impedance	10	220	88,000	ohms
Source Impedance	50	220	88,000	ohms
Load Impedance	4,500	4,500	4,500	ohms
Power Output (5% distortion)	45	40	42	mw
Power Gain	25	33	13	db

EQUIVALENT CIRCUIT:

OUTLINE DRAWING

APPROXIMATE CONVERSION FORMULAE
"h" TO "r" PARAMETERS (ASSUME $r_b \ll r_c$)

$$r_e = h_{11} - \frac{h_{12}}{h_{22}} (1 + h_{21})$$

$$r_b = \frac{h_{12}}{h_{22}}$$

$$r_c = \frac{1}{h_{22}}$$

$$a = - h_{21}$$

"h" PARAMETERS

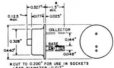

COLLECTOR
BASE
EMITTER

X CUT TO 0.200" FOR USE IN SOCKETS
LEAD DIAMETER —0.017"
MOUNTING POSITION—ANY
WEIGHT —0.05 OZ.
BASE CONNECTED TO TRANSISTOR SHELL

(TENTATIVE DATA)

GENERAL ELECTRIC

Review Problems

1. (a) Name the three elements in a point-contact transistor.
(b) Draw a diagram showing the basic construction of a point-contact transistor.

2. Explain the current relations in a point-contact transistor.

3. (a) What does the symbol "α" stand for in transistor terminology?
(b) Give a typical value for α.
(c) Show by formula how this value is determined.

4. Explain how a point-contact transistor can have voltage and power gain even though it is basically a current operated device.

5. Name two serious disadvantages of point-contact transistors as compared to junction types.

6. In diagrammatic form show the basic circuitry for an N-P-N transistor. Label the elements.

7. Explain the current relations in N-P-N transistor operation.

8. (a) What is meant by collector cutoff current?
(b) What is the symbol for this current?

9. (a) Give a typical value for α for a junction transistor.
(b) Can a value of $\alpha = 20$ be obtained? Explain.

10. How do voltage and power gains for a junction transistor compare with point-contact units? Explain.

11. Explain how a P-N-P transistor differs from an N-P-N unit (a) in construction; (b) in basic circuitry.

12. Explain the current relations in P-N-P transistor operation.

13. (a) Draw the graphic symbols for P-N-P and N-P-N transistors.
(b) How can you tell which is which?

14. (a) What does the symbol "β" stand for in transistor terminology?
(b) Show by formula how it can be determined.
(c) Show by formula its relation to α.

15. What two families of static characteristic curves are generally plotted for transistors?

16. (a) On characteristic curves, why are collector voltages sometimes shown as negative quantities?
(b) Why are collector currents sometimes shown as negative quantities?

17. Why is it impractical to evaluate transistor parameters directly from characteristic curves?

18. (a) Name the three possible configurations in which transistors can be connected.

(b) Show by basic diagrams (less power supply and associated circuitry) each of these three connections.

19. (a) Name three parameters of a transistor that are similar to plate resistance in a vacuum tube.

    (b) Give the equation by which each of these parameters can be evaluated.

20. (a) What is the main reason for poor high-frequency operation of a transistor?

    (b) What causes this condition?

21. (a) Name two techniques used in the manufacturing of junction transistors.

    (b) Explain each method briefly.

22. Explain what is meant by the alpha cutoff frequency.

23. Why is the transistor essentially a low power device?

24. Explain briefly how "power" transistors were achieved.

25. In what respect does the power ratings for transistors differ from vacuum-tube ratings?

26. What is the basic difference between a "standard" junction transistor and a tetrode transistor?

27. Show by diagrammatic sketch the basic circuitry used with tetrode transistors.

28. Explain how current flow in a tetrode transistor differs from the "standard" transistor.

29. (a) What is the advantage of the tetrode transistor?

    (b) Explain in two respects how this advantage is realized.

CHAPTER 11

Phototubes and Photo-
electric Cells

-▀--▀--▀-▀--▀--▀--▀--▀-▀--▀--▀--▀-▀--▀--▀--▀--▀--▀--▀-▀--▀--▀--▀-▀--▀--▀-✓

When light energy strikes certain materials, changes in electrical characteristics are noticed. These *photoelectric* effects can take one of three forms:

> 1. *Photoemissive effect.* Electrons are emitted from the surface
> of the material.
> 2. *Photovoltaic effect.* A voltage is produced across the faces of
> the material.
> 3. *Photoconductive effect.* The electrical resistance of the material
> is reduced.

Photoelectric effects were noticed many years ago. As far back as
1839 Edmond Becquerel discovered the photovoltaic effect. In his experiments using a pair of electrodes immersed in a liquid electrolyte, he observed a flow of current when the cell was illuminated with sunlight. The
photoconductive effect was discovered by Willoughby Smith in 1873 when
he noticed that the resistance of selenium bars dropped by as much as 100
percent when exposed to sunlight. The discovery of the photoemissive
effect was more of an accident. Heinrich Rudolph Hertz, while experiment-
ing with oscillators and spark gaps, noticed that longer sparks were obtained when the spark gaps were exposed to light.

Each of these effects will be discussed in more detail shortly. However, since they are all dependent on light energy, a brief review of the basic light principles and terminology is in order.*

Light Waves

Light waves are electromagnetic waves, and travel through space at the speed of 186,000 miles per second or in metric units at 300,000,000 meters per second. Visible light waves range from red through violet. The difference between these colors is due to the *frequency* of the waves, with red as the lowest and violet as the highest frequency. At still lower frequencies in the electromagnetic spectrum are the infrared waves, heat waves, and radio waves. Above the visible light waves come the ultraviolet, *x*-rays, and cosmic rays. These electromagnetic waves are more often differentiated in terms of their *wavelengths* rather than their frequencies. The term wavelength is used to denote the physical length (in feet, inches, meters, or other units of distance) corresponding to the *distance occupied by one cycle of variation in space.*

To make this idea clearer, let us examine a water wave. If we drop a stone in a pond, ripples or water waves will travel outward in *space* surrounding the spot where the stone was dropped. The water will have high spots or crests and low spots or troughs. This is shown in Fig. 11-1, *for a specific instant of time.* The distance between any two peaks is the *wavelength* of this water wave. Now let us notice one particular spot on this

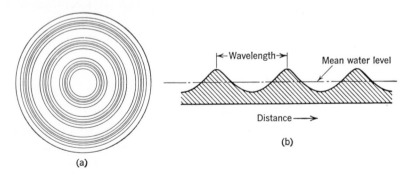

(a)

Wavelength | Mean water level | Distance

(b)

Fig. 11-1. Water waves at a given instant, showing wavelength: (a) top view; (b) cross-sectional view.

water wave. For ease of observation a cork could be floated at this spot. The cork will be seen to rise above and fall below the mean water level.

---

* For details consult Shortley, G., and Williams, D., *Elements of Physics,* 2nd Ed. (Prentice-Hall, Inc., 1955).

These are variations with *time,* and the rate of rise and fall determine the frequency of the wave.

There is a simple relation between frequency and wavelength. The higher the frequency, the shorter the wavelength, or by equation,

$$\text{wavelength } (\lambda) = \frac{v}{f}$$

where v is the velocity of the wave motion and f is the frequency in cycles per second.

If the velocity is expressed in feet per second, the wavelength determination will also be in feet. Similarly, if the velocity is expressed in meters per second, the wavelength will be in meters.

Light waves are waves of very high frequencies. (You will recall we said that their position in the electromagnetic spectrum is above radio waves, and we already know of radio waves above 30,000 megacycles.) Consequently their wavelengths are very short—minute fractions of an inch and even of a centimeter. To avoid such small fractional or decimal numbers, two new units of length—the *angstrom unit* or the *micron* are used. These units are decimally related to the meter and to each other:

$$1 \text{ meter} = 10^{10} \text{ angstrom units} = 10^6 \text{ microns}$$
$$1 \text{ micron} = 10^4 \text{ angstrom units}$$

The visible light spectrum ranges from violet at the high frequency end to red at the lower frequency. The sensation of violet is produced by vibrations of approximately 7.5×10^{14} cycles per second. This corresponds to a wavelength of

$$\lambda \text{ (meter)} = \frac{v}{f} = \frac{3 \times 10^8}{7.5 \times 10^{14}} = 0.4 \times 10^{-6} \text{ meter}$$

or

$$0.4 \times 10^{-6} = 0.4 \text{ micron}$$

or

$$0.4 \times 10^{-6} \times 10^{10} = 4000 \text{ angstrom units}$$

Figure 11-2 shows a section of the electromagnetic wave spectrum including the region of visible light.

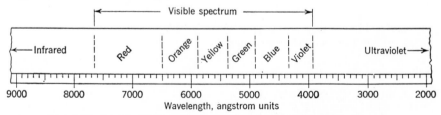

Fig. 11-2. Visible portion of the spectrum of electromagnetic radiation, showing approximate wavelength of the various colors.

Light Units

The original unit for comparing the light-giving power of various light sources was the candlepower and was defined as the light output of a very specific candle.* Although this candle is no longer used, as the standard, the unit is still retained. The amount of light given off by a light source (or received by some object) is called *luminous flux* and is measured in *lumens*. The lumen is evaluated as follows: Imagine a one-candlepower source of light located at the center of a spherical shell of one foot in radius. (The inside surface of the sphere should be dead black to prevent reflection effects.) The amount of light, or luminous flux, that falls on each square foot of this spherical surface is equal to one lumen. Since the total surface of such a sphere is $4\pi r^2$, it follows that the total luminous flux from a one-candlepower source is 4π lumens.

If the one-candlepower source were inclosed in a sphere of three-foot radius, what would happen to the total luminous flux? Nothing! By definition, this source has a total luminous flux of 4π lumens, and regardless of where this light source is located, the luminous flux does not change. Is that clear? Good. Now for another question: How much light (luminous flux) will fall on a one-square-foot section on the surface of this sphere? The total surface of this sphere is $4\pi r^2 = 4\pi \times 9$, or 36π square feet. Since the total flux is 4π lumens, each square foot receives

$$\frac{4\pi \text{ lumens}}{36\pi \text{ sq ft}} = \frac{1}{9} \text{ lumen}$$

Notice that by *tripling* the radius of the sphere the luminous flux per square foot has dropped to *one-ninth*. This is an important relation: *The amount of light falling on any given surface varies inversely as the square of the distance from the light source.*

This brings us to our final light unit, *intensity of illumination*. Let us assume we have a surface with an area of two square feet and that the total luminous flux on this surface is two lumens. The intensity of illumination is one lumen per square foot. This intensity is called one *foot-candle*. Notice then that intensity corresponds to luminous flux density or flux per unit area, and that the term foot-candle is the unit of intensity of illumination and is equal to an intensity of one lumen per square foot. If the above surface area were cut down to only one-half square foot, what

---

* This was the British Standard Candle made of spermaceti, weighing $2\frac{3}{5}$ ounces and burning at the rate of 120 grains of spermaceti per hour.

change would there be in the intensity of illumination? There would be no change! Since the light source was not changed and the distance from the source was not changed, the intensity of illumination is not affected. However, the total amount of light falling on this new surface would be less. The total flux is the product of intensity times area or

$$\text{total flux} = 1 \text{ ft-candle} \times \tfrac{1}{2} \text{ sq ft} = \tfrac{1}{2} \text{ lumen}$$

Light Energy

We have already mentioned that light is an electromagnetic wave and that radio waves, heat waves, x-rays, and cosmic rays are some of the other waves in the spectrum of electromagnetic waves. All of these waves have energy and their energy is transmitted through space by variations in their electric and magnetic fields. Albert Einstein suggested the *quantum theory* —that the energy of radiation is not continuous, but consists of closely packed discrete bundles of energy. These bundles are called *quanta* (plural of quantum). The amount of energy in a quantum varies directly with the frequency of the particular wave.* Thus there is more energy in a quantum of light wave than a heat wave; more again in a quantum of x-ray than light; still more in a quantum of cosmic ray. When speaking of light waves these quanta of energy are also called *photons*. Since red light has the longest wavelength in the visible light spectrum, a photon of red light has less energy than photons of the other colors. A photon at the violet end of the spectrum would contain more energy.

Photoelectric Emission

When light strikes the surface of certain metals, the free electrons at or near the surface can absorb sufficient energy from the photons of light to break through the surface potential barrier and escape into space. This is similar to thermionic emission except that the source of added energy comes from light photons rather than from heat. In order to get maximum emission from a given amount of illumination, low work function materials are desirable as cathodes. In this connection, the alkali metals, lithium, sodium, potassium, cesium, and rubidium seemed most suitable. The choice of material used depended mainly on the color (wavelength) of the light source; for example, lithium has its maximum sensitivity at about 4100 angstrom units, while at the other extreme, cesium has its maximum sensi-

---

* The energy (in joules) contained in a quantum is equal to hf where h is Planck's constant, 6.62×10^{-34} joule-second, and f is the frequency in cycles per second.

tivity at about 5400 angstrom units. This would make lithium most useful for colors in the violet-ultraviolet range and cesium for blue light. Neither of these basic metals is well suited to light in the red region, which incidentally is the region of maximum output from a tungsten incandescent lamp.

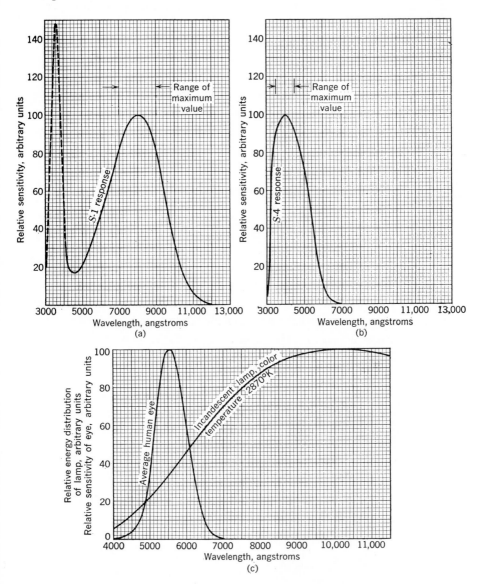

Fig. 11-3. Comparison of spectral characteristics of (a) S-1 and (b) S-4 cathode surfaces with (c) human eye and tungsten lamp.

In thermionic emission, you will recall that thin oxide layers were found to be much more efficient emitters (lower work function) than pure metals. Experiments along the same lines developed many composite photosensitive films which are far superior to pure metal cathodes. For standardization, the Radio Manufacturers Association (RMA) and the National Electrical Manufacturers Association (NEMA) jointly adopted a classification of commercial cathode surfaces based on their spectral response characteristics. These surfaces are designated as S-1 through S-10. The two most commonly used surfaces are S-1 with a cesium-oxygen-silver surface and S-4 with an antimony-cesium surface. The spectral response of these surfaces is shown in Fig. 11-3 together with the visual sensitivity of the "average" human eye and the light output of a tungsten lamp at 2870°K. (This tungsten lamp is used as the light source for photometric measurements.)

Vacuum Phototube

Phototubes are used in many applications where it is desired to control electrical circuits by means of light beams, or modulate electrical currents by variations in light intensities. These tubes are the heart of such devices as automatic door openers, color-sorting equipment, burglar alarms, and movie projectors with sound tracks. Basically, a phototube consists of a photoemissive cathode and an anode in a glass shell similar to other vacuum tubes. A typical phototube and its schematic symbol are shown in Fig. 11-4. The cathode structure is made large so as to intercept as much light as possible. Similarly, the anode or plate is made small so as to allow a maxi-

Fig. 11-4. Typical phototube and its schematic symbol.

mum of light to reach the cathode. The curvature of the cathode structure helps to direct the emitted electrons toward this small anode.

The electrical characteristics of a phototube can be obtained by connecting the tube to a variable d-c supply and measuring the current flow for various values of anode voltage. If this is repeated for various values of illumination a complete family of curves is obtained. Such a circuit and the resulting curves are shown in Fig. 11-5. The light flux is obtained from

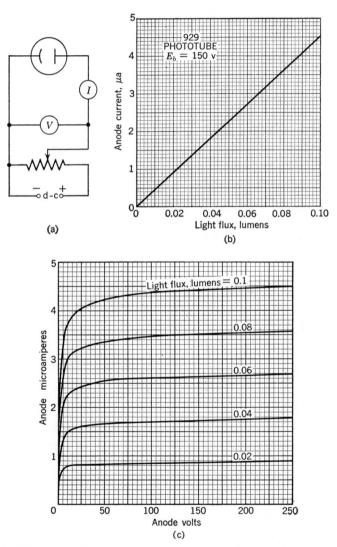

Fig. 11-5. Test circuit and electrical characteristics of the 929 vacuum phototube.

a calibrated lamp. (The candlepower of such a lamp is specified for a given operating voltage.) The lumens falling on the phototube can then be calculated from the distance to the light source and the surface area of the cathode. As the distance to the light source is increased the amount of light (lumens) falling on the cathode decreases. You will recall that this is an inverse square ratio. For accurate results, such an experiment should be performed in a suitable dark room to prevent stray light or reflected light from reaching the cathode. This effect can also be produced by using a photometric black box in which to enclose the light source and phototube.

Notice from Fig. 11-5(c) that, regardless of the amount of luminous flux, the current rises rapidly at first and then levels off, or saturates, even at relatively low voltage values. This can be explained as follows. When light strikes the cathode, electrons are emitted. Some of these electrons will have enough initial velocity (and proper direction) to hit the anode. Therefore some current flows even when the anode voltage is zero. As the anode is made positive, electrons are attracted to the anode and the plate current increases. At some particular anode voltage *all* the emitted electrons are drawn to the anode and beyond this voltage no further increase in current can be obtained, regardless of the applied voltage. The higher the level of illumination, the greater the cathode emission and the later the saturation point. Phototubes are generally operated at voltages well beyond the saturation point. Under this condition the plate current is directly proportional to the amount of luminous flux or to the intensity of illumination. This is shown in Fig. 11-5(b), for an anode voltage of 150 volts. This curve can be obtained either from the family of curves of Fig. 11-5(c), or experimentally by keeping the applied voltage constant and varying the distance from the phototube to the light source.

Gas Phototubes

If you refer back to Fig. 11-5, you will notice that the currents produced through this vacuum phototube are extremely low—only a few microamperes. Such low currents are not enough for direct operation of even the most sensitive relays. Appreciably higher current flow can be obtained, for the same amount of incident light, by adding a small amount of inert gas into a vacuum phototube. The tube is now called a gas phototube. The ratio of the current flow obtained in a gas tube to the current that would flow *in the same tube* without gas is called the *gas amplification factor*. Amplification factors of three to as high as ten are common. The presence of gas in the gas phototube is shown schematically by adding a black dot to the phototube symbol.

Figure 11-6 shows a gas phototube and its electrical characteristics. (This particular tube responds to light received from the end of the bulb rather than from the side.) Compare the shape of the curves of this tube with those of the vacuum phototube. For low anode voltages—up to approximately 25 volts—there is a distinct similarity. The current rises rapidly at first and then reaches a saturation value. But now, in this gas tube, as the anode voltage is raised above 25 volts, the current starts to increase again. This is particularly obvious for higher illumination values. The rise in current becomes very sharp at higher anode voltages, and if the voltage is increased further, the current would rise to destructive values. These characteristic curves can be obtained using the circuit of Fig. 11-5(a), with one modification. As in any gas tube, a protective resistor must be added in series with the supply voltage to keep the anode current from exceeding the maximum rated value at full supply voltage.

At low anode potentials the gas has no effect. Therefore the characteristic curves are similar to those of a vacuum phototube. As the plate potential is increased, the electrons emitted by photoemission will be accelerated. At some potential, they will have sufficient velocity to cause ionization by collision when they strike the neutral gas atoms. This creates additional electrons. They, in turn, can also cause ionization by collision with other neutral gas atoms. Meanwhile the positive gas ions are attracted to the cathode. They can bombard the cathode and produce additional electrons by secondary emission. At the higher anode potential these effects proceed at a faster rate and ionization may become cumulative. This can be seen by the sharp rise in current at the high voltage end of the curves and particularly at higher illumination levels. To prevent "runaway" currents due to cumulative ionization, gas phototubes should be operated with protective current limiting resistors in series with the supply voltage.

The addition of gas to a phototube has a drawback in that it reduces the *dynamic response,* or the speed with which the anode current can follow changes in illumination. This limits the maximum frequency of light variation at which gas phototubes can be used. However, this limitation does not extend down to audio frequencies, and these tubes are used extensively for sound reproduction from films.

One measure of comparison for phototubes is in terms of their *luminous sensitivity.* This is a ratio of the anode current to the amount of luminous flux falling on the cathode, and is expressed in microamperes per lumen.

Fig. 11-6. Gas phototube and its electrical characteristics.

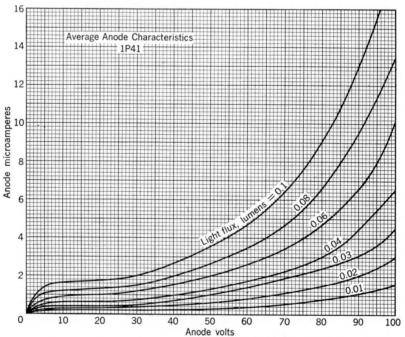

For vacuum phototubes this figure ranges from a low of approximately 7 to as high as 70, with most common values between 20 to 30 microamperes per lumen. Gas phototubes have sensitivities as high as 250 microamperes per lumen.

Multiplier Phototubes

We have seen that adding gas to a tube resulted in current amplifications up to 10, as compared to the vacuum-type phototube. But even gas phototubes have insufficient output at low illumination levels. In fact, the output of the above phototubes may even be too low for satisfactory amplification by vacuum tube or transistor amplifiers. The noise produced in the amplifiers may exceed the signal level. This situation can be remedied by use of *multiplier phototubes,* which make use of secondary emission effects to increase the output current.

These tubes have a photoemissive cathode, several "intermediate plates" called *dynodes,* and finally the output plate or anode. Each of the dynodes is operated at a successively higher positive potential, with the output plate having the maximum positive potential. Anode voltages of over 2000 volts are used in some photomultiplier tubes.

The basic principle of electron multiplication by secondary emission is fairly simple. Light strikes the photosensitive cathode and electrons are emitted. These electrons are directed to the first dynode. By operating this first dynode at a sufficiently positive polarity, the electrons are accelerated toward the dynode and strike the surface with sufficient force to knock off secondary emission electrons. The number of secondary emission electrons may exceed the number of electrons striking the anode by as much as 5 to 1. The ratio depends on the velocity with which the electrons strike the surface and is a function of the dynode voltage.

These secondary emission electrons are in turn directed toward the second dynode. The second dynode has a higher positive potential than the first dynode. The resulting electrostatic field accelerates the electrons toward the second dynode. When they strike the surface, more secondary emission electrons are produced. For example, assuming a secondary emission ratio of 5 to 1, for every electron produced by photoemission from the cathode, we would have 5 electrons emitted from the first dynode, 25 electrons from the second dynode, 125 electrons from the third dynode, etc. This effect can be seen from Fig. 11-7(b). The total amplification therefore depends on the number of stages (number of dynodes) and the voltage per stage.

Figure 11-7 shows a multiplier phototube having 9 stages. When op-

erated at 100 volts per stage, it is capable of amplifying the feeble photoelectric currents produced at the cathode by a factor of 1,000,000 times.

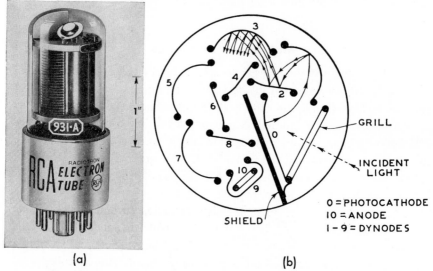

(a)　　　　　　　　　　　　　　　　(b)

Fig. 11-7. A 9-stage multiplier phototube: (a) external view; (b) cross-
section view.

The current amplification factor is reduced to 150,000 at 75 volts per
stage. By the ingenious arrangement of the elements shown in Fig. 11-7(b),
it was possible to fit the tube into the standard T-9 bulb (maximum over-all
dimensions $1\frac{5}{16}$ inches diameter, $3\frac{11}{16}$ inches length). Curvature of the
dynode surfaces assists in focusing or directing the secondary emission
electrons toward the next dynode.

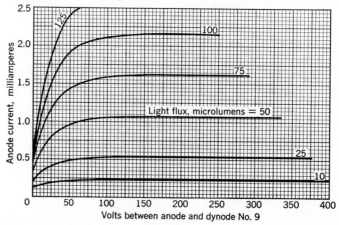

Fig. 11-8. Average anode characteristics, type 931-A multiplier phototube.

The electrical characteristics of this tube (931-A) are shown in Fig. 11-8. At first glance, the current values might seem rather low, but notice that the luminous flux values are extremely low—in *microlumens*.

Another multiplier phototube is shown in Fig. 11-9. This tube (6810) is a head-on type employing 14 stages. When operated with a supply voltage of 2000 volts the gain is 12,500,000. An increase in supply voltage to 2300 volts raises the gain to 66,000,000!

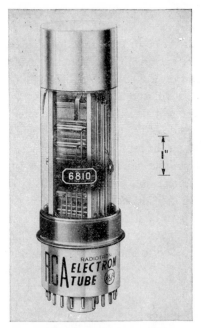

Fig. 11-9. A 14-stage head-on multiplier phototube.

From the basic principles and a comparison of the two tubes shown above, it would seem that infinite amplification could be obtained by raising the stage-to-stage voltages and by using more stages. Theoretically, this might be so, but in practice a limit is reached. As the number of stages is increased, it becomes increasingly difficult to prevent interaction and feedback. It is also more difficult to keep the electron stream focused. The high electron densities in the later stages can produce a space-charge effect that would actually reduce current flow. Also, with more stages and particularly as the voltage per stage is raised, power dissipation in the final stages becomes a problem.

Photoconductive Cells

Photoconductive effects were first noticed in connection with selenium bars. Their resistance was reduced drastically when exposed to sunlight.

This phenomenon is a semiconductor property and is exhibited to various degrees by other semiconductor materials. To understand why this is so, let us think back to the semiconductor fundamentals covered in Chapter 7. You will recall that the valence electrons in these materials are arranged in a crystal-lattice structure with strong covalent bonds between the electrons of adjacent atoms. As a result, pure semiconductors should have no conductivity whatsoever. One of the reasons for the slight conduction exhibited by these materials was the absorption of energy—heat or light—by the valence electrons. If the energy absorbed is sufficient, the covalent bonds can be broken, creating free electrons and holes, each of which are current carriers. The resistance of a semiconductor material will therefore depend on the amount of light falling on it, and the ambient temperature.

If a voltage is applied across a semiconductor photoconductive cell, current will flow through the circuit, and for a given supply voltage the magnitude of the current will depend on the light intensity, or foot-candles, falling on the semiconductor surface. But, even if the light intensity is zero, electron-hole pairs can be created by heat energy, even at room temperature! Therefore, current will still flow. This current is known as the *dark current,* and the corresponding cell resistance as the *dark resistance.* When a cell is to be used at low illumination levels, the dark resistance should be high, otherwise the dark current could readily mask the small change in current due to small changes in illumination.

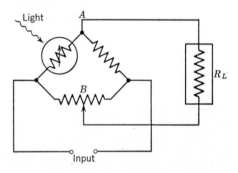

Fig. 11-10. Photoconductive cell in a bridge circuit.

One way of circumventing the masking action of this dark current is to use the cell as one arm of a Wheatstone bridge. Such a circuit is shown in Fig. 11-10. The bridge is balanced before exposing the cell to the light source. At balance, regardless of the dark current flowing through the cell, the voltage between points A and B is zero. No current flows through the relay or load resistor (R_L). When light strikes the cell, its resistance decreases, unbalancing the bridge. The current flowing in the output circuit will operate the relay or produce a voltage across R_L.

A commercial photoconductive cell is shown in Fig. 11-11, together with its characteristic curve. This cell uses cadmium sulfide as the semiconductor material and features high luminous sensitivity, low dark current, and extremely low background noise. The cell is of the head-on variety. Its spectral response covers the visible range from 3500 to 5500 angstrom units, with maximum response in the blue-green region at 5000 angstrom units. Other semiconductor surfaces have their maximum sensi-

Fig. 11-11. A commercial photoconductive cell and its characteristic curve.

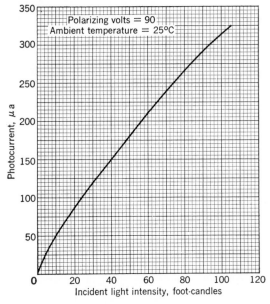

tivities at other wavelengths. For example, lead sulfide photoconductive cells have high sensitivity in the red and infra red region and are most useful in "invisible ray" applications such as burglar alarms.

Photoconductive cells can be used in much the same applications as vacuum and gas phototubes.

Semiconductor Photodiode

When studying the semiconductor diodes, whether of the point-contact or P-N junction variety, we learned that if these units are biased in the reverse direction, they have a high inverse resistance and current flow is negligibly low. For the P-N junction [see Fig. 7-4(b)], this was due to the lack of current carriers in the region surrounding the junction. What will happen if light energy is made to strike directly at the junction? Electron-hole pairs will be formed. But these are current carriers—the junction will now act as a conductor! In other words, the P-N junction diode, when operated with reverse bias, exhibits the same effects as a photoconductive cell. The conductivity is low at low illumination levels, and increases in proportion to the light intensity falling on the junction.

The sensitivity of the junction photodiode and the photoconductive cell are of the same order. However, the photodiode has one advantage, in that its dark current is much lower. On the other hand, with photodiodes, the light must be carefully focused on the junction area. If the incident light misses the junction area even by one hundredth of an inch, the sensitivity is cut approximately in half. The explanation for this is fairly simple. In a diode with reverse bias, there are practically no current carriers at the junction region. As was mentioned above, light energy striking this area produces current carriers, increasing the conductivity of the device. Light energy striking at some distance from the junction also produces electron-hole pairs, or current carriers. But most of these carriers disappear by recombination before they reach the junction.

Figure 11-12(a) shows an alloyed junction germanium photodiode. It is enclosed in an evacuated, hermetically sealed glass envelope, with a built-in lens at one end to focus the light on the junction region. A typical set of characteristic curves is shown in Fig. 11-12(b). This photodiode is usable over a wide frequency spectrum covering the visible light and the infra red region with a maximum sensitivity at approximately 15,000 angstrom units.

Since these units are essentially semiconductor diodes, they are represented in schematic diagrams by the standard semiconductor diode symbol. To distinguish it as a photosensitive device, a wiggly arrow (incident light) is aimed at the junction. Photodiodes can be used in many of the photoelectric applications previously mentioned. Their small size make them particularly desirable in such applications as punched card or punched tape readout, to reduce the size and power dissipation of computing machines.

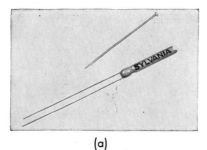

(a)

Fig. 11-12. External view and characteristic curves of the 1N77A photodiode.

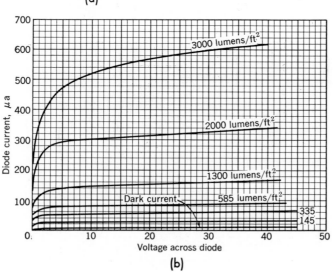

(b)

Phototransistors

The term phototransistor is used somewhat loosely with reference to semiconductor photosensitive devices with point contact or P-N junctions. Basically, the principle of photoconductivity is still involved. Light energy increases the number of current carriers and increases conductivity. Some manufacturers apply the term phototransistors to two-terminal units such as the photodiode described above. Their justification in using this terminology is by considering the incident light as the emitter.

The point-contact phototransistor shown in Fig. 11-13 falls in this category. It consists of a pellet of N-type germanium (the base), with a point or "catwhisker" (the collector) making a pressure contact to one face. A reverse bias voltage is applied between base and collector. This can be seen from the circuit diagram inset of Fig. 11-13(c). When incident light energy strikes the forward face of the germanium pellet, current car-

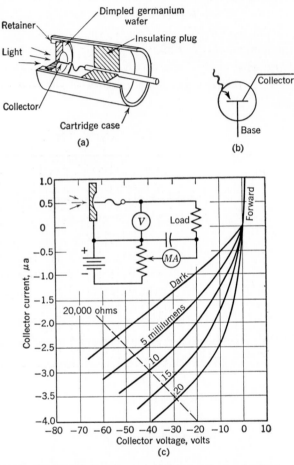

Fig. 11-13. Point-contact phototransistor: (a) longitudinal section view; (b) symbol and (c) characteristics.

riers (holes and electrons) are produced. The electrons are attracted toward the cartridge case because of its positive potential and the holes diffuse toward the collector point. This latter action is similar to the "hole injection" of the emitter in a point-contact transistor, and a "current gain" results.

For good sensitivity, it is important that the light strikes the cell directly in front of the collector point contact. Otherwise many of the carriers will recombine before the above action can take place. As in the photo-diode, this effect can be achieved by fitting a lens into the end of the cart-ridge so as to focus the light energy at the right spot.

Another type of phototransistor is the N-P-N or P-N-P type, similar in construction to the junction transistor. Figure 11-14 shows a germanium P-N-P alloyed junction phototransistor. Notice the general resemblance with the junction transistors of Chapter 10. (See Figs. 10-3 and 10-13.) The spectral response of this unit covers the visible region and extends into the infra red with the maximum sensitivity at approximately 10,000 angstrom units.

Fig. 11-14. Junction phototransistor.

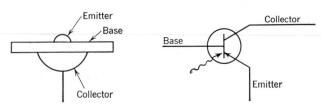

Phototransistors perform the same functions as phototubes and other photosensitive devices. Their advantages are smaller size, lower power dissipation, and greater sensitivity. Comparing the last three types discussed, the point-contact transistor has a sensitivity of from two to three times that of the photodiode (also called a P-N phototransistor), while the P-N-P or N-P-N ranges from 50 to 500 times more sensitive than the photodiode.

Photovoltaic Cells

The photoelectric devices discussed so far, whether of the vacuum-tube type, gas-tube type, or semiconductor type, all require electrical power for their operation. In contrast, the photovoltaic cell generates its own electrical power. As was mentioned earlier in this chapter, the photovoltaic effect was first discovered by Becquerel in 1839. It was discovered again by W. G. Adams and R. E. Day in 1876, and by C. E. Fritts in 1884 as he was working on selenium for large area rectification. In all experimentation with photovoltaic action and large area rectifiers strong correlation was noted. Rectifying contacts produced a photovoltage when exposed to bright light, and vice versa, good photoelectric cells were also good rectifiers. So it is not surprising that the development of one paralleled the other.

The early photovoltaic cells used selenium or copperoxide as the semiconductor. In the middle 1950's with the great advances in germanium and silicon devices, these semiconductors were also used in commercial photocells. In construction, the photovoltaic cell is similar to the semiconductor power rectifiers. This can be seen by comparing the basic construction of a selenium photovoltaic cell, Fig. 11-15, with Figs. 9-1 and 9-2 for the

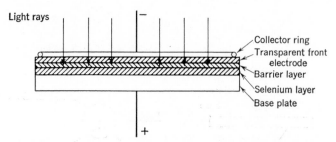

Fig. 11-15. Basic construction of a selenium photovoltaic cell.

basic area-rectifier cell. The transparent front electrode and the barrier layer are of molecular thickness, while the selenium layer is from 0.002 to 0.003 inch thick. The completed cell is coated with a protective lacquer and represents a rugged shatterproof unit immune to shock and vibration.

When light falls on the cell, it penetrates through the transparent front electrode to the selenium, creating electron-hole pairs. Depending on the relative work functions of the metal front electrode and of the semiconductor, electrons from the semiconductor can gain enough energy from the light photons to escape from the semiconductor surface into metal. This creates a negative charge on the front electrode (and collector ring) and a positive charge on the selenium layer (and base plate). This polarity is indicated on the cell of Fig. 11-15. As long as light shines on the cell, a difference of potential is maintained. This difference of potential disappears when the source of light energy is removed and the electrons, "trapped" in the metal front electrode, leak back through the barrier layer.

The emf (electromotive force) produced in the photoelectric cell increases with the intensity of illumination. The increase is logarithmic, rising fairly rapidly and linearly at low levels of illumination but gradually levelling off asymptotically. This relation is shown in Fig. 11-16 for a

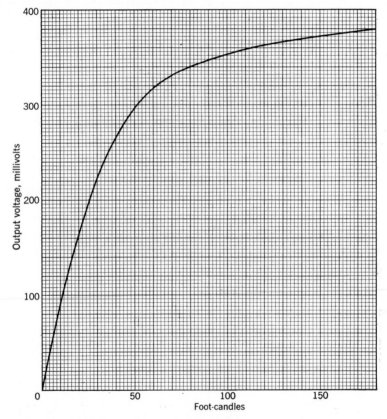

Fig. 11-16. Open-circuit voltage as a function of illumination, for a DP-5 photocell.

selenium photocell. The maximum open circuit voltage for this cell approaches 600 millivolts when exposed to direct sunlight (10,000 foot-candles). This maximum voltage for any cell depends on the difference in the work functions of the two substances in contact at the photoactive interface, i.e., front electrode and semiconductor. *The open circuit voltage is independent of the area of the photocell illuminated.* This is similar to a battery—where the emf developed is dependent on the material used for the electrodes and electrolyte and not on the area or size of the battery.

Since the photovoltaic cell is a semiconductor device, and since it has a P-N junction (barrier layer to semiconductor), it follows that this cell should exhibit photoconductive effects—and it does. The dark internal resistance is high (15,000 to 20,000 ohms for a cell area of 1 square inch) but it drops to well under 1000 ohms under bright illumination. Advantage is taken of this relation when designing circuit applications for the photovoltaic cell. The current in any circuit depends on the voltage available and the circuit resistance. With a photovoltaic cell the voltage increases with illumination—but not at a linear rate. However, at the same time, the internal resistance of the cell decreases, and if the load resistance is low, the total circuit resistance will also decrease with illumination. For certain values of load resistance, the decrease in circuit resistance will offset the non-linear rise in emf and the total circuit current will rise with illumination *at a linear rate.* The effect of load resistance on linearity can be seen in Fig. 11-17.

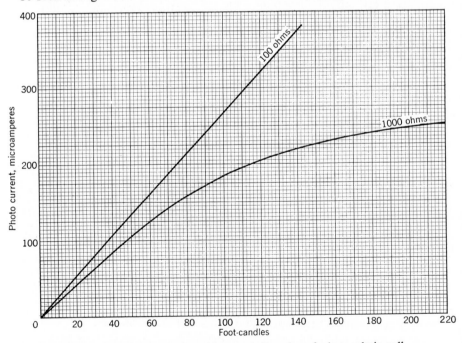

Fig. 11-17. Effect of load resistance on linearity of photovoltaic cell current, for A-5 cell.

Again, since these cells are semiconductor devices, they are subject to temperature effects. Both the emf and internal resistance are affected by temperature, but again, their effects tend to counteract, so that the short-

Fig. 11-18. Commercial applications of the photovoltaic cell.

circuit current is nearly independent of temperature. To obtain good linearity and to avoid instability due to temperature effects, photovoltaic cells are generally operated with very low external load resistances—approaching short-circuit. However, low value load resistance is not a cure-all. The sensitivity of these cells can be permanently impaired if they are subjected to too high a temperature.

Photovoltaic cells can be used in many industrial applications where light intensities are involved or where control can be made dependent on change or interruption of light beams. The advantage of these cells over previous photosensitive devices is that they can be operated without any additional power source. The short-circuit current is usually enough to operate a sensitive relay. In addition, its good linearity over a wide range of illumination levels makes these units ideal for use in measurement of light intensities. Figure 11-18 shows several commercial applications of the photovoltaic cell; in (a) as an exposure meter for photographic work; in (b) as a foot-candle meter for measuring illumination levels and checking its adequacy for various types of work; and in (c) as an automatic on-off control of artificial lighting when natural light falls below some fixed level.

Sun or Solar Batteries

You are probably familiar with portable radios, and you know that they operate from batteries. Up until the middle 1950's the carbon zinc or "dry battery" was extensively used. These batteries (for filament and plate power) are fairly expensive and many a "portable" owner would try to get the "last ounce of power" out of his batteries. The result was that quite often these receivers failed because of dead batteries.

With the development of transistors and their application to portable electronic equipment, the amount of power required to operate the equipment was drastically reduced. The power requirements were now within the limits of the photovoltaic cell! This gave rise to electronic equipment that could be operated from sunlight (or other light source). The photovoltaic cells used to convert radiant energy into electrical energy are called *sun batteries* or *solar batteries*. In general, the use of the term photovoltaic cell is limited to devices not expressly intended for the purpose of supplying power, whereas the term battery is used when the cell's primary purpose is to supply power. The term battery, as used in this application, should not be confused with batteries such as the lead-acid (automobile battery) storage battery. These are charged and can be used for some period of time thereafter—until they are discharged. The cycle can be repeated over and over. *The sun or solar battery cannot hold a charge and will deliver power only while exposed to light.*

There are many different semiconductor materials that may be used for solar batteries. Typical materials used are selenium, germanium, silicon, and cadmium sulphide.

Sun battery cells are available in various sizes. This affects the internal resistance and the current rating of the cell, but the output voltage remains constant. For example, with selenium sun cells, the output voltage at optimum load resistance is 0.25 volt regardless of cell size, whereas the current into the load (at 10,000 foot-candles) varies from 3.5 milliamperes for a cell area of 0.26 square inch to 100 milliamperes for a cell area of 9.41 square inches. Similarly parallel connection of cells will result in an increase in current output almost in direct proportion to the number of cells used—*if the external resistance is low*. Series connection of cells (in attempting to increase the supply voltage) will increase the internal resistance and the internal voltage drop so that the load voltage and load current are not changed. Therefore, when used to power low resistance circuits solar cells should be connected in parallel if increased power output at moderate illumination values is desired.

On the other hand, with high resistance loads, the effect of the internal

Fig. 11-19. Photovoltaic cells and sun batteries.

resistance of the cell becomes negligible. The current now depends on external resistance only. Now, we can connect cells in series and since the internal resistance is negligible (in comparison), the load voltage and load current will increase. A word of caution regarding the use of series cells— if any one cell is not illuminated, its high internal resistance may cause a very high internal voltage drop and the load voltage may approach zero. For maximum power transfer, the internal cell resistance should match the load resistance. Proper matching—depending on load resistance values, size of cells used, and level of illumination at which the cells will generally be used—may require series, parallel, or even series-parallel arrangements.

Figure 11-19 shows a variety of mounted and unmounted photovoltaic cells. The lower left is generally used as a sun battery cell. This cell has an active area of 0.26 square inch. In the background is a sun battery made up of a combination of cells. These cells can be arranged in series, parallel, or series-parallel.

Review Problems

1. (a) What is meant by the general term "photoelectric effect"?
   (b) State three specific forms of this effect.
   (c) Explain each of these specific effects, briefly.
2. (a) What is the visible distinction between light waves of different frequencies?
   (b) What is the relation between frequency and wavelength?
3. (a) Name two units commonly used in specifying wavelengths of light waves.
   (b) Express each of these units in meters.
4. (a) What unit is used to specify the intensity, or light-giving power, of a light source?
   (b) What term is used to designate the total light given off by a light source?
   (c) What unit is used to measure this total light?
5. How much total light is given off by:
   (a) a 10-candlepower source?
   (b) a 32-candlepower source?
6. The luminous flux falling on a given surface is 36 lumens. Find the amount of light that would fall on this same surface if:
   (a) the distance to the light source is tripled;
   (b) the distance to the light source is cut in half.
7. (a) What is the unit used to measure the intensity of the illumination falling on any surface?

(b) If a total luminous flux of 40 lumens falls on a surface area of 5 square feet, what is the intensity of illumination?

8. If 80 lumens falls on a surface area of 0.4 square foot, find the intensity of illumination.

9. A photocell has an active surface area of 10 square inches. The intensity of illumination falling on it is 5000 foot-candles. Find the total flux falling on the cell.

10. (a) What is a quantum? (b) What is a photon?

11. Explain the principle of photoelectric emission.

12. Draw the schematic symbol for a vacuum phototube.

13. Explain the reason for the shape of the characteristic curve of the vacuum phototube of Fig. 11-5(c).

14. Using a 929 vacuum phototube what value of anode current would flow for:

(a) An anode voltage of 80 volts and a luminous flux of 0.08 lumens?

(b) An anode voltage of 120 volts and a luminous flux of 0.04 lumens?

15. Using a 929 vacuum phototube, at an anode voltage of 150 volts how much luminous flux would be needed for a current of (a) 3.80 microamperes? (b) 1.90 microamperes? (c) 0.95 microampere?

16. What is the advantage of a gas phototube over a vacuum type?

17. Explain the reason for the shape of the characteristic curves of the gas tube in Fig. 11-6.

18. Why do gas-tube circuits use resistors in series with the supply voltage?

19. (a) What advantage does a multiplier phototube have over vacuum or gas tubes?

(b) Explain briefly how this advantage is obtained.

20. Explain briefly the principle of photoconduction.

21. (a) What is the significance of the term "dark current"?

(b) Should this value be high or low? Explain.

(c) Explain how its effect can be nullified.

22. (a) What light intensity is needed with the photoconductive cell of Fig. 11-11 in order to produce a current of 220 microamperes at a polarizing voltage of 90 volts?

(b) The sensitive area of the cell is 0.020 inch by 0.018 inch. What total flux is necessary to produce the intensity required in (a) above?

23. Explain briefly the principle of the junction photodiode.

24. (a) With photodiodes, why must the light energy be focused carefully to strike at the junction area?

(b) How is this generally accomplished?

25. With 24 volts across the photodiode of Fig. 11-12, find the current that would flow at a light intensity of 2000 foot-candles.

26. (a) Name two types of phototransistors.

(b) Compare the sensitivity of each of these two types to the photodiode.

27. Explain briefly the principle of the photovoltaic cell.

28. What determines the maximum voltage available from photovoltaic cells?

29. (a) What factors determine the internal resistance of these cells?

(b) Give the general range of values from dark to bright.

30. (a) State two reasons why these cells are often operated with load resistances approaching short-circuit.

(b) Explain briefly why this is so.

31. What is the advantage of photovoltaic cells over other photosensitive devices?

32. (a) What is a sun or solar battery?

(b) How is it distinguished from a photovoltaic cell?

(c) How do they differ from dry cells or storage batteries?

33. When operating into low resistance loads, will the use of series-connected solar batteries increase the voltage at the load? Explain.

34. What determines whether solar battery cells should be connected in series, parallel, or series-parallel?

SELECTED VACUUM TUBE CHARACTERISTICS

TYPE 6J5

Medium-Mu Triode

Heater voltage .... 6.3 volts
Heater current .... 0.3 ampere

Maximum Ratings

Plate voltage .... 300 max volts
Grid voltage .... 0 min volts
Plate dissipation .... 2.5 max watts
Peak heater—cathode voltage ...... 90 max volts
Cathode current .... 20 max ma

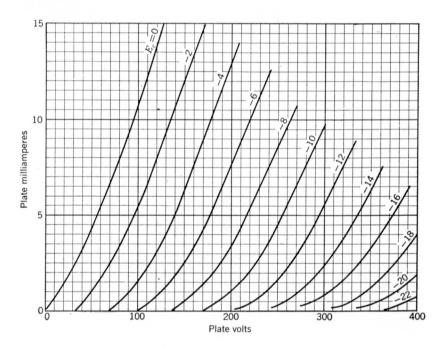

SELECTED VACUUM TUBE CHARACTERISTICS

TYPE 6BG7

Medium-Mu Duotriode

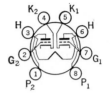

Heater voltage .... 6.3 volts
Heater current .... 0.3 ampere

Maximum Ratings

Plate voltage .... 110 max volts
Plate dissipation .... 1.0 max watts
Peak heater-cathode voltage .... 90 max volts
Cathode current .... 20 max ma

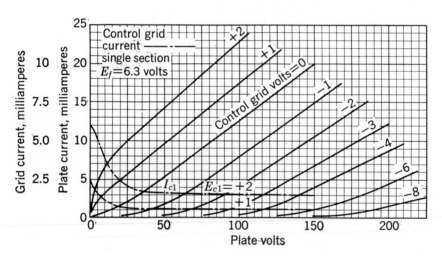

SELECTED VACUUM TUBE CHARACTERISTICS

TYPE 12AX7

High-Mu Twin Triode

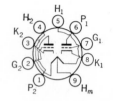

Heater voltage .... 12.6/6.3 volts
Heater current .... 0.15/0.3 ampere

Maximum Ratings

Plate voltage .... 300 max volts
Plate dissipation .... 1 max watts
Grid voltage .... 0 min volts
Peak heater-cathode voltage .... 180 max volts

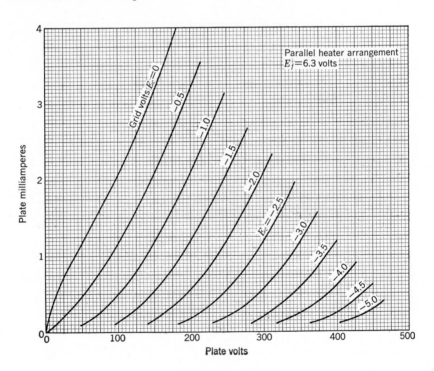

SELECTED VACUUM TUBE CHARACTERISTICS

TYPE 6SF5

High-Mu Triode

Heater voltage .... 6.3 volts
Heater current .... 0.3 ampere

Maximum Ratings

Plate voltage .... 300 max volts
Grid voltage .... 0 min volts
Peak heater-cathode voltage .... 90 max volts

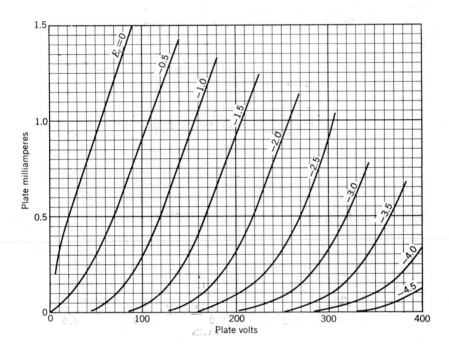

SELECTED VACUUM TUBE CHARACTERISTICS

TYPE 6SK7

Remote-Cutoff Pentode

Heater voltage ....   6.3   volts
Heater current ....   0.3   ampere

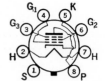

Maximum Ratings

Plate voltage   300   max volts
Grid No. 2 voltage   125   max volts
Grid No. 1 voltage   0   min volts
Plate dissipation ....   4.0   max watts
Grid No. 2 dissipation ....   0.4   max watts
Peak heater-cathode voltage   90   max volts

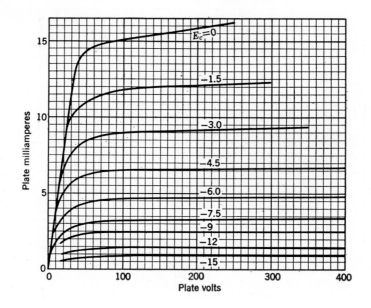

SELECTED VACUUM TUBE CHARACTERISTICS

TYPE 6CB6

Sharp-Cutoff Pentode

Heater voltage .... 6.3 volts
Heater current .... 0.3 ampere

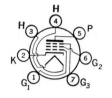

Maximum Ratings

Plate voltage .... 300 max volts
Grid No. 2 voltage .... 150 max volts
Plate dissipation .... 2.0 max watts
Grid No. 2 dissipation .... 0.5 max watts
Peak heater-cathode voltage .... 200 max volts

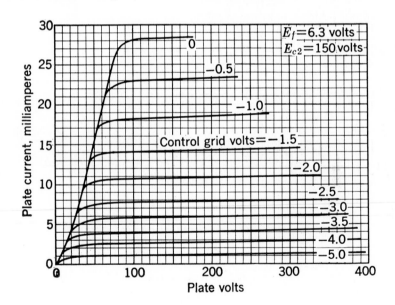

SELECTED VACUUM TUBE CHARACTERISTICS

TYPE 6B4G

Power Triode

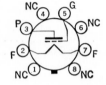

Heater voltage .... 6.3 volts

Heater current .... 1.0 ampere

Maximum Ratings

Plate voltage .... 300 max volts

Plate dissipation .... 15 max watts

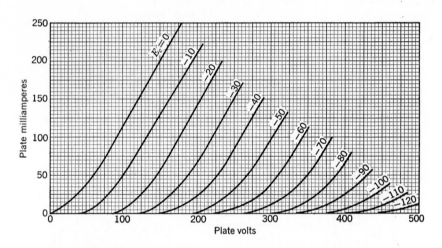

SELECTED VACUUM TUBE CHARACTERISTICS

TYPE 6CD6G

Beam Power Amplifier

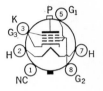

Heater voltage	6.3	volts
Heater current	2.5	ampere

Maximum Ratings

Plate voltage (d-c)	700	max volts
Peak positive-plate voltage	6000	max volts
Grid No. 2 voltage (d-c)	200	max volts
Plate current	170	max ma
Plate dissipation	15	max watts
Grid No. 2 dissipation	3	max watts
Peak heater-cathode voltage	135	max volts

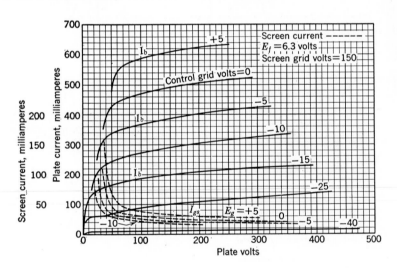

SELECTED POWER TRIODES

TYPE	DESCRIPTION FEATURES AND NOTES	Basing	Base	CONSTRUCTION Length, inches	Diameter, inches	Filament*	CATHODE Volts	Amperes
826	Air cooled UHF type with high efficiency. Has a center-tapped filament, zirconium coated plate, and a medium molded-flare base.	7BO	7-pin Septar	$3\frac{11}{16}$	$2\frac{3}{8}$	T.T.	7.5	4.0
833A	Forced air cooled, 100 watt triode with a zirconium plated anode and special post terminals.	833A	Spec.	$8\frac{13}{16}$	$4\frac{19}{32}$	T.T.	10	10
838	Air cooled, high mu zero bias class B modulator with high power output and low distortion. Jumbo base.	4E	4-pin	$7\frac{7}{8}$	$2\frac{5}{16}$	T.T.	10	3.25
845	Air cooled modulator and AF power amplifier. Jumbo base.	4E	4-pin	$7\frac{7}{8}$	$2\frac{5}{16}$	T.T.	10	3.25
5513	Forced air cooled, grounded-grid RF amplifier and oscillator capable of dissipating 1200 watts. Full ratings up to 220 Mc.	5513	Spec.	$7\frac{1}{2}$	3	T.T.	6.3	30
5514	All-purpose power triode with high mu allowing low or zero bias operation. Replaces types HY30Z, HY40, HY40Z, HY51A, HY51B and HY51Z.	4BO	4-pin	$6\frac{9}{16}$	$2\frac{7}{16}$	T.T.	7.5	3.0
5518	Transmitting triode for use as a grounded-grid class C RF amplifier.	5518	Spec.	$11\frac{11}{16}$	$5\frac{1}{2}$	T.	6.3	235

☐ ICAS (Intermittent Commercial and Amateur Service).

★ Design Center Values.

▲ Values shown are CCS (Continuous Commercial Service) unless otherwise noted.

*Thoriated tungsten filament (T.T.); pure tungsten filament (T.)

†Explanation of abbreviations in APPLICATION column:
A Audio — Class A Audio Frequency Amplifier or Modulator.
AB₁ Audio — Class AB₁, Audio Frequency Amplifier or Modulator.
B — Class B Push-Pull Audio Frequency Modulator.
CBT — Class B Television.
CP — Class C Plate Modulated Amplifier (100% Moaulation).
CT — Class C Telegraphy Power Amplifier and Oscillator.

2N

3N

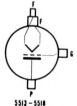

5513 – 5518

[*Note:* Appendices 2, 3, 4, 5, 6, and 8 are reproduced through the courtesy of CBS-Hytron.]

Appendix 2
SELECTED POWER TRIODES

APPLICATION†	Frequency in Mc for Full Input	Plate Volts	D-C Input Watts	Plate Dissipation Watts	Plate Volts	Grid Volts	Peak Grid Volts	Plate Amps	Grid Amps, D-C	Plate-to-Plate Load Resistance Ohms	Amplification	Driving Watts	Output Watts	TYPE
USE		**MAX RATINGS (Absolute Max.) ▲**			**CHARACTERISTICS—TYPICAL OPER**									
CPL1	250	1000	95	45	1000	−160	320	.095	.04	—	31	11.5	70	826
CTL1	250	1000	130	55	1000	−70	183	.13	.035	—	—	5.8	90	
B	...	3000	1125	300	3000	−70	400	0.1	—	—	—	20	1650	833A
CP	30	2500	835	200	2500	−300	460	.335	.075	—	—	30	635	
CT	30	3000	1250	300	3000	−200	360	.415	.055	—	—	20	1000	
B	—	1250	220	100	1250	0	200	.148	—	9000	Variable	7.5	260	838
CP	30	1000	175	67	1000	−135	255	.15	.06	—	—	16	100	
CT	30	1250	220	100	1250	−90	200	.15	.03	—	—	6	130	
AB1 Audio	—	1250	150	100	1250	−225	440	.04	—	6600	5.3	—	115	845
CBT	220	3000	3300	1200	2000	−20	240	.967	.18	—	220	223	1125	5513
CT	—	4000	3600	1200	3750	−150	250	.94	.159	—	—	377	2690	
CT	60	1500	262.5	65	1500	−106	197	.175	.06	—	—	12	200	5514
CP					1250	−84	172	.142	.06	—	—	10	135	
B					1500	−4.5	146	.35	.088	10500	—	6.5	400	
CT	—	7000	12000	4000	6600	−520	940	1.3	0.20	—	145	180	6500	5518

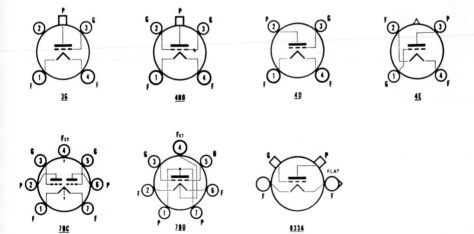

3G 4BB 4D 4E

7BC 7BQ 833A

SELECTED SPECIAL RECEIVING TUBES

| TYPE | DESCRIPTION | | CONSTRUCTION | | | CATHODE | | |
	FEATURES AND NOTES	Basing	Base	Length, inches	Diameter, inches	Heater–Filament	Volts	Amperes
6AJ5	Sharp cutoff pentode voltage amplifier. 28-volt-plate version of type 6AK5.	7BD	7-pin Min.	1¾	¾	Htr.	6.3	0.175
6AS6	Sharp cutoff pentode with grid 1 & grid 3 control for application in delay circuits, gated amplifier circuits and gain controlled amplifier circuits.	7CM	7-pin Min.	1¾	¾	Htr.	6.3	0.175
6AS7G	Low-mu duotriode with high perveance and an A-C plate resistance of 280 ohms. Used as a regulator tube in d-c power supplies, a d-c amplifier, etc.	8BD	8-pin O.	5⁵⁄₁₆	2¹⁄₁₆	Htr.	6.3	2.5
12AY7	Medium-mu duotriode for application in the first stages of audio amplifiers having high gain where primary considerations are reduction in microphonics, leakage noise, and hum.	9A	9-pin Min.	2³⁄₁₆	⅞	Htr.	12.6 6.3	0.15 0.3
26A7GT	Twin beam power tube for use with low voltage B+ power supplies.	8BU	8-pin O.	3¹¹⁄₁₆	1⁹⁄₃₂	Htr.	26.5	0.6
1620	Sharp cutoff pentode similar to 6J7. For use where microphonics is critical. Metal type with a miniature cap.	7R	7-pin O.	3⅛	1⁵⁄₁₆	Htr.	6.3	0.3
1635	High-mu power duotriode for Class B amplifier applications.	8B	8-pin O.	3⁵⁄₁₆	1⁵⁄₁₆	Htr.	6.3	0.6
5879	Sharp cutoff pentode used as an audio amplifier in which reduced hum, microphonics, leakage and noise are desirable.	9AD	9-pin Min.	2³⁄₁₆	⅞	Htr.	6.3	0.15
6072	Low noise, low microphonic duotriode used primarily in the low-level stages of high gain AF amplifiers	9A	9-pin Min.	2³⁄₁₆	⅞	Htr.	6.3 12.6	0.35 0.175

*Each unit.
†Grids 2 and 3 tied to plate.
‡Values are for two units.

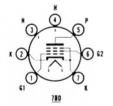

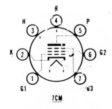

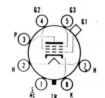

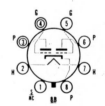

Appendix 3

SELECTED SPECIAL RECEIVING TUBES

APPLICATION	Plate Supply Volts	Grid 1 Volts	Grid 2 Supply Volts	Plate Ma	Grid 2 Ma	A-C Plate Resistance, Ohms	Transconductance	Amplification	Load Resistance, Ohms	Output Watts	TYPE
RF Amp.	28	−1.0	28	2.7	1.0	100,000	2500	---	---	---	6AJ5
Class A Amp.	120	−2.0	120	5.2	3.5	110,000	3200	---	---	---	6AS6
D-C Amp.	Maximum Ratings — Plate Volts = 250, Plate Diss. = 13, Plate Ma = 125, Peak Heater — Cathode Volts = + or − 300, Grid Circuit Resistance for Cathode Bias Op. = 1 meg.										6AS7G
Class A Amp.	250	−4.0	---	3.0	---	22,800	1750	40	---	---	12AY7
Class A Amp.*	26.5	−4.5	26.5	20	1.9	---	5700	---	1500	0.18	26A7GT
AB₁ Audio	26.5	−7.0	26.5	19	2.0	---	---	---	2500	0.5	
Class A Amp. (Pentode)	100	−3.0	100	---	0.5	1 meg	1185	---	---	---	1620
	250	−3.0	100	5.3	0.5	>1 meg	1225	---	---	---	
	180	−5.3	---	5.3	---	11,000	1800	20	---	---	
	250	−8.0	---	6.5	---	10,500	1900	20	---	---	
Class B Amp.‡	300	0	---	6.6	---	1,000 ohms impedance	---	---	12,000	10.4	1635
Class A Amp. (Pentode)	250	−3.0	100	1.8	0.4	2 meg	---	---	---	---	5879
Class A Amp. (Triode)†	100	−3.0	---	2.2	---	17,000	1240	21	---	---	
Class A Amp.*	250	−4.0	---	3.0	---	25,000	1750	44	---	---	6072
Low Level Amp.*	150	Plate Load Resistor = 20,000 ohms Grid Resistor = 0.1 meg.				Cathode Resistor = 2700 ohms Cathode Capacitor = 40 µf			Voltage Gain = 12.5		

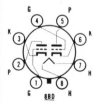

G P
K 3 / 5 K
P 2 / 6
G 1 / 7 H
8BD

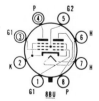

P G2
G1 3 / 4 / 5
K 2 / 6 H
1 / 7 H
G1 8BU P

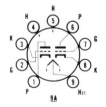

H H
K 4 / 5 / 6
G 3 / 7 G
2 / 8 K
P 9 Hct
9A

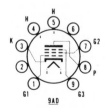

H H
K 4 / 5 / 6
K 3 / 7 G2
2 / 8 P
G1 9 G3
9AD

267

Appendix 4

SELECTED GAS DIODES

TYPE	DESCRIPTION FEATURES AND NOTES	CONSTR. Basing	Base†	MAXIMUM RATINGS Starting Current Ma	Operating Ma Min.	Max.*	Ambient Temp.**
OA2	Glow Tube — 150 Volts	5BO	7-pin Min.	75	5	30	−55 to +90°C
OA2WA JANOA2WA USNOA2WA	Glow Tube — 150 Volts	5BO	7-pin Min.	Same as 6626 below.			
OA3(VR75)	Glow Tube — 75 Volts	4AJ	6-pin O.	100	5	40	−55 to +90°C
OB2	Glow Tube — 105 Volts	5BO	7-pin Min.	75	5	30	−55 to +90°C
OB2WA JANOB2WA USNOB2WA	Glow Tube — 105 Volts	5BO	7-pin Min.	Same as 6627 below			
OB3(VR90)	Glow Tube — 90 Volts	4AJ	6-pin O.	—	5	30	—
OC3(VR105)	Glow Tube — 105 Volts	4AJ	6-pin O.	100	5	40	−55 to +90°C
OD3(VR150)	Glow Tube — 150 Volts	4AJ	6-pin O.	100	5	40	−55 to +90°C
5651	Glow Tube — 87 Volts	5BO	7-pin O.	—	1.5	3.5	−55 to +90°C
6626 6626/OA2WA USN6626/ OA2WA	Glow Tube — 150 Volts Reliable operation under adverse conditions.	5BO	7-pin Min.	{ 75 —	5 6	30 10	−55 to +150°C −55 to +150°C
6627 6627/OB2WA USN6627/ OB2WA	Glow Tube — 105 Volts Reliable operation under adverse conditions.	5BO	7-pin Min.	{ 75 —	5 6	30 10	−55 to +110°C −55 to +150°C
6830	Glow Tube — 150 Volts	2AV	7-pin Min. with flying leads	75	5	30	−55 to +90°C
6831	Glow Tube — 105 Volts	2AV	7-pin Min. with flying leads	75	5	30	−55 to +90°C

*Use sufficient series resistance to limit current at all times to not more than the rated values.

**Ambient temperature for tubes operated at maximum ratings; if ratings are decreased, the ambient temperature may be increased.

†All miniature tubes listed except types 6830 and 6831 are 2⅝ in. high and ¾ in. in diameter. Types 6830 and 6831 have the same diameter but their over-all length is greater because flying leads have been substituted for the base pins. The octal types are 4¼ in. high and 1⁹⁄₁₆ in. in diameter.

RED

BLACK

2AV

268

Appendix 4
SELECTED GAS DIODES

APPLICATION	SERVICE		TYPICAL OPERATION			TYPE
	Min. Supply Volts, D-C	Operating Volts, D-C	Max. Shunt Capacitor, μf	Regulation Average Volts		
Voltage Regulator	185	150	0.1	2		OA2
Voltage Reg. & Ref.	Same as 6626. Tested for military applications.					OA2WA JANOA2WA USNOA2WA
Voltage Regulator	105	75	—	5		OA3(VR75)
Voltage Regulator	133	108	0.1	1		OB2
Voltage Reg. & Ref.	Same as 6627. Tested for military applications.					OB2WA JANOB2WA USNOB2WA
Voltage Regulator	125	90	—	5		OB3(VR90)
Voltage Regulator	133	108	—	2		OC3(VR105)
Voltage Regulator	185	150	—	3.5		OD3(VR150)
Voltage Reference	115	87	0.02 Stability = 0.1 V	3.0 max.		5651
Voltage Regulator	165	148	0.1	2		6626
Voltage Reference	165	148	Stability = 0.2 V	0.5		6626/OA2WA USN6626/ OA2WA
Voltage Regulator	130	108	0.1	1.5		6627
Voltage Reference	130	107	Stability = 0.2 V	0.2		6627/OB2WA USN6627/ OB2WA
Voltage Regulator	185	150	0.1	2.0		6830
Voltage Regulator	133	108	0.1	1.0		6831

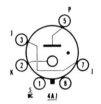

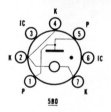

Appendix 5

SELECTED GAS TRIODES AND TETRODES

TYPE	DESCRIPTION — FEATURES AND NOTES	Basing	Base	Length, inches	Diameter, inches	Heater–Filament	Volts	Amperes	APPLICATION	Approx. Tube Drop Volts	Temperature Range Ambient °C	Peak Forward Anode Volts	Peak Inverse Anode Volts	Peak Cathode Current, Amps	Average Cathode Current, Amps	Surge Current, Amps	TYPE
OA4G	Cold cathode gas triode for application in calculating machines and carrier current relay systems.	4V	6-pin O.	4 1/8	1 9/16	Cold Cathode			Relay Service	70	Peak Starter Electrode Voltage = 75 to 90 V	225	0.10	.025	—	—	OA4G
1C21	Similar to OA4G but for d-c operation only.	4V	6-pin O.	2 5/8	1 9/16	Cold Cathode			Relay Service	73	Peak Starter Electrode Voltage = 66 to 80 V	180	0.10	.025	—	—	1C21
2A4G	Control grid type gaseous triode.	5S	7-pin O.	4 1/8	1 9/16	Fil.	2.5	2.5	Control Tube	15	−55 to +70	200	1.25	.10	—	—	2A4G
2D21	Gas tetrode with negative control operable in a high sensitivity circuit directly from a high-vacuum phototube.	7BN	7-pin Min.	2 5/8	3/4	Htr.	6.3	0.6	Grid-Controlled Rectifier Relay Tube	8	−75 to +90	1300	0.5	.10	Grid 1 Resistance = 1 meg	10	2D21
3C23	Mercury-vapor triode thyratron with negative control.	3G	4-pin	6 1/8	2 1/16	Fil.	2.5	7.0	Relay Control	15	−40 to +80*	1250	6.0	1.5	120	—	3C23
6D4	Gas triode for application as a relay tube or relaxation oscillator.	5AY	7-pin Min.	2 5/8	3/4	Htr.	6.3	0.25	Relay Service	16	−55 to +90	350	0.11	.025	—	—	6D4
FG27A	Mercury-vapor thyratron with negative control for use in relay circuits. Requires only a small amount of grid power.	4CF	4-pin	7 1/4	3	Fil.	5.0	4.5	Relay Service	16	−40 to +80	1000	10	2.5	200	—	FG27A
FG95	See data for 5560/FG95																FG95
FG97	Mercury-vapor, double grid thyratron for use where grid power is small and actuation of the grid from a high impedance source is desired.	FG97	4-pin	6 1/4	2 1/16	Fil.	2.5	5.0	Relay Service	16	+40 to +80*	1000	2.0	0.5	40	—	FG97
884	Gas type triode with negative control. Recommended for new equipment design.	6Q	6-pin O.	4 1/8	1 9/16	Htr.	6.3	0.6	Relaxation Oscillator	14	−75 to +90 — For Relaxation Oscillator (Sweep Circuit Service): Peak Anode Volts = 300. Peak Cathode Amps = 0.3.	1000	2.0	0.3	0.075	40	884
2050	Gas type tetrode with negative control which can be operated directly from a high-vacuum phototube.	6BS	8-pin O.	4 1/8	1 9/16	Htr.	6.3	0.6	High Sensitivity Relay Control	8	−55 to +70 — Grid 1 Circuit Resistance = 10 meg. max.	1500	1.0	0.1	10	—	2050
5545	Gas filled triode with negative control used for control applications.	4BZ	4-pin	9	2 5/8	Fil.	2.5	21	Control Tube	16	−55 to +70	1500	80	6.4	1120	—	5545

MAX. RATINGS (Absolute Values)

CONSTRUCTION — CATHODE — SERVICE — APPLICATION

Type	Basing	Socket	Length	Dia.	Cathode	Volts	Amps	Service		Temp. Range					
5560/FG95	4CD	4-pin	7 11/16	2 1/4	Htr.	5.0	4.5	Relay Control and Ignitor Firing	16	−40 to +80*	1000	1000	15	2.5	200
5696	7BN	7-pin Min.	1 3/4	3/4	Htr.	6.3	0.15	High Sensitivity Relay Control	10	−55 to +90	500	500	0.1	.025	2
5823	4CK	7-pin Min.	2 3/8	3/4	Cold Cathode			Relay Service							
6012	6CO	6-pin O.	4 1/4	1 21/32	Htr.	6.3	2.6	Relay Service	10	−75 to +90	650	1300	5.0	0.5	20
6807	6807	4-pin	9	2 5/8	Fil.	2.5	21	Control Tube	16	−55 to +70	1500	1500	80	6.4	1120

Notes within table:

- **5560/FG95** — Mercury-vapor triode thyratron with negative control characteristics. Low grid power requirement.
- **5696** — Gas type tetrode thyratron for relay applications such as counter circuits where low heater current gain and short deionization time are important.
- **5823** — Glow discharge, cold cathode type for "on-off" control of low current electrical circuits.
- **6012** — Negative control thyratron for relay and grid controlled rectifier service, especially motor control and low-power inverter service.
- **6807** — Negative control gas triode for control applications.

For 5696 — Typical Operating Conditions for Relay Service:
A-C Anode Volts (RMS) = 117 V Peak Grid Signal Volts = 5 V
Grid 1 Bias Volts (RMS) = 5 V Grid 1 Circuit Resistance = 0.1 meg.

For 5823 — Peak Anode and Starter Electrode Volts (Inverse and Forward) = 200 V
Peak Starter Electrode Breakdown Volts = +73 to +105V

*Condensed Mercury °C

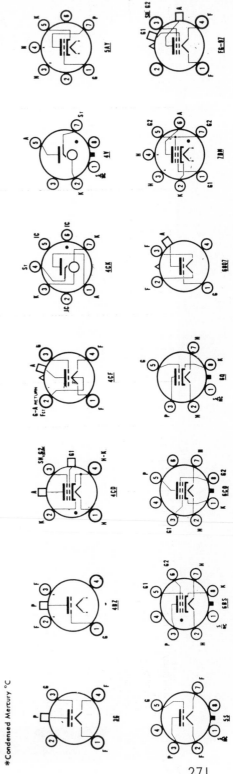

Appendix 6. CRYSTAL DIODES

Type	Application or Description	Mechanical Specifications (See Page 11)	Temperature Range, °C	Continuous Reverse Working Voltage (Volts)	Recurrent Peak Anode Current (ma)	Average Anode Current (ma)	Surge Current (ma 1/sec. max.)	Peak Reverse Voltage (volts min.)	Forward Current at -1 volt (ma min.)	Reverse Current (ua max.)	Forward Resistance at -1 volt (ohms max.)	Reverse Resistance (ohms min.)
1N34A	60 volt	Fig. A	-50 to +75	60	150	50	500	70	5	30 at -10v, 500 at -50	200	333K at -10v, 100K at -50v
1N35	Matched Pair (Note 1)	Fig. C	-50 to +75	50	60	22.5	100	70	7	10 at -10v	143	1 meg. at -10v
1N38A	100 volt	Fig. A	-50 to +90	100	150	50	500	120	4	6 at -3v, 500 at -100v	250	500K at 3v, 200K at -100v
1N38B	100 volt (Note 2)	Fig. A	-50 to +90	100	150	50	500	120	4	6 at -3v, 500 at -100v	250	500K at -3v, 200K at -100v
1N39A	200 volt	Fig. A	-50 to +90	200	150	50	500	225	4 (25 max.)	100 at -100v, 600 at -200v	250	1 meg. at -100, 333K at -200v
1N40	Plug-in Varistor (Note 3)	Fig. E	-50 to +75	25	60	22.5	100	70	12.7 at 1.5v	40 at -10v	120	250K at -10v
1N41	Packaged Varistor (Note 3)	Fig. D	-50 to +75	25	60	22.5	100	70	12.7 at 1.5v	40 at -10v	120	250K at -10v
1N42	100 volt Varistor (Note 3)	Fig. E	-50 to +75	100	60	22.5	100	120	12.7 at 1.5v	750 at -100v	120	133K at -100v
1N54A	High Back Resistance	Fig. A	-50 to +90	50	150	50	500	70	5	7 at -10v, 100 at -50v	208	1.4 meg. at -10v, 500K at -100v
1N55A	150 volt (Note 2)	Fig. A	-50 to +90	150	150	50	500	165	4	500 at -150v	250	300K at -150v
1N56A	High Conduction (Note 2)	Fig. A	-50 to +90	50	200	60	1000	50	15	300 at -30v	67	100K at -30v
1N58A	100 volt	Fig. A	-50 to +90	100	150	50	500	50	4	600 at -100v	250	167K at -100v
1N59A	250 volt	Fig. A	-50 to +90	250	150	50	500	115	4	600 at -250v	333	200K at -150v
1N60	Video Detector	Fig. A	-50 to +90	25	150 (Note 4)	50 (Note 4)	500	270	Note 5	Note 6	-	150K (Note 6)
1N63	High Back Resistance	Fig. A	-55 to +90	100	150	50	500	120	4	50 at -50v	250	1 meg. at -50v
1N65	70 volt	Fig. B	-55 to +90	70	150	50	500	80	2.5	200 at -50v	400	250K at -50v
1N67A	Miniature—High Back (Note 2)	Fig. A	-55 to +90	80	90	30	300	100	4	5 at -5v, 50 at -50v	250	1 meg. at -5v and -50v
1N69	60 volt	Fig. A	-55 to +90	60	125	40	400	75	5	5 at -10v, 850 at -50v	200	333K at -10v, 100K at -50v
1N69A	60 volt (Note 2)	Fig. A	-55 to +90	60	125	40	400	75	5 (25 max.)	30 at -10v, 500 at -50v	200	333K at -10v, 100K at -50v
1N70	100 volt	Fig. A	-55 to +90	100	90	30	350	125	3	25 at -10v, 300 at -50v	333	400K at -10v, 167K at -50v
1N70A	100 volt (Note 2)	Fig. E	-50 to +90	100	90	30	350	125	3 (25 max.)	25 at -10v, 300 at -50v	333	400K at -10v, 167K at -50v
1N71	Low Impedance Varistor (Note 2)	Fig. E	-50 to +75	40	200	60	1000	50	15	300 at -30v	67	100K at -30v
1N77A	Photodiode	Fig. F	0 to +90	Note 8	-	-	-	Note 9	15	15 at -10v, 100 at -50v (Dark)	333	670K at -10v, 500K at -50v
1N81	Low Voltage	Fig. A	-55 to +90	40	90	30	350	50	3	10 at -10v	333	1 meg. at -10v
1N81A	Low Voltage (Note 2)	Fig. A	-55 to +90	40	90	30	350	50	3 (25 max.)	10 at -10v	333	1 meg. at -10v
1N82	UHF Mixer	Fig. A	-50 to +90	Note 10	-	-	-	-	Note 10	-	-	-
1N82A	UHF Mixer	Fig. A	-50 to +90	Note 10	-	-	-	-	Note 10	-	-	-
1N90	Miniature—General Purpose	Fig. B	-55 to +90	60	90	30	300	75	5	750 at -50v	200	67K at -50v
1N98	Miniature—High Back	Fig. B	-55 to +90	80	90	30	300	100	20	8 at -5v, 100 at -50v	500	62.5K at -5v, 500K at -50v
1N100	Miniature—High Back	Fig. B	-55 to +90	80	90	30	300	100	20	5 at -5v, 50 at -50v	500	1 meg. at -5v and -50v
1N111	60 volt Computer	Fig. A	-50 to +90	60	150	25	500	70	5	Note 11	200	400K (Note 11)
1N112	60 volt Computer	Fig. A	-50 to +90	60	150	25	500	70	5	Note 11	200	200K (Note 11)
1N113	60 volt Computer	Fig. A	-50 to +90	60	150	25	500	70	2.5	Note 11	400	400K (Note 11)
1N114	60 volt Computer	Fig. A	-50 to +90	60	150	25	500	70	2.5	Note 11	400	200K (Note 11)
1N115	60 volt Computer	Fig. A	-50 to +90	60	150	25	500	70	2.5	Note 11	400	100K (Note 11)
1N118	Miniature—High Conduction	Fig. A	-50 to +90	60	150	90	250	75	20	100 at -50v	50	500K at -50v
1N119	60 volt—Computer	Fig. A	-50 to +90	60	150	25	500	70	5	Note 11 and Note 12	200	400K (Note 11)
1N120	60 volt—Computer	Fig. A	-50 to +90	60	150	25	500	70	5	Note 11 and Note 12	200	200K (Note 11)
1N126	Miniature—60 volt	Fig. B	-55 to +90	60	150	30	350	75	5	50 at 10v, 850 at 50v	200	200K at -10v, 58K at -50v

*Ratings are limiting values assigned by the manufacturer to operating or storage conditions (electrical, mechanical, or environmental) under the control of the user. If values are exceeded, permanent impairment of the device and/or performance may result.

Type	Application or Description	Mechanical Specifications (See Page 11)	Temperature Range °C	Continuous Reverse Working Voltage (Volts)	Recurrent Peak Anode Current (ma)	Average Anode Current (ma)	Surge Current (ma 1 sec. max.)	Peak Reverse Voltage	Forward Current at -1 Volt (ma min.) for Zero Dynamic Resistance (Volts min.)	Reverse Current (ua max.)	Forward Resistance at -1 volt (ohms max.)	Reverse Resistance (ohms min.) (Note 11)
1N126A	Miniature—60 volt (Note 2)	Fig. B	-55 to +90	60	90	30	350	75	5 (25 max.)	50 at -10v, 850 at -50v	200	200K at -10v, 58K at -50v
1N127	Miniature—100 volt	Fig. B	-55 to +90	100	90	30	300	125	3	25 at -10v, 300 at -50v	333	400K at -10v, 167K at -50v
1N127A	Miniature—100 volt (Note 2)	Fig. B	-55 to +90	100	90	30	300	125	3 (25 max.)	25 at -10v, 300 at -50v	333	400K at -10v, 167K at -50v
1N128	Miniature—High Back (Note 2)	Fig. B	-55 to +90	40	90	30	300	50	3	10 at -10v	333	1 meg. at -10v
1N191	Miniature—Computer	Fig. B	-55 to +90	90	90	30	300	—	5	Note 11 and Note 12	200	400 ohms (Note 11)
1N193	High Temperature	Fig. A	-50 to +150	50	50	30	100	Note 13	1.0 at +2v (Note 14)	20 at -10v, 40 at -40v (Note 14)	2000	500K at -10v, 125K at -50v (Note 11)
1N194	High Temperature	Fig. A	-50 to +150	40	50	30	100	Note 13	1.5 at +2v	10 at -40v (Note 12 and Note 14)	1333	400K at -10v
1N194A	High Temperature	Fig. A	-50 to +150	40	50	30	100	Note 13	1.5	10 at -40v (Note 12 and Note 14)	667	400K at -10v
1N195	High Temperature	Fig. A	-50 to +150	40	50	30	100	Note 13	2.0 at +2v	10 at -40v (Note 12 and Note 14)	1000	400K at -10v
1N196	High Temperature	Fig. A	-50 to +150	50	50	30	100	Note 13	1.0 at +2v	10 at -40v (Note 12 and Note 14)	2000	400K at -10v
1N198	Miniature—75°C	Fig. B	-55 to +90	80	90	30	300	100	4	10 at -10v, 50 at -50v (Note 15)	250	1 meg. at -10v and -50v
1N198A	Miniature—75°C (Note 2)	Fig. A	-55 to +90	80	90	30	300	100	4 (25 max.)	10 at -10v, 50 at -50v (Note 15)	250	1 meg. at -10v and -50v
1N355	High Back (Note 16)	Fig. C	-55 to +90	80	150	500	500	100	4	5 at -5v, 50 at -50v	250	1 meg. at -10v and -50v
1N417	Computer	Fig. A	-55 to +75 / Note 17	60 / Note 18	150 / Note 19	60	100	—	Note 20	Note 11 and Note 12	—	500K (Note 11)
1N418	Computer	Fig. A	-55 to +75 / Note 17	60 / Note 18	45	16	100	—	7	Note 11 and Note 12	143	500K (Note 11)
1N419	Computer	Fig. A	-50 to +75 / Note 17	80 / Note 18	150 / Note 21	60	Note 21	—	125	Note 11 and Note 12	8	500K (Note 11)
1N447	VLI (Very Low Impedance)	Fig. A	-55 to +75	30	200	60	500	75	25	20 at -10v, 60 at -30v	40	500K at -10v and -30v
1N448	VLI	Fig. A	-55 to +75	100	200	60	500	120	25	30 at -30v, 100 at -100v	40	1 meg. at -30v and -100v
1N449	VLI	Fig. A	-55 to +75	30	200	60	500	50	50	10 at -10v, 30 at -30v	20	1 meg. at -10v and -30v
1N450	VLI	Fig. A	-55 to +75	100	200	60	200	120	50	30 at -30v, 100 at -100v	20	1 meg. at -30v and -100v
1N451	VLI	Fig. A	-55 to +75	150	200	60	200	170	50	150 at -150v	20	1 meg. at -150v
1N452	VLI	Fig. A	-55 to +75	30	250	80	500	50	100	30 at -30v	10	1 meg. at -30v
1N453	VLI	Fig. A	-55 to +75	100	250	80	300	120	100	30 at -30v, 100 at -100v	10	1 meg. at -30v and -100v
1N454	VLI	Fig. A	-55 to +75	50	300	100	500	75	200	50 at -50v	5	1 meg. at -50v
1N455	VLI	Fig. A	-55 to +75	30	300	100	500	50	300	30 at -30v	5	1 meg. at -10v and -30v
1N631	Miniature—Computer	Fig. B	-50 to +75	60	150 / Note 19	60	—	—	Note 20	Note 11 and Note 12	—	500K (Note 11)
1N632	Miniature—Computer	Fig. B	-50 to +75 / Note 17	60	45	16	100	—	7	Note 11 and Note 12	143	500K (Note 11)
1N633	Miniature—Computer	Fig. B	-50 to +75 / Note 17	80	150 / Note 21	60	Note 21	—	125	Note 11 and Note 12	8	500K (Note 11)
1N634	Miniature—VLI	Fig. B	-50 to +75 / Note 17	60	200	60	300	120	50	35 at -30v, 115 at -100v	20	850K at -30v and -100v
1N635	Miniature—VLI	Fig. B	-50 to +75 / Note 17	60	200	60	200	170	50	175 at -150v	20	850K at -150v
1N1093	Computer	Fig. A	-50 to +75 / Note 17	15	—	50	400	25	Note 22	25 at -5v and 75 at -15v at 55°C	8	200K at -5v and -15v at 55°C

*Ratings are limiting values assigned by the manufacturer to operating or storage conditions (electrical, mechanical, or environmental) under the control of the user. If values are exceeded, permanent impairment of the device and/or performance may result.

Appendix 6 (cont.) CRYSTAL DIODES

Note 1: Units are matched in the forward direction at 1 volt so that the current flowing through the lower resistance unit is within 10% of that through the higher resistance unit. Ratings are shown for each diode.

Note 2: Available to military performance specifications.

Note 3: Consists of four specially selected and matched diodes whose resistances are balanced within ±2.5% in the forward direction at 1.5 volts. For additional balance, the forward resistance of each varistor pair is matched to within three ohms. Ratings shown are for each diode.

Note 4: Sixty cycle, resistance loaded half-wave rectifier service.

Note 5: Units are tested in a circuit employing an input of 1.6 volts rms at 40 MC, 75% modulated at 400 cycles. Demodulated output across a 4700 ohm resistor shunted by a 5 uuf capacitor is a minimum of 1.50 volts peak to peak.

Note 6: Minimum specified reverse resistance applies to all points between 0 and —10 volts with 60 cps sweep.

Note 7: Consists of four specially selected diodes whose forward currents are matched within a range of 1 ma. with 1 volt applied. Ratings shown are for each diode.

Note 8: For type 1N77A continuous operating voltage maximum is —50 volts and maximum power dissipation is 20 milliwatts.

Note 9: Light sensitivity = 16 to 40 volts peak to peak across 100K ohms in series with the photodiode and a reverse supply voltage of 45 volts; light supplied at 2 lumens per sq. ft. having a color temperature of 2750 ± 100°K and interrupted at 200 to 400 cycles per second.

Note 10: Types 1N82 and 1N82A peak reverse voltage maximum rating is 5 volts and absolute maximum oscillator voltage is 25 ma. These types are designed for operation as mixers up to 1000 megacycles and are capable of low noise operation as a mixer for UHF television in the 470-890 mc band. Overall noise selection limit for 1N82 is 16 db maximum and for 1N82A is 14 db maximum.

Note 11: Minimum specified resistance limit applies for all points as indicated below when the reverse characteristic is swept between 0 and —70 volts at 60 cycle rate,

Type 1N111	—20v to —50v	At 55°C
1N112	—10v to —50v	At 55°C
1N113	—10v to —50v	At 55°C
1N114	—10v to —50v	At 55°C
1N115	—10v to —50v	At 55°C
1N119	—20v to —50v	At 55°C
1N120	—20v to —50v	At 55°C
1N191	—10v to —50v	At 55°C
1N417	—10v to —60v	At 25°C
1N418	—10v to —60v	At 25°C
1N419	—20v to —90v*	At 25°C
1N631	—20v to —60v	At 25°C
1N632	—20v to —60v	At 25°C
1N633	—20v to —90v*	At 25°C

*For 0 to —100v sweep

Note 12: Reverse recovery time is specified and defined as the time required for the diode to recover to a specified reverse current when the operating coltage necessary to give 30 ma forward conduction is rapidly switched to —35 volts.

Type	Recovery Current	Recovery Time
1N119	700 ua	0.5 usec
	87.5	3.5
1N120	700	0.5
	175	3.5
1N191	700	0.5
	87.5	3.5
1N193	400	0.5
1N194	300	0.2
1N194A	300	0.2
1N195	300	0.3
1N196	100	0.1
1N417*	500	0.3
1N418*	500	0.3
1N419*	500	0.3
1N631*	500	0.3
1N632*	800	0.3
1N633*	1650	0.3

*Forward current = 5 ma, Reverse voltage = 40 ± 2v, Circuit resistance = 2000 ohms.

Note 13: If continuous reverse working voltage is exceeded, breakdown will occur at some higher value of the inverse voltage and suitable means must be provided to limit the current flow to less than 1 ma.

Note 14: At 150°C, maximum reverse currents are as follows:
1N193 = 200 ua at —10v, 500 ua at —50v
1N194 = 300 ua at —40v
1N194A = 300 ua at —40v
1N195 = 300 ua at —40v
1N196 = 300 ua at —40v

Note 15: For type 1N198A at 75°C, the maximum reverse current at —10 volts is 75 ua and at —50 volts is 250 ua. Also at 75°C, the forward current at 1 volt is 5 to 35 ma.

Note 16: Available as pairs, matched for forward conduction at +1.5 volts and dynamic impedance.

Note 17: Storage temperature as indicated, operating temperature range is +10 to +55°C.

Note 18: For 1N417 maximum reverse voltage pulse = 90 volts (1 sec. max.)
For 1N418 maximum reverse voltage pulse = 90 volts (1 sec. max.)
For 1N419 maximum reverse voltage pulse = 120 volts (1 sec. max.)

Note 19: For types 1N417 and 1N631, peak forward current = 150 ma at 20% duty cycle.

Note 20: For types 1N417 and 1N631, the forward voltage peak for a 50 ma current peak from a half sine wave of 0.1 usec pulse width and 100 kc pulse repetition frequency is 3.5 volts.

Note 21: For types 1N419 and 1N633, peak forward pulse = 150 ma for 2.0 usec pulse.

Note 22: For type 1N1093, the maximum forward voltage is 0.4 volts for a current of 5.0 ma at 25°C. At both 10°C and 50°C the forward characteristics are controlled at both 1.0 ma and 10.0 ma forward currents.

Appendix 7. REGISTERED RETMA TRANSISTOR TYPES

For explanation of symbols, ratings, and manufacturing symbols see page 279.

RETMA No.	Type	Mfr.	Use	Dwg. No.	MAX. RATINGS				TYPICAL VALUES					Closest GE
					P_C mw @ 25°C	BV_{CE}	I_C ma	T_J °C	h_{fe}	f_{ab} mc	G_e db	P_o mw Class A	P_o mw Class B	
2N22	Pt	WE	SW	1	120	-100	-20	55	1.9α					
2N23	Pt	WE	SW	2	80	-50	-40	55	1.9α					
2N24	Pt	WE	AF	1	120	-30	-25	50	2.2α					
2N25	Pt	WE	AF	1	200	-50	-30	60	2.5α					
2N26	Pt	WE	SW	2	90	-30	-40	55						
2N27	NPN	WE	AF	1	50	35	100	85	100	1				
2N28	NPN	WE	AF	1	50	30	100	85	100	.5				
2N29	NPN	WE	AF	1	50	35	30	85	100	1	17			
2N30	Pt	GE	Obsolete	3	100	30	7	40	2.2α	2				old G11
2N31	Pt	GE	Obsolete	3	100	-30	-7	40	2.2α	2	21			old G11A
2N32	Pt	RCA		5	50	-40	-8	40	2.2α	2.7				
2N33	Pt	RCA	RF	5	30	-8.5	-7	40		50Mc	Osc.			
2N34	PNP	RCA	AF	6	50	-25	-8	50	40	.6	40			2N190
2N35	NPN	RCA	IF	6	50	-25	-8	50	40	.8	40		125	2N169A
2N36	PNP	CBS	AF	4	50	-20	-8	50	45		45			2N191
2N37	PNP	CBS	AF	4	50	-20	-8	50	30		36			2N190
2N38	PNP	CBS	AF	4	50	-20	-8	50	15		32			2N189
2N38A	PNP	CBS	AF	4	50	-20	-8	50	18		32			2N189
2N41	PNP	RCA	AF	7	50	-25	-15	50	40	1	40			2N190
2N43	PNP	GE	AF	8	150	-20*	-50	100	50	1	40	40		2N43
2N43A	PNP	GE	AF	8	150	-20*	-50	100	40		40	40		2N43A
2N44	PNP	GE	AF	8	150	-20*	-50	100	20	1	39	40		2N44
2N45	PNP	GE	AF	8	150		-50	100	12	1	38	40		2N45
2N46	PNP	RCA		7		see 2N41								2N196
2N47	PNP	Phil	AF	13	50	-35	-20	65	38	8	40			2N190 25V
2N48	PNP	Phil	AF	13	50	-35	-20	65	32	8	40			2N189 25V
2N49	PNP	Phil	AF	13	50	-35	-20	65	38	8	40			2N190 25V
2N50	Pt	Cle	SW	1	50	-15	-1	50	2α	3	20			
2N51	Pt	Cle	SW	1	100	-50	-8	50			20			
2N52	Pt	Cle	RF	1	120	-50	-8	50			20			
2N53	Pt	Cle	RF	1	100	-50	-8	50	2α	.5	20			
2N54	PNP	W	AF	9	200	-45	-10	60	32	.5	40			2N190 25V
2N55	PNP	W	AF	9	200	-45	-10	60	20	.5	39			2N190 25V
2N56	PNP	W	AF	9	200	-45	-10	60	12	.5	38			2N189 25V
2N57	PNP	W	PWR	12	20W	-60	-8A		60		14		5W	
2N62	PNP	Phil	Obsolete		50	-35	-20		40					
2N63	PNP	Ray	AF	10	100	-22	-10	85	22	6	39	40		2N107
2N64	PNP	Ray	AF	10	100	-15	-10	85	45	8	41	40		2N191
2N65	PNP	Ray	AF	10	100	-12	-10	85	90	1.2	42	40		2N192

[*Note:* Appendix 7 reproduced through courtesy of General Electric Company.]

Appendix 7 (cont.) REGISTERED RETMA TRANSISTOR TYPES

For explanation of symbols, ratings, and manufacturing symbols see page 279.

RETMA No.	Type	Mfr.	Use	Dwg. No.	Pc mw @25°C	BV_CE	Ic ma	Tj °C	hfe	fab mc	Ge db	Po mw A	Po mw B / Class	Closest GE
2N68	PNP	Syl	PWR	11	2W/4W	-25	-1.5A	70	40	.4	23	600	5W	
2N71	PNP	W	PWR	21	1W	-50	-250	60		.25	25	400		
2N72	Pt	RCA	Obsolete		50	-40	-20	55		2.5				
2N73	PNP	W	AF SW	9	200	-50					low level			
2N74	PNP	W	AF SW	9	200	-50					high level			
2N75	PNP	W	AF SW	9	200	-50					very low level			
2N76	PNP	GE	AF	8	50	-20	-10	60	20	1	38	50		2N190
2N77	PNP	RCA	AF	19	35	-25	-15	50	55	7	44			2N191
2N78	NPN	GE	RF	14	75	-15	-20	85	50	4	22			2N169 or 2N168A
2N79	PNP	RCA	AF	20	35	-30	-50		46	.7	44	50		2N191
2N80	PNP	CBS	AF	4	50	-25	-8	Hi	80					2N192
2N81	PNP	GE	AF	8	50	-20	-15	100	30					use 2N189
2N82	PNP	CBS	AF	15	35	-20	-15	Hi	30	3	38	600		{ 2N169A (and 2N123 PNP) }
2N94	NPN	Syl	RF Sw	10	30	-20	-50	75	30		38			
2N94A	NPN	Syl	RF Sw	10	30	-20	-50	75	40	6				
2N95	NPN	Syl	Pwr	11	2.5W/4W	25	1.5A	70	40	.4	23	600	5W	2N169 15V
2N97	NPN	GP	IF	10	50	30	10	75	13	1	20			2N169A 25V
2N97A	NPN	GP	IF	10	50	40	10	85	13	1	20			
2N98	NPN	GP	IF	10	50	40	10	75	38	2.5	22			2N169A 25V
2N98A	NPN	GP	IF	10	50	40	10	85	38	2.5	22			2N169A 25V
2N99	NPN	GP	IF	10	50	40	10	75	38	3.5	22			2N169A 25V
2N100	NPN	GP	IF	10	25	-25	-5	50	100	5	23	600		2N170 6V
2N101	PNP	Syl	Pwr	28	1W	-25	-1.5A	70			23	600	5W	
2N102	NPN	Syl	Pwr	28	1W	-25	1.5A	70			23			
2N103	NPN	GP	Genl IF	10	50	35	10	75	5	.75	15			2N170 6V
2N104	PNP	RCA	AF	20	70	-30	-50	70	44	.7	41			2N190 25V
2N105	PNP	RCA	AF	23	35	-25	-15	50	55	.75	42			2N191
2N106	PNP	Ray	AF	10	100	-6	-10	85	45	.8	36	40		2N189
2N107	PNP	GE	AF	8	50	-6	-10	60	20	1	38			2N107
2N108	PNP	CBS	AF Out	16	50	-20	-15						35	
2N109	PNP	RCA	AF Out	20	50	-12	-35	50	70	3	33	75	150	2N188-2N192
2N111	PNP	Ray	IF	10	100	-6	-5	85	40	5	30			2N135-2N135
2N112	PNP	Ray	RF	10	100	-6	-5	85	40		32			2N136-2N135
2N113	PNP	Ray	RF	10	100	-6	-5	85	45	10	33			2N137
2N114	PNP	Ray	RF Sw	10	100	-6	-5	85	65	20				2N137 or 2N123
2N117	NPN	TI	Si	10	150	30	25	150	12	4				
2N118	NPN	TI	Si	10	150	30	25	150	24	5				2N123
2N123	PNP	GE	RF Sw	8	100	-20	-125	85	50	8				2N168
2N124	NPN	TI	RF Sw	10	50	10	8	75	18	3				
2N125	NPN	TI	RF Sw	10	50	10	8	75	32	5				2N167
2N126	NPN	TI	RF Sw	10	50	10	8	75	60	5				2N167
2N127	NPN	TI	RF Sw	10	50	10	8	75	130	5				2N167
2N128	PNP	Phil	SB Osc	13	30	-4.5	-5	85	35	60	29			
2N129	PNP	Phil	SB Osc	13	30	-4.5	-5	85	20	40				
2N135	PNP	GE	IF	8	100	-12	-50	85	20	4.5				2N135

276

Type	Material	Mfr.	Use											Substitute
2N136	PNP	GE	RF	8	100	-12	-50	85	40		31		50	2N136
2N137	PNP	GE	RF	8	100	-6	-50	85	60		33		100	2N137
2N138	PNP	Ray	AF Out		50	-12	-20	40	140		30			2N192
2N138A	PNP	Ray	AF Out	20	50	-45	-100	85	48	4.7	29			2N187 25V
2N139	PNP	RCA	IF	20	35	-16	-15	70	45	7	29			2N136-2N135
2N140	PNP	RCA	Osc		35	-16	-15	70		7	28			2N136
2N141	PNP	Syl	Pwr	26	1.5W/4W	-30	-.8A	65	40	.4	26	600	5W	
2N142	NPN	Syl	Pwr	26	1.5W/4W	-30	-.8A	65	40	.4	26	600	5W	
2N143	PNP	Syl	Pwr	26	1W/4W	-30	-.8A	65	40	.4	26	600	5W	
2N144	NPN	Syl	Pwr	26	1W/4W	30	.8	65	40	.4	26	600	5W	2N169 or 2N292
2N145	NPN	TI	IF	10	65	20	5	75			33 max			2N169 or 2N292
2N146	NPN	TI	IF	10	65	20	5	75			36 max			
2N147	NPN	TI	Osc	10	65	20	5	75			39 max			2N168A or 2N293
2N148	NPN	TI	lo IF	10	65	16	5	75			35 max			2N169 or 2N292
2N148A	NPN	TI	lo IF	10	65	32	5	75			35 max			2N169A
2N149	NPN	TI	lo IF	10	65	16	5	75			38 max			2N169 or 2N292
2N149A	NPN	TI	lo IF	10	65	32	5	75			38 max			2N169A
2N150	NPN	TI	lo IF	10	65	16	5	75			41 max			2N169 or 2N292
2N150A	NPN	TI	lo IF	10	65	32	5	75	48	.3	41 max	2W	9W	2N169A
2N155	PNP	CBS	Pwr	27	1.5W/5W	-30	-3A	85	40	.3	33	2W	9W	
2N156	PNP	CBS	Pwr	22	1.5W/5W	-30	-3A	85		.3	36	2W	17W	
2N158	PNP	CBS	Pwr Sw	22	1.5W/5W	-60	-3A	85	40	.3	40			
2N159	Pt	Sprague	Si IF		80	-50	-10	150	14	2				
2N160	NPN	GP	Si IF	10	150	40	25	150	14	4	34			
2N160A	NPN	GP	Si RF	10	150	40	25	150	28	4	34			
2N161	NPN	GP	Si RF	10	150	40	25	150	28	5	37			
2N161A	NPN	GP	Si RF	10	150	40	25	150		5	37			
2N162	NPN	GP	Si RF	10	150	40	25	150	38	8	38			
2N162A	NPN	GP	Si RF	10	150	40	25	150	38	8	38			
2N163	NPN	GP	Si RF	10	150	40	25	150	28	8	40			
2N163A	NPN	GP	Si RF	10	150	40	25	150	50	6	40			2N167
2N167	NPN	GE	Sw	14	65	30	75	85	36	8	39 max			use 2N293
2N168	NPN	GE	RF	14	55	15	20	75	20	6				
2N168A	NPN	GE	Osc	14	65	15	20	85	40	8	39 max			2N168A
2N169	NPN	GE	IF	14	55	15	20	75	40	4	35 max			2N169
2N169A	NPN	GE	IF	14	55	25	20	75	30	5	35 max			2N169A
2N170	NPN	GE	RF	14	55	.6	5	50	20	4	27			2N170
2N172	NPN	TI	IF	10	65	16	-7A	75		.6	28		20W	2N168A
2N173	PNP	Dlc	Pwr	18	40W	-60	-2	90	100	.2		8	80W	
2N174	PNP	Dlc	Pwr	18	40W	-80	-7A	90	45	.8	43	20		2N192
2N175	PNP	RCA	AF	20	20	-10	-2	50	65	.7	25	3W		
2N176	PNP	Motor	Pwr	27		-12	-600	80		.7		3W	110	
2N178	PNP	Motor	Pwr	27	10W	-12	-600	80	30	.7	29		300	2N188
2N180	PNP	CBS	AF Out		150	-30	-25	75	60	3.5	37		600	2N188A 25V
2N181	PNP	CBS	AF Out	25	250	-30	-38	75	60	7.5	34			
2N182	NPN	CBS	IF	4	100	25	10	75	25					2N167
2N183	NPN	CBS	Sw	4	100	25	10	75	40					2N167
2N184	NPN	CBS	Sw	4	100	25	10	75	60	12				2N167
2N185	PNP	TI	AF	10	150	-20	-150	50	55	.8	40.5	2	250	2N188A
2N186	PNP	GE	AF Out	8	75	-25	-200	60	24	.8	28		300	2N186A
2N186A	PNP	GE	AF Out	8	180	-25	-200	60	24		28		750	2N186A

277

For explanation of symbols, ratings, and manufacturing symbols see page 279.

RETMA No.	Type	Mfr.	Use	Dwg. No.	P_C mw @ 25°C	BV_{CE}	I_C ma	T_J °C	h_{fe}	f_{ab} mc	G db	P_o mw Class A	P_o mw Class B	Closest GE
2N187	PNP	GE	AF Out	8	75	−25	−200	60	36	1	30		300	2N187
2N187A	PNP	GE	AF Out	8	180	−25	−200	60	36	1	30		750	2N187A
2N188	PNP	GE	AF Out	8	75	−25	−200	60	54	1.2	32		300	2N188
2N188A	PNP	GE	AF Out	8	180	−25	−200	60	54	1	32	1		2N188A
2N189	PNP	GE	AF	8	75	−25	−50	60	24	.8	37	1		2N189
2N190	PNP	GE	AF	8	75	−25	−50	60	36	1	39		750	2N190
2N191	PNP	GE	AF	8	75	−30	−50	60	54	1.2	41	1		2N191
2N192	PNP	GE	AF	8	75	−10	−50	60	75	1.5	43	1		2N192
2N194	NPN	Syl	Osc	10	50	−10	50	75	7.5	3.5	15			2N169
2N206	PNP	RCA	AF	19	75	−30	−50	85	47	.8	46			2N191
2N211	NPN	Syl	Osc	10	50	−10	50	75	30	3.5				2N293
2N212	NPN	Syl	Osc	10	50	−10	50	75	15	.6	22			2N293
2N214	NPN	Syl	AF Out	10	125	−25	75	70	70	.8	29		200	2N188 (PNP)
2N215	PNP	RCA	AF	19	50	−30	−50	70	44	.7	41			2N191
2N216	NPN	Syl	IF	10	50	−15	50	75	15	.3	26			2N169
2N217	PNP	RCA	AF	19	50	−25	−70	50	70	4.7	33		160	2N192
2N218	PNP	RCA	IF	19	35	−16	−15	70	48		30			2N135
2N219	PNP	RCA	Osc	19	35	−16	−15	70	45	.7	27			2N136
2N220	PNP	RCA	AF Out	19	20	−10	−2	50	65	.8	43		100	2N192
2N228	NPN	Syl	AF Out	10	50	−25	40	75	70	.8	26			2N169
2N229	NPN	Syl	AF	10	50	−12		75	25	1.6				2N169
2N230	PNP	Mall	Pwr	27	15W	−30	−2A	85	83	.014 (β)	44			2N192 25V
2N237	PNP	NAC	AF		150	−45	−20	55	70	1	42m			2N191
2N238	PNP	TI	AF	10	50	−20		60						
2N240	PNP	Phil	SB Sw	8	10	−6	−15	60	16	1.2	34		300	2N241
2N241	PNP	GE	AF Out	8	100	−25	−200	60	60	1.2	34		750	2N241A
2N241A	PNP	GE	AF Out	8	180	−25	−200		60					
2N242	PNP	Syl	Pwr	27	35	−45	−2A	100	40	5Kc (β)	30	2.5W	500	2N188A
2N247	PNP	RCA	Drift RF	24		−35	−10	85	60	30 (37 @ 1.5Mc)	31	50		
2N249	PNP	TI	AF Out	17	350	−25	−200	60	45					
2N250	PNP	TI	Pwr	27	12W	−30	−2A	80	50	6 Kc	34	6W		
2N251	PNP	TI	Pwr	27	12W	−60	−2A	80	50	6 Kc	34	6W		2N293
2N253	NPN	TI	IF	10	65	−12	5	75			30			
2N254	NPN	TI	IF	10	65	−20	−5	75	40	.2	34			2N293
2N255	PNP	CBS	Pwr	27	1.5W/6.25W	−15	−3A	85	40	.2	23	1W	5W	
2N256	PNP	CBS	Pwr	27	1.5W/6.25W	−30	−3A	85			26	2W	10W	2N293
2N257	PNP	Cle	Pwr	27	2W/25W	−20		85	50	7 Kc (β)	30	1W		
2N260	PNP	Cle	Si	4	200	−10	−50	150	16	1.8	38			
2N260A	PNP	Cle	Si	4	200	−30	−50	150	16	1.8	38			
2N261	PNP	Cle	Si RF	4	200	−75	−50	150	10	1.8	36			
2N262	PNP	Cle	Si RF	4	200	−10	−50	150	20	6	40			
2N262A	PNP	Cle	Si RF	4	200	−30	−50	150	20	6	40			
2N265	PNP	GE	AF	8	75	−25	−50	60	110	1.5	45			2N265
2N268	PNP	Cle	Pwr		2W/25W	−30	−100	70	7	6 Kc (β)	28			2N123
2N269	PNP	RCA	Sw	8	35	−20			35	4				
2N292	NPN	GE	IF	14	55	15	20	75	80	6	35 max			2N292
2N293	NPN	GE	RF	14	55	15	20	75	35	4	39 max			2N293

EXPLANATION OF SYMBOLS

TYPES AND USES:

Si—Silicon High Temperature Transistors (all others germanium)

Pt—Point contact types

AF—Audio Frequency Amplifier–Driver

AF Out—High current AF Output

Pwr—Power output 1 watt or more

RF—Radio Frequency Amplifier

Osc—High gain High frequency RF oscillator

IF—Intermediate Frequency Amplifier

Io IF—Low IF (262 Kc) Amplifier

Sw—High current High frequency switch

AF Sw—Low frequency switch

RATINGS:

P_c=*Maximum collector dissipation* at 25°C (76°F) ambient room temperature. Secondary designations are ratings with connection to an appropriate heat sink.

BV_{CB}=*Minimum collector-to-emitter breakdown voltage.* GE transistors measured with Base-to-emitter resistance as follows:

    10K for AF and AF Out PNP

    1 Meg for RF, IF, and Osc PNP

    Open circuit for NPN

*BV_{CB}=45 Minimum collector-to-base breakdown voltage (for grounded base applications).

I_c=*Maximum collector current.* (Negative for PNP, Positive for NPN.)

T_J=Maximum centigrade *junction temperature.* P_C must be derated linearly to 0 mw dissipation at this temperature.

h_{fe}=Small signal base to collector *current-gain*, or Beta (except for Pt Contact types where emitter to collector gain, alpha α, is given).

f_{ab}=*Alpha cut-off-frequency.* Frequency at which the emitter to collector current gain, or alpha, is down to $\sqrt{2}$ or .707 of its low frequency audio value. For some power transistors, the Beta or base-to-collector current-gain cutoff–frequency is given as noted.

G_c=Grounded-emitter *Power Gain.*

    AF, AF Out, and Pwr Gain measured at 1 Kc.

    RF, IF, and Osc Gains at 455 Kc.

(Sw Gain is dependent on circuit and wave-shape.) (All measured at typical power output level for given transistor type.)

P_o=Maximum *Power Output* at 5% harmonic distortion, in mw except where noted as watts. Class A single-ended, Class B Push Pull.

MANUFACTURERS:

CBS—CBS–Hytron.

Cle—Clevite Transistor Products.

DLc–Delco Radio Div., General Motors Corp.

GE—General Electric Company.

GP–Germanium Products Corp.

Mall—P. R. Mallory and Company, Inc.

Mar–Marvelco, National Aircraft Corp.

Motor–Motorola, Inc.

Phil–Philco.

Ray–Raytheon Manufacturing Company.

RCA–RCA.

Sprague–Sprague Electronics Company.

Syl–Sylvania Electric Products Company.

TI–Texas Instruments, Inc.

W–Westinghouse Electric Corp.

WE–Western Electric Company.

NOTE:

Closest GE types are given only as a general guide and are based on available published electrical specifications. However, General Electric Company makes no representation as to the accuracy and completeness of such information.

Where the maximum voltage rating of the GE unit is not equal to or greater than the given transistor, the GE rating is also given. Note that physical dimensions vary considerably among manufacturers and may be the limiting factor in some replacement applications.

Since manufacturing techniques are not identical, the General Electric Company makes no claim, nor does it warrant, that its transistors are exact equivalents or replacements for the types referred to.

SELECTED PHOTOTUBES

TYPE	FEATURES AND NOTES	Basing	Base	Length, inches	Diameter, inches	Wavelength Angstroms	Sensitivity μa/μ watt
1P39	Vacuum type similar to type 929 except for non-hygroscopic base. For high humidity conditions. Blue sensitive.	3J	6-pin O.	3¹⁄₁₆	1⁹⁄₃₂	4000	.042
1P40	Gas type similar to 930 except for non-hygroscopic base. For high humidity conditions. Red sensitive.	3J	6-pin O.	3¹⁄₁₆	1⁹⁄₃₂	8000	.0135
868	Gas type phototube for the reproduction of sound.	2K	4-pin	4⅛	1⅛	8000	.009
918	Used for the reproduction of sound, for relay controls, and for measurements. Red sensitive.	2K	4-pin	4⅛	1⅛	8000	.015
921	Gas cartridge type for relay applications and light measurements. Red sensitive.	2AQ	Spec.	1²³⁄₃₂	⅞	8000	.0135
922	Cartridge vacuum type for relay applications. Red sensitive.	2AQ	Spec.	1²³⁄₃₂	⅞	8000	.002
923	For replacement purposes. Types 1P40 or 930 recommended for new equipment. Gas type.	2K	4-pin	3⁹⁄₁₆	1¹⁄₁₆	8000	.0135
927	Gas type for 16 mm. sound equipment, relay and measurement applications.	2F	Spec.	2¹³⁄₃₂	²¹⁄₃₂	8000	.0125
929	Vacuum type for light measurement and relay application. Blue sensitive.	3J	6-pin O.	3¹⁄₁₆	1⁹⁄₃₂	4000	.042
930	Gas type for sound reproduction and relay use. Red sensitive.	3J	6-pin O.	3¹⁄₁₆	1⁹⁄₃₂	8000	.0135
931A	High sensitivity multiplier type used in facsimile transmission, sound reproduction, and research. Blue sensitive.	11K	Spec.	3¹¹⁄₁₆	1⁵⁄₁₆	4000	18600
5581	Gas type similar to 930. Designed for sound reproduction from a dye-image sound track used with an incandescent light source.	3J	6-pin O.	3¹⁄₁₆	1⁹⁄₃₂	4000	.125

*Averaged over any interval of 30 seconds maximum.

▼ Ratio of anode sensitivity to cathode sensitivity.

☐ With 100 volts/dynode stage and 90 volts between final dynode and anode.

★ At 90 volts for all gas types; 250 volts for all vacuum types at 25°C.

‡Measured with 2870°K light source.

△ May be doubled when anode supply voltage is limited to 70 volts.

▲ May be doubled when anode supply voltage is limited to 80 volts.

SELECTED PHOTOTUBES

Anode Supply D-C or Peak A-C Volts	Peak Cathode Current, μa	Peak Cathode Current Density μa/sq. in.	Average Cathode Current, μa*	Gas Amplification Factor	I_b Dark Max. D-C; μa*	0 cps	5000 cps	10000 cps	TYPE
250	20	100	5	—	.005	45	45	45	1P39
90	10	100	3△	10	.005	135	111	101	1P40
100	20	100	5▲	8	.10	90	77	67	868
90	20	100	5△	10.5	.10	150	120	105	918
90	10	100	3△	10	.10	135	119	108	921
500	15	100	5	--	.005	20	20	20	922
90	10	100	3△	10	.10	135	111	101	923
90	6	100	2△	10	.10	125	110	100	927
250	20	100	5	-.-	.125	45	45	45	929
90	10	100	3△	10	.10	65	56	50	930
1250	Supply Volts between Final Dynode & Anode = 250 Peak Anode Ma = 10 Average Anode Ma = 1.0 Ambient Temp. = 75°C D-C Anode Dark Current = 0.1 μa Anode Luminous Sensitivity □ = 20 amp/lumen Equivalent Noise Input □ = 7 x 10⁻¹² lumens Current Amplification □▼ = 1 x 10⁻⁶								931A
100	10	100	3▲	5.5	.05	135	124	108	5581

281

SELENIUM SUN BATTERIES

Sun Battery is a semiconductor photovoltaic energy converter that supplies electrical power to a load when exposed to sunlight or artificial light sources. The battery consists of a number of series connected selenium "Sun Battery Cells" that are specially processed for high illumination level and high current density operation.

SUN BATTERY CELL...RATINGS	
Maximum Operating Temperature:	Continuous duty at 85°C Intermittent duty 100°C
Maximum Illumination:	15,000 foot candles

SUN BATTERY CELL...ELECTRICAL CHARACTERISTICS AT 25°C								
Standard Cell Types	Overall Dimensions inch x inch	Active Area Square Inch	Typical Output Power for Optimum Match to Load					
			2000 foot candles		5000 foot candles		10,000 foot candles	
			volts	milliamps	volts	milliamps	volts	milliamps
1B2	0.72 x 0.44	0.26	0.24	1.0	0.25	2.0	0.26	3.5
B2M	Cell mounted on angle bracket with pigtail leads (see opposite page)							
1B5	1.44 x 0.64	0.76	0.24	3.0	0.25	6.0	0.26	10.0
1B10	1.69 x 0.88	1.26	0.24	5.0	0.25	10.0	0.26	17.0
1B15	1.69 x 1.69	2.25	0.24	9.0	0.25	18.0	0.26	30.0
1B20	2.0 x 2.0	3.27	0.24	12.0	0.25	23.0	0.26	37.0
1B30	3.25 x 3.25	9.41	0.24	32.0	0.25	60.0	0.26	100

All standard sun battery cells are available with 6" color coded pigtail leads attached (add suffix pl to cell nomenclature). The cells are also available, on request, individually mounted on a straight or angle bracket and with pigtail leads attached. These bracket mounted cells are impregnated for further protection against humidity and atmospheric contaminants.

SUN BATTERY...STANDARD TYPE

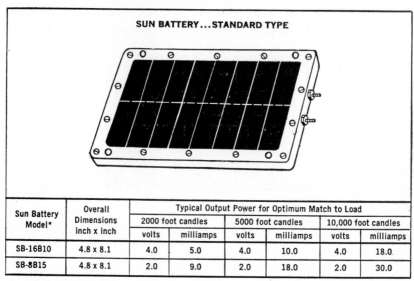

Sun Battery Model*	Overall Dimensions inch x inch	Typical Output Power for Optimum Match to Load					
		2000 foot candles		5000 foot candles		10,000 foot candles	
		volts	milliamps	volts	milliamps	volts	milliamps
SB-16B10	4.8 x 8.1	4.0	5.0	4.0	10.0	4.0	18.0
SB-8B15	4.8 x 8.1	2.0	9.0	2.0	18.0	2.0	30.0

*The model SB sun batteries are sealed in a phenolic case with plastic window, as shown in drawing above. The nomenclature following the SB indicates the number and type of sun battery cells, all connected in series. Four holes are provided in the frame for mounting purposes.

[*Note:* Reproduced through courtesy of International Rectifier Corp.]

Appendix 10
TRANSISTOR LETTER SYMBOL STANDARDS

A. *Quantity symbols:*

1. Instantaneous values are represented by lower-case letters (*i, e, p* for current, voltage, and power, respectively).
2. Maximum, average (d-c), and RMS values are represented by upper-case letters (*I, V, P*).

B. *Subscripts:*

1. Instantaneous *total* values and d-c values are represented by upper-case subscripts (*C, E, B* for collector, emitter, and base, respectively).
2. Varying (a-c) component values are represented by lower-case letters (*c, e, b*).

C. *Double and triple subscripts:*

1. Double subscripts are used to indicate between which two electrodes a voltage is measured; that is, V_{EB} designates the potential of the emitter with respect to base. (Note that the second subscript is the reference electrode.)
2. *Supply* voltages are indicated by repeating the electrode subscript. The reference electrode may then be designated by a third subscript. For example, the supply voltage between collector and base would be V_{CCB}.

Index

A

Acceptor, 164
Aging, rectifier cell, 184
Alpha cutoff, 215
Amplification factor:
  current (α), 200, 205
  current (β), 208
  gas phototube, 234
  vacuum tube, 19
Angstrom unit, 228
Anode, 8
Aquadag, 109, 121, 124

B

Base, 199
Beam power tube, 55
Breakdown potential, 99

C

Capacitance, interelectrode, 24
Cathode:
  heat shield, 83
  oxide coated, 7
  sheath, 82
  thoriated, 6
  tungsten, 6
  types of, 4
Cathode-ray oscilloscope, 134–159
  amplifiers for, 136
  block diagram, 134
  synchronization, 138
  time base, 137
Cathode-ray tubes, 107–131
  aluminized, 131
  construction, 108–113
  metal, 109

Characteristics (*see* specific types)
Collector, 199
Copper-oxide rectifier, 184
Covalent pairs, 163
Crystal diodes, 170–179
  characteristics, 173
  graphic symbol, 177
  specifications, 176
  table of, 178
  types of, 171
Crystal lattice, 163
Current amplification factor:
  alpha (α), 200, 205
  beta (β), 208

D

Deflection:
  balanced, 123
  electromagnetic, 126
  electrostatic, 116
  plates, 112
  sensitivity, 118
  yoke, 126
Diode:
  crystal, 170–179
  vacuum tube, 8–15
Disc seal tubes, 66
Discharge:
  abnormal, 100
  arc, 100
  glow, 99
  self maintained, 99
  Townsend, 99
Dissipation:
  maximum plate, 61
  maximum screen, 61
Donors, 164

285

E

Edison effect, 9
Electromagnetic:
    deflection, 126
    focusing, 124
Electron emission (*see* Emission)
Electron gun, 111
    bent, 129
    diagonal cut, 129
Electron-ray tube, 57
Electrostatic:
    deflection, 116
    focusing, 114
Emission:
    current, 10
    electron, 2
    field, 3
    photoelectric, 4, 230
    secondary, 3, 43
    thermionic, 3, 4
Emitter, 199

F

Figure of merit, 25
Fluorescence, 112
Flyback time, 138
Focusing:
    anode, 111
    coil, 125
    control, 116, 121
    electromagnetic, 124
    electrostatic, 114
Foot-candle, 229
Frequency measurement (CRO), 153
Frequency response (CRO), 156

G

Gaseous conduction, 96
    stages in, 97
Gas tubes, 76–104
    diode, cold cathode, 96
    diode, hot cathode, 79
    hydrogen thyratron, 93
    ignitron, 102
    multianode, 104
    residual, 76
    shield grid thyratron, 94
    triode, thyratron, 84
Germanium power rectifier, 190

Glow:
    discharge, 99
    tubes, 100
Grid, 15
    bias, 16
    screen, 39
    shield, 94
    suppressor, 46

H

Holes, 165
Hydrogen thyratron, 93

I

Ignition potential, 99
Ignitron, 102
Image charge, 3
Intensifier bands, 119
Intensity control, 113, 121
Interelectrode capacitance, 24
Inverse voltage, 61
Ion, 76
    spot, 128
    trap, 129
        magnet, 129
Ionization, 77
Ionizing potential, 77

J

Junction transistor, 202–220
    alloyed, 214
    configurations, 211
    current amplification, 205, 208
    diffused, 214
    frequency limitations, 214
    graphic symbols, 207
    grown, 214
    life expectancy, 219
    N-P-N, 204
    P-N-P, 206
    parameters, 212
    power, 215
    static characteristics, 209
    tetrode, 216

K

Klystron, 67

L

Letter symbols:
  chart, 36
  transistors, 283
  tubes, 34
Light:
  energy, 230
  frequencies, 227
  units of, 229
  wavelength, 227
Lighthouse tube, 65
Lissajous figures, 146
Load line, 31
Lumens, 229
Luminous flux, 229

M

Magic-eye tube, 60
Magnesium-copper sulphide rectifier, 187
Magnetron, 67, 68–72
Majority carriers, 167
Mercury pool tubes:
  ignitron, 102
  multianode, 104
Micron, 228
Microwave tubes, 66
Minority carriers, 167
Multielement tubes, 39–75
Multiplier phototubes, 237
Multi-unit tubes, 57
Mutual:
  characteristics, 18
  conductance, 22

O

Oscilloscope (*see* Cathode-ray oscilloscope)

P

Pentode, 46–54
  characteristics, 48
  coefficients, 50
  construction, 47
  remote cutoff, 50
Persistence, 112
Phanotron, 84
Phase-shift measurement, 145–153

Phosphorescence, 112
Photoconductive:
  cells, 239
  effect, 226
Photodiode, 242
Photoelectric:
  cells, 226–254
  emission, 4, 230
Photoemissive effect, 4, 226
Photon, 230
Phototransistor, 243
Phototube, 226–254
  gas, 234
  multiplier, 237
  sensitivity, 235
  vacuum, 232
Photovoltaic:
  cells, 246
  effect, 226
Plasma, 82
Plate, 8
  current, 9
  dissipation, 61
  resistance, 12, 21
P-N junction, 167
Point-contact rectifier, 170
Point-contact transistor, 198–202
  current amplification, 200
  limitations, 201
  voltage and power gain, 201
Positioning controls, 120
Power tubes, 54

Q

Quanta, 230
Quiescent value, 36

R

Ratings:
  crystal diodes, 176
  power rectifier cells, 182
  power transistors, 216
  tubes, 61–63
Rectifier:
  area, 180–197
  cell characteristics, 182
  copper-oxide, 184
  crystal, 170–179
  diode (tube), 15

Rectifier (*Cont.*):
  dry, 180
  germanium, power, 190
  magnesium-copper sulphide, 187
  metallic, 180
  point contact, 170
  P-N junction, 167
  selenium, 188
  semiconductor, power, 180–197
  silicon, power, 194
Rectigon, 84
Resistance:
  dark, 240
  plate, 12, 21
Retrace time, 138

S

Saturation:
  current, 10
  space charge, 12
  temperature, 11
  voltage, 10
Screen grid, 39
  dissipation, 61
Selenium rectifier, 188
Semiconductor, 161
  area rectifier, 180–197
  crystal lattice, 163
  fundamentals, 160–169
  materials, 161
  N-type, 166
  photodiode, 242
  P-type, 166
Sheath:
  cathode, 82
  positive ion, 82
Shield grid thyratron, 94
Shot effect, 79
Silicon power rectifier, 194
Solar battery, 249
Space charge, 7
Square-wave testing, 156
Striking potential, 99
Sun battery, 249
Suppressor grid, 46
Surface barrier potential, 3
Sweep generator, 137
  simple circuit, 140
  synchronization, 143
  thyratron circuit, 142

T

Tetrode, 39–46
  characteristics, 41
  coefficients, 44
  limitations, 45
Thyratron, 84–96
  hydrogen, 93
  shield grid, 94
  phase shift control, 94
Time base, 137
Townsend discharge, 98, 99
Transconductance, 22
Transistors, 160, 198–223
  characteristics, 209
  configurations, 211
  frequency limitations, 214
  junction, 202
  life expectancy, 219
  parameters, 212
  photo, 243
  point-contact, 198
  power, 215
  tetrode, 216
Transit time, 163
Travelling wave tube, 67, 72
Triode, 15–25
  amplification factor, 19
  construction, 15
  mutual characteristics, 18
  mutual conductance, 22
  plate characteristics, 17
  plate resistance, 21
  symbol, 15
Tungar, 84

V

Valence electrons, 162
Voltage:
  measurement (CRO), 144
  regulator, 101
  saturation, 10
  zener, 175

W

Wavelength, light, 227
Work function, 2

Z

Zener voltage, 175